APPLICATIONS OF THE THEORY OF MATRICES

APPLICATIONS OF THE THEORY OF MATRICES

by F. R. GANTMACHER
(Ф. Р. ГАНТМАХЕР)

Translated and revised by
J. L. BRENNER, Stanford Research Institute
with the assistance of
D. W. BUSHAW, State College of Washington
and S. EVANUSA, Baltimore, Maryland

19 59

INTERSCIENCE PUBLISHERS, INC., NEW YORK
INTERSCIENCE PUBLISHERS LTD., LONDON

PHYSICS

FIRST PUBLISHED 1959

LIBRARY OF CONGRESS CATALOG CARD NUMBER 58-13804

INTERSCIENCE PUBLISHERS, INC.
250 Fifth Avenue, New York 1, N.Y.

For Great Britain and Northern Ireland:
INTERSCIENCE PUBLISHERS LTD.
88/90, Chancery Lane, London W.C. 2, England

PRINTED IN THE NETHERLANDS
BY DIJKSTRA'S DRUKKERIJ N.V., VOORHEEN BOEKDRUKKERIJ GEBROEDERS HOITSEMA, GRONINGEN

TRANSLATOR'S PREFACE

Applications of the Theory of Matrices is a translation, with revisions, of the second part of *A Theory of Matrices* published in 1954. The first (untranslated) section contains general material which is easily available in texts in English and other Western languages. In order to make the present volume a self-contained whole, appendices and footnotes of explanation have been added.

The inclusion of many references to books and articles in Western languages should make the volume more useful than a straight translation would have been. Where appropriate, references have been made to developments subsequent to 1954.

The textual matter includes chapters of interest to applied mathematicians. The chapter on differential equations is full and readable; the chapter on the Routh-Hurwitz problem is (so far as I know) the only modern exposition in book form of the theory which a control engineer needs in studying stability of a servomechanism. The chapter on matrices with nonnegative elements is most useful in numerical analysis and engineering. The numerical analyst will notice, too, that the algorithm expounded in the last chapter can be used directly to evaluate the roots of a (complex or real) polynomial; codes for this method already exist.

Some care has been expended to make this translation more than a mere translocation of words. Besides this, several misprints in the original edition have been corrected. I cannot suppose that no misprints have been added, and would be grateful for any corrections communicated by readers.

Mr. Evanusa's valuable help extended through several months, and his support was untiring in spite of the press of other professional responsibilities. Professor Bushaw translated the entire last chapter and aided significantly with the other chapters and the reading of proofs.

Stanford Research Institute   J. L. BRENNER
Menlo Park, California

May, 1959

CONTENTS

CHAPTER I

Complex Symmetric, Antisymmetric and Orthogonal Matrices

CHAPTER II

Singular Bundles of Matrices

CHAPTER III

Matrices with Nonnegative Elements

CHAPTER IV

Applications of the Theory of Matrices to the Study of Systems of Linear Differential Equations

CHAPTER V

The Routh-Hurwitz Problem and Related Questions

CHAPTER I

Complex Symmetric, Antisymmetric and Orthogonal Matrices

In any investigation of linear operators in a Euclidean space, one studies *real* symmetric, antisymmetric and orthogonal matrices, i.e., *real* square matrices which are characterized by the following relationships, respectively:

$$S' = S, \quad K' = -K, \quad O' = O^{-1}$$

(here ' indicates formation of the transposed matrix). It is known that, over the field of complex numbers, all these matrices have linear elementary divisors, and one knows canonical forms for these matrices, i.e., "most simple" real symmetric, antisymmetric and orthogonal matrices, to which arbitrary matrices of the types under discussion are equivalent.

The canonical forms are block diagonal, and each block is a 1×1 or a 2×2 matrix. For a symmetric, antisymmetric or orthogonal matrix, the 2×2 blocks are symmetric, antisymmetric, or orthogonal. In the last case, moreover, the 1×1 blocks are all $+1$ or -1.

In this chapter we study *complex* symmetric, antisymmetric and orthogonal matrices. We find what elementary divisors these matrices can have, and what canonical forms are established for them. These forms have a considerably more complicated structure than the corresponding normal forms in the real case. The first section establishes interesting relationships between complex orthogonal, unitary matrices and real symmetric, antisymmetric and orthogonal matrices.

1

§ 1. Some formulas for complex orthogonal and unitary matrices

Let us commence with the following lemma.

LEMMA 1. *1. If the matrix G is simultaneously Hermitian and orthogonal* $(G' = \bar{G} = G^{-1})$, *then it can be represented in the form*

$$G = Ie^{iK} \tag{1}$$

where I is a real symmetric involutory matrix, and K a real antisymmetric matrix which is permutable with it:

$$I = \bar{I} = I', \quad I^2 = E, \quad K = \bar{K} = -K' \tag{2}$$

2. If in addition G is a positive definite Hermitian matrix [1], *then in formula* (1) $I = E$, *and*

$$G = e^{iK}. \tag{3}$$

Proof. *1.* Set

$$G = S + iT \tag{4}$$

where S and T are real matrices. Then

$$\bar{G} = S - iT, \quad G' = S' + iT'. \tag{5}$$

Thus $\bar{G} = G'$ implies $S = S'$, $T = -T'$; i.e., S is a symmetric, T is an antisymmetric matrix.

Further, if we substitute the expressions for G and $\bar{G}$ from (4) and (5) in the complex equality $G\bar{G} = E$, the latter is seen to amount to the two real equalities

$$S^2 + T^2 = E, \quad ST = TS. \tag{6}$$

The second of these equalities indicates that S and T commute.

But two commutative normal matrices S and T can be brought into block-diagonal canonical form by one and the same real orthogonal transformation. Therefore [2]

[1] That is, $G = G^* \equiv \bar{G}'$, and $x^*Gx > 0$ ($x^*x > 0$); or what is the same thing, G is the matrix of coefficients of a positive definite Hermitian form.

[2] First simultaneously into (complex) diagonal form by a unitary transformation (Appendix I), then into real block diagonal form as shown. The product of the two transformations must be real. The diagonal elements in $O^{-1}SO$ must repeat as shown, if $ST = TS$ holds.

$$S = O\{s_1, s_1, s_2, s_2, \ldots, s_q, s_q, s_{2q+1}, \ldots, s_n\} O^{-1}, \quad {}^{2a}$$

$$T = O\left\{\begin{bmatrix} 0 & t_1 \\ -t_1 & 0 \end{bmatrix}, \begin{bmatrix} 0 & t_2 \\ -t_2 & 0 \end{bmatrix}, \ldots, \begin{bmatrix} 0 & t_q \\ -t_q & 0 \end{bmatrix}, 0, \ldots, 0\right\} O^{-1}$$

$$(O = \bar{O} = O'^{-1}) \quad (7)$$

(the numbers s_i and t_i are real.) Hence

$$G = S + iT = O\left\{\begin{bmatrix} s_1 & it_1 \\ -it_1 & s_1 \end{bmatrix}, \begin{bmatrix} s_2 & it_2 \\ -it_2 & s_2 \end{bmatrix}, \ldots, \begin{bmatrix} i_q & it_q \\ -it_q & s_q \end{bmatrix}, \right.$$

$$\left. s_{2q+1}, \ldots, s_n\right\} O^{-1}. \quad (8)$$

On the other hand, substituting the expressions (7) for S and T in the first of equalities (6), we find that the following holds:

$$s_1^2 - t_1^2 = 1, \ s_2^2 - t_2^2 = 1, \ldots, s_q^2 - t_q^2 = 1, \ s_{2q+1} = \pm 1, \ldots, s_n = \pm 1. \quad (9)$$

It is now a simple matter to check that a matrix of the type

$$\begin{bmatrix} s & it \\ -it & s \end{bmatrix} \text{ with } s^2 - t^2 = 1$$

can always be represented in the form

$$\begin{bmatrix} s & it \\ -it & s \end{bmatrix} = \varepsilon \exp i\begin{pmatrix} 0, & \varphi \\ -\varphi, & 0 \end{pmatrix},$$

where

$$|s| = \operatorname{ch} \varphi, \quad \varepsilon t = \operatorname{sh} \varphi, \quad \varepsilon = \operatorname{sign} s.$$

Therefore, on the strength of (8) and (9) we have:

$$G = O\left\{ \pm \exp i\begin{bmatrix} 0 & \varphi_1 \\ -\varphi_1 & 0 \end{bmatrix}, \pm \exp i\begin{bmatrix} 0 & \varphi_2 \\ -\varphi_2 & 0 \end{bmatrix}, \ldots, \right.$$

$$\left. \pm \exp i\begin{bmatrix} 0 & \varphi_q \\ -\varphi_q & 0 \end{bmatrix}, \pm 1, \ldots, \pm 1\right\} O^{-1}, \quad (10)$$

i.e.,

$$G = Ie^{iK},$$

$$I = O\{\pm 1, \pm 1, \ldots, \pm 1\} O^{-1},$$

where

$$K = O\left\{\begin{bmatrix} 0 & \varphi_1 \\ -\varphi_1 & 0 \end{bmatrix}, \ldots, \begin{bmatrix} 0 & \varphi_q \\ -\varphi_q & 0 \end{bmatrix}, 0, \ldots, 0\right\} O^{-1} \quad \left.\right\} \quad (11)$$

^{2a} The symbol $\{A, B, \ldots\}$ denotes a diagonal block matrix with $A, B, \ldots$ ranged along the diagonal.

and

$$IK = KI.$$

Equalities (2) follow from (11).

2. Suppose in addition it is known that G is a positive definite Hermitian matrix. Then all characteristic numbers of the matrix G are certainly positive ($Gx = x\lambda \Rightarrow x^*Gx = (x^*x)\lambda$). On the strength of formula (10), however, these characteristic numbers are the numbers

$$\pm e^{\varphi_1}, \ \pm e^{-\varphi_1}, \ \pm e^{\varphi_2}, \ \pm e^{-\varphi_2}, \ldots, \pm e^{\varphi_q}, \ \pm e^{-\varphi_q}, \ \pm 1, \ldots, \pm 1$$

[here the signs correspond to the signs in formula (10)].

Therefore, in formula (10) and the following formula (11), the ambiguous $\pm$ signs must all be $+$. Consequently

$$I = O\{1, \ 1, \ldots, 1\}O^{-1} = E,$$

which is what we were required to prove. The lemma is completely proved.

The lemma will now be applied to proving the following theorem:

THEOREM 1. *A complex orthogonal matrix O can always be represented in the form*

$$O = Re^{iK} \tag{12}$$

where R is a real orthogonal, and K a real antisymmetric, matrix

$$R = \bar{R} = R'^{-1}, \quad K = \bar{K} = -K'. \tag{13}$$

Proof. Suppose that formula (12) holds. Then the following is true:

$$O^* = \bar{O}' = e^{iK}R'$$

and

$$O^*O = e^{iK}R'Re^{iK} = e^{2iK}.$$

On the strength of the preceding lemma, a real antisymmetric matrix K can be defined from the condition

$$O^*O = e^{2iK}, \tag{14}$$

since the matrix O^*O is a positive definite Hermitian orthogonal matrix. After matrix K has been found from (14), we find R from (12):

$$R = Oe^{-iK}. \tag{15}$$

Then the following holds:

$$R^*R = e^{-iK} O^*O\bar{e}^{iK} = E,$$

i.e., R is a unitary matrix. On the other hand, it follows from (15) that the matrix R, as the product of two orthogonal matrices, is itself orthogonal: $R'R = E$. Thus, R is at the same time unitary and orthogonal, and, consequently, is real orthogonal. Formula (15) can be written in the form (12).

The theorem is proved.[3]

Let us now establish the following lemma.

LEMMA 2. *If the matrix D is at the same time symmetric and unitary $(D = D' = \bar{D}^{-1})$, then it can be represented in the form*

$$D = e^{iS}, \tag{16}$$

where S is a real symmetric matrix $(S = \bar{S} = S')$.

Proof. Define U, V from

$$D = U + iV \quad (U = \bar{U}, V = \bar{V}). \tag{17}$$

Then the relations

$$\bar{D} = U - iV, \quad D' = U' + iV'$$

hold. The complex identity $D = D'$ implies the two real identities:

$$U = U', \quad V = V'.$$

Thus, U and V are real symmetric matrices.

The equality $D\bar{D} = E$ implies the following:

$$U^2 + V^2 = E, \quad UV = VU. \tag{18}$$

---

[3] Formula (12), like the polar decomposition of a complex matrix, is intimately connected with an important theorem of Cartan, which establishes well-known representations for automorphisms of semisimple complex Lie groups.

According to the second of these equalities, the matrices U and V commute. Thus there is a real orthogonal matrix O such that

$$U = O\{s_1, s_2, \ldots, s_n\}O^{-1}, \quad V = O\{t_1, t_2, \ldots, t_n\}O^{-1}. \quad (19)$$

Here s_k and t_k $(k = 1, 2, \ldots, n)$ are real numbers. Now the first of equalities (18) gives:

$$s_k^2 + t_k^2 = 1 \quad (k = 1, 2, \ldots, n).$$

Therefore there exist real numbers φ_k $(k = 1, 2, \ldots, n)$ such that

$$s_k = \cos \varphi_k, \quad t_k = \sin \varphi_k \quad (k = 1, 2, \ldots, n).$$

Substituting these expressions for s_k and t_k in (19) and applying (17), we find:

$$D = O\{e^{i\varphi_1}, e^{i\varphi_2}, \ldots, e^{i\varphi_n}\}O^{-1} = e^{iS},$$

where

$$S = O\{\varphi_1, \varphi_2, \ldots, \varphi_n\}O^{-1}. \quad (20)$$

From (20) it follows that $S = \bar{S} = S'$. The lemma is proved.

By means of this lemma, we can prove the following theorem:

THEOREM 2. *A unitary matrix U can be represented in the form*

$$U = Re^{iS} \quad (21)$$

where R is a real orthogonal, and S a real symmetric matrix:

$$R = \bar{R} = R'^{-1}, \quad S = \bar{S} = S'. \quad (22)$$

Proof. Formula (21) would imply

$$U' = e^{iS}R'; \quad (23)$$

combining (21) and (23), we obtain

$$U'U = e^{iS}R'Re^{iS} = e^{2iS}$$

by using (22).

But by lemma 2, there is a real symmetric matrix S satisfying

$$U'U = e^{2iS} \quad (24)$$

since the matrix $U'U$ is a symmetric unitary matrix. After the matrix S is determined, the matrix R can be determined from the equality

$$R = Ue^{-iS}. \tag{25}$$

Then the relation

$$R' = e^{-iS}U' \tag{26}$$

holds, and thus, from (24), (25) and (26) it follows that

$$R'R = e^{-iS}U'Ue^{-iS} = E,$$

i.e., R is an orthogonal matrix.

On the other hand, according to (25), R is a product of two unitary matrices and, consequently, R is a unitary matrix. Since R is at the same time orthogonal and unitary, R is a real matrix. Obviously, formula (25) can be rewritten in the form (21). The theorem is proved.

§ 2. Polar decomposition of a complex matrix

Let us prove the following theorem:

THEOREM 3. *Any nonsingular $n \times n$ matrix $A = (a_{ik})$ with complex elements can be decomposed as follows:*

$$A = SO \tag{27}$$

and

$$A = O_1 S_1 \tag{28}$$

where S and S_1 are complex symmetric, and O and O_1 are complex orthogonal matrices. Also,

$$S = (AA')^{\frac{1}{2}} = f(AA'), \quad S_1 = (A'A)^{\frac{1}{2}} = f_1(A'A),$$

where $f(\lambda)$, $f_1(\lambda)$ are polynomials in λ.

In the decomposition (27), [(28)] the factors S and O [O_1 and S_1] are permutable if and only if the matrices A and A' are permutable.

Proof. It is sufficient to establish the factorization (27). For if such a decomposition is carried out for the matrix A', the factorization (28) of A follows automatically, since O' is orthogonal if O is orthogonal.

If formula (27) holds, then

$$A = SO, \quad A' = O^{-1}S;$$

therefore

$$AA' = S^2. \tag{29}$$

Conversely, since AA' is a nonsingular matrix $[(AA')^{-1} = (A^{-1})'A^{-1}]$ then the function $x^{\frac{1}{2}}$ is defined on the spectrum of this matrix [4] and, consequently, there exists an interpolation polynomial $f(\lambda)$ such that

$$(AA')^{\frac{1}{2}} = f(AA') \tag{30}$$

We denote symmetric matrix (30) by $S = (AA')^{\frac{1}{2}}$. Then (29) will hold, and, consequently, det $S \neq 0$. We define the matrix O from equality (27):

$$O = S^{-1}A.$$

It is easy to see that this matrix is orthogonal. Thus, the decomposition (27) is established.

If the factors S and O in decomposition (27) are permutable, then the following matrices are also permutable:

$$A = SO \quad \text{and} \quad A' = O^{-1}S,$$

because

$$AA' = S^2, \quad A'A = O^{-1}S^2O.$$

Conversely, if $AA' = A'A$, then

$$S^2 = O^{-1}S^2O,$$

i.e., the matrix O is permutable with $S^2 = AA'$. But then the matrix O is permutable with the matrix $S = f(AA')$. Thus, the theorem is completely proved.

[4] We are taking a single-valued branch of the function $\sqrt{\lambda}$ in a simply connected region, which contains all the characteristic numbers of the matrix AA', and does not contain the number 0.

As an application of the polar decomposition theorem, we prove the theorem:

THEOREM 4. *If two complex symmetric, or antisymmetric, or orthogonal matrices are similar*

$$B = T^{-1}AT \tag{31}$$

these matrices are orthogonally similar, i.e., there exists an orthogonal matrix O such that

$$B = O^{-1}AO. \tag{32}$$

Proof. From the condition of the theorem, there follows (see below) the existence of a polynomial $q(\lambda)$ such that

$$A' = q(A), \quad B' = q(B). \tag{33}$$

In the case of symmetric matrices, the polynomial $q(\lambda)$ is identically equal to λ, and in the case of antisymmetric matrices, it is identically equal to $-\lambda$. If A and B are orthogonal matrices, then $q(\lambda)$ is an interpolation polynomial for $1/\lambda$ on the entire spectrum of matrices A and B.

By relying on equalities (33), we will find a proof of the given theorem in a manner very similar to the proof of the corresponding theorem in the real case. It follows from (31) that

$$q(B) = T^{-1}q(A)T,$$

or, on the strength of (33)

$$B' = T^{-1}A'T.$$

Hence

$$B = T'AT'^{-1}.$$

Comparing this equality with (31), we easily find that

$$TT'A = ATT'. \tag{34}$$

Since T is nonsingular, it has a polar decomposition

$$T = SO \quad (S = S' = f(TT'), \quad O' = O^{-1}).$$

Since according to (34) the matrix TT' is permutable with A, the matrix $S = f(TT')$ is also permutable with A. Therefore, substituting in (31) the product SO for T, we obtain:

$$B = O^{-1}S^{-1}ASO = O^{-1}AO.$$

The theorem is proved.

§ 3. Normal form of a complex symmetric matrix

Let us prove the following theorem.

THEOREM 5. *There exists a complex symmetric matrix with any preassigned elementary divisors.*[5]

Proof.   Let H be the $n \times n$ matrix of nth order, in which the elements of the first superdiagonal are equal to unity, and all the remaining elements are equal to zero. We will prove the existence of a symmetric matrix S which is similar to the matrix H:

$$S = THT^{-1}. \tag{35}$$

To find the transforming matrix T, we start with the condition

$$S = THT^{-1} = S' = T'^{-1}H'T'.$$

This condition can be rewritten as follows:

$$VH = H'V \tag{36}$$

where V is a symmetric matrix connected with T by the equality [6]

$$T'T = -2iV. \tag{37}$$

Direct calculation shows that any solution V of matrix equation (36) has the following form:

---

[5] Concerning the contents of this section, and also of Sections 4 and 5 following, see [71].

[6] To simplify later formulas, it is convenient at this time to introduce the factor $2i$.

$$V = \begin{bmatrix} 0 & & \cdots & & 0 & a_0 \\ & & & \cdot & a_0 & a_1 \\ \cdot & & & \cdot & \cdot & \cdot \\ \cdot & & \cdot & \cdot & \cdot & \cdot \\ \cdot & \cdot & \cdot & \cdot & & \cdot \\ 0 & \cdot & \cdot & & & \cdot \\ a_0 & a_1 & \cdots & & & a_{n-1} \end{bmatrix}, \tag{38}$$

where $a_0, a_1, \ldots, a_{n-1}$ are arbitrary complex numbers.

Since it is sufficient for us to find one transforming matrix T, then in this formula we place $a_0 = 1$, $a_1 = \ldots = a_{n-1} = 0$, i.e., we define the matrix V by the equality [7]

$$V = \begin{bmatrix} 0 & \ldots & 0 & 1 \\ 0 & \ldots & 1 & 0 \\ \cdot & \cdot & \cdot & \cdot \\ 1 & \ldots & 0 & 0 \end{bmatrix}. \tag{39}$$

In addition, we will require the transforming matrix T to be symmetric:

$$T = T'. \tag{40}$$

Then equation (37) for T becomes

$$T^2 = -2iV. \tag{41}$$

Now we require the matrix T to be a polynomial in V, which is no loss in generality. Since $V^2 = E$, such a polynomial can be taken to be a polynomial of the first degree:

$$T = aE + bV.$$

From equation (41), taking into consideration the equality $V^2 = E$, we find that

$$a^2 + b^2 = 0, \quad 2ab = -2i.$$

[7] The matrix V is at the same time symmetric and orthogonal.

These relations are satisfied if we take $a = 1$, $b = -i$. Thus

$$T = E - iV. \tag{42}$$

The nonsingularity of T follows from (41) since V is non-singular. Thus (since $V^2 = E$) $T^{-1} = \frac{1}{2}iV^{-1}T = \frac{1}{2}iVT$, i.e.,

$$T^{-1} = \frac{1}{2}(E + iV), \tag{43}$$

and this formula gives an inverse of T in any case.

Thus, a symmetric transform S of the matrix H is defined by the equality

$$S = THT^{-1} = \frac{1}{2}(E - iV)H(E + iV), \quad V = \begin{bmatrix} 0 \dots 0 & 1 \\ 0 \dots 1 & 0 \\ \cdot \cdot \cdot \cdot \cdot \\ 1 \dots 0 & 0 \end{bmatrix}. \tag{44}$$

Since matrix S satisfies equation (36) and since $VHV = H'$, equality (44) can also be rewritten as follows:

$$2S = (H + H') + i(HV - VH)$$

$$= \begin{bmatrix} 0 & 1 & & \dots & & 0 \\ 1 & \cdot & \cdot & & & \cdot \\ \cdot & \cdot & \cdot & \cdot & & \cdot \\ \cdot & & \cdot & \cdot & \cdot & \cdot \\ \cdot & & & \cdot & \cdot & 1 \\ 0 & & \dots & & 1 & 0 \end{bmatrix} + i \begin{bmatrix} 0 & & \dots & & 1 & 0 \\ \cdot & & & & \cdot & -1 \\ \cdot & & & \cdot & \cdot & \cdot \\ \cdot & & \cdot & \cdot & & \cdot \\ 1 & \cdot & \cdot & & & \cdot \\ 0 & -1 & & \dots & & 0 \end{bmatrix}. \tag{45}$$

Formula (45) defines the symmetric transform S of the matrix H.

Henceforth, if n is the order of matrix H, $H = H^{(n)}$, then the corresponding matrices T, V and S will be denoted by: $T^{(n)}$, $V^{(n)}$ and $S^{(n)}$.

Let the following elementary divisors be given:

$$(\lambda - \lambda_1)^{p_1}, \quad (\lambda - \lambda_2)^{p_2}, \dots, (\lambda - \lambda_u)^{p_u}. \tag{46}$$

We form the corresponding Jordan matrix

$$J = \{\lambda_1 E^{(p_1)} + H^{(p_1)}, \quad \lambda_2 E^{(p_2)} + H^{(p_2)}, \dots, \lambda_u E^{(p_u)} + H^{(p_u)}\}.$$

For each matrix $H^{(p_j)}$ we will introduce the corresponding symmetric form $S^{(p_j)}$. From

$$S^{(p_j)} = T^{(p_j)} H^{(p_j)} \, [T^{(p_j)}]^{-1} \quad (j = 1, 2, \ldots, u)$$

it follows that

$$\lambda_j E^{(p_j)} + S^{(p_j)} = T^{(p_j)} [\lambda_j E^{(p_j)} + H^{(p_j)}] \, [T^{(p_j)}]^{-1}.$$

Therefore, placing

$$\tilde{S} = \{\lambda_1 E^{(p_1)} + S^{(p_1)}, \; \lambda_2 E^{(p_2)} + S^{(p_2)}, \ldots, \lambda_u E^{(p_u)} + S^{(p_u)}\}, \quad (47)$$

$$T = \{T^{(p_1)}, \; T^{(p_2)}, \ldots, T^{(p_u)}\}, \quad (48)$$

we will have

$$\tilde{S} = TJT^{-1}.$$

$\tilde{S}$ is a symmetric transform of the Jordan matrix J. The matrix $\tilde{S}$ is similar to the matrix J and has the same elementary divisors (46) as the matrix J. The theorem is proved.

COROLLARY 1. *An arbitrary square complex matrix* $A = (a_{ik})_1^n$ *is similar to a symmetric matrix.*

Applying Theorem 4, we obtain:

COROLLARY 2. *The arbitrary complex symmetric matrix* $S = (s_{ik})_1^n$ *is orthogonally similar to a symmetric matrix which has the normal form* $\tilde{S}$, *i.e., there exists an orthogonal matrix* O *such that*

$$\tilde{S} = O\tilde{S}O^{-1}. \quad (49)$$

A complex symmetric matrix can be transformed into a "partitioned diagonal" matrix

$$\tilde{S} = \{\lambda_1 E^{(p_1)} + S^{(p_1)}, \; \lambda_2 E^{(p_2)} + S^{(p_2)}, \ldots, \lambda_u E^{(p_u)} + S^{(p_u)}\}, \quad (50)$$

where every element is zero except the boxes shown; these are along the main diagonal; and the boxes $S^{(p)}$ are determined as follows [see (44) and (45)]:

$$S^{(p)} = \tfrac{1}{2}[E^{(p)} - iV^{(p)}]H^{(p)}[E^{(p)} + iV^{(p)}]$$
$$= \tfrac{1}{2}[H^{(p)} + H^{(p)\prime} + i(H^{(p)}V^{(p)} - V^{(p)}H^{(p)})]$$

$$= \tfrac{1}{2}\begin{bmatrix} 0 & 1 & & \cdots & & 0 \\ 1 & \cdot & \cdot & & & \\ & \cdot & \cdot & \cdot & & \\ & & \cdot & \cdot & \cdot & \\ & & & \cdot & \cdot & 1 \\ 0 & & \cdots & & 1 & 0 \end{bmatrix} + \tfrac{1}{2}i\begin{bmatrix} 0 & & \cdots & & 1 & 0 \\ & & & & \cdot & \cdot \\ & & & & \cdot & -1 \\ & & & \cdot & \cdot & \\ 1 & & \cdot & \cdot & & \\ 0 & -1 & \cdots & & & 0 \end{bmatrix}. \tag{51}$$

§ 4. Normal form of a complex antisymmetric matrix

Let us see what elementary divisors an antisymmetric matrix can have. We will employ the following theorem:

THEOREM 6. *The rank of an antisymmetric matrix is an even integer.*

Proof. Let the antisymmetric matrix K have rank r. Then among the rows of the matrix K there are r linearly independent ones; namely those with indices $i_1, i_2, \ldots, i_r$; all the remaining rows are linear combinations of these rows. Since the columns of the matrix K are obtained from the corresponding rows, by multiplying the elements of the latter by -1, then any column of the matrix K is a linear combination of the columns with indices $i_1, i_2, \ldots, i_r$. Therefore, an arbitrary minor of rth order of matrix K can be represented in the form

$$\alpha K\begin{bmatrix} i_1, & i_2, & \ldots, & i_r \\ i_1, & i_2, & \ldots, & i_r \end{bmatrix},$$

where α is some number.

Hence it follows that

$$K\begin{bmatrix} i_1, & i_2, & \ldots, & i \\ i_1, & i_2, & \ldots, & i \end{bmatrix} \neq 0.$$

But an antisymmetric determinant of odd order is always equal to zero. Consequently, r is an even number. The theorem is proved.

THEOREM 7. *Let K have order n and rank r; $K' = -K$.*

1. If λ_0 is a characteristic number of the antisymmetric matrix K, and if the corresponding elementary divisors are

$$(\lambda - \lambda_0)^{f_1}, \quad (\lambda - \lambda_0)^{f_2}, \ldots (\lambda - \lambda_0)^{f_t},$$

then $-\lambda_0$ is also a characteristic number of the matrix K; and the corresponding elementary divisors are:

$$(\lambda + \lambda_0)^{f_1}, \quad (\lambda + \lambda_0)^{f_2}, \ldots, (\lambda + \lambda_0)^{f_t}.$$

Note the equality as regards cardinal number and degree.

2. If the number zero is a characteristic number of the antisymmetric matrix [8] *K, then the system of elementary divisors of matrix K contains each elementary divisor of even degree which corresponds to the characteristic number zero (repeated) an even number of times.*

Proof. *1.* The transposed matrix K' has the same elementary divisors as matrix K. But $K' = -K$, and the elementary divisors of matrix $-K$ are obtained from the elementary divisors of matrix K, if in the latter all the characteristic numbers λ_1, λ_2, ... are replaced by $-\lambda_1$, $-\lambda_2$, ... Hence follows the first part of our theorem.

2. Let δ_1 elementary divisors of the form λ, and δ_2 elementary divisors of the form λ^2, etc., correspond to the characteristic number zero of matrix K. In general, we will use the symbol δ_p to indicate the number of elementary divisors of the form λ^p ($p = 1, 2, \ldots$). We will prove that δ_2, δ_4, ... are even numbers.

The defect $d(= n - r)$ of the matrix K is equal to the number of linearly independent characteristic vectors which correspond to the characteristic number zero, or, what is the same thing, to the number of elementary divisors of the form λ, λ^2, λ^3, ... Therefore

$$d = \delta_1 + \delta_2 + \delta_3 + \ldots \tag{52}$$

Since according to Theorem 6 the rank of matrix K is an even number, and $d = n - r$, then the number d has the same parity as the number n. Such a statement can be made concerning the

[8] That is, if $\det K = 0$. When n is odd, $\det K$ is always equal to 0.

defects d_3, d_5, . . . of the matrices K^3, K^5, . . ., since the uneven powers of an antisymmetric matrix are again antisymmetric Therefore, all the numbers $d_1 = d$, d_3, d_5, . . . have one and the same parity.

On the other hand, in raising matrix K to the power m each elementary divisor λ^p of this matrix for $p < m$ splits into p elementary divisors (of the first degree), and for $p \geqq m$, into m elementary divisors.[9] Therefore the number of elementary divisors of the matrices K, K^3, . . ., which are powers of λ, will be determined by the formulas

$$d_3 = \delta_1 + 2\delta_2 + 3(\delta_3 + \delta_4 + \ldots),$$
$$d_5 = \delta_1 + 2\delta_2 + 3\delta_3 + 4\delta_4 + 5(\delta_5 + \delta_6 + \ldots). \tag{53}$$

Comparing (52) and (53) and remembering that all the numbers $d_1 = d$, d_3, d_5, . . . have one and the same parity, the conclusion can easily be made that δ_2, δ_4, . . . are even numbers. The theorem is proved completely.

The following converse of Theorem 7 holds.

THEOREM 8. *There exists an antisymmetric matrix with any preassigned elementary divisors which satisfy restrictions 1, 2 of the preceding theorem.*

Proof.   Let us first find an antisymmetric transform of the

[9] This follows most simply from the fact that, if

$$J = \lambda E + H = \begin{bmatrix} \lambda & 1 & & 0 \\ & \cdot & \cdot & \\ & & \cdot & \cdot \\ & & & \cdot & 1 \\ & & & & \cdot \\ 0 & & & & \lambda \end{bmatrix}$$

then

$$f(J) = \begin{bmatrix} f(\lambda), & f'(\lambda)/1! & f''(\lambda)/2! \ldots f^{(p-1)}(\lambda)/(p-1)! \\ 0 & f(\lambda) & f'(\lambda)/1! \ldots \ldots \ldots \\ & \cdot \cdot \cdot \cdot \cdot \cdot \cdot \cdot \cdot \cdot \cdot \cdot \cdot \cdot \cdot \cdot \cdot \cdot \end{bmatrix}$$

where $f(J) = J^m$ in this case. See footnotes 15, 16.

block diagonal matrix of order $2p$:

$$J_{\lambda_0}^{(pp)} = \{\lambda_0 E + H, -\lambda_0 E - H\}, \tag{54}$$

which has the two elementary divisors $(\lambda - \lambda_0)^p$ and $(\lambda + \lambda_0)^p$; here $E = E^{(p)}$, $H = H^{(p)}$. [λ_0 is allowed to be 0.]

We seek a transforming T such that the matrix

$$T J_{\lambda_0}^{(pp)} T^{-1}$$

will be antisymmetric, i.e., such that the following equality holds:

$$T J_{\lambda_0}^{(pp)} T^{-1} + T'^{-1} [J_{\lambda_0}^{(pp)}]' T' = 0$$

or

$$W J_{\lambda_0}^{(pp)} + [J_{\lambda_0}^{(pp)}]' W = 0, \tag{55}$$

where W is a symmetric matrix connected with the matrix T by the equality [10]

$$T'T = -2iW. \tag{56}$$

Let us partition the matrix W into four square blocks, each of order p:

$$W = \begin{bmatrix} W_{11} & W_{12} \\ W_{21} & W_{22} \end{bmatrix}.$$

Then (55) can be rewritten as follows:

$$\begin{bmatrix} W_{11} & W_{12} \\ W_{21} & W_{22} \end{bmatrix} \begin{bmatrix} \lambda_0 E + H & 0 \\ 0 & -\lambda_0 E - H \end{bmatrix}$$
$$+ \begin{bmatrix} \lambda_0 E + H' & 0 \\ 0 & -\lambda_0 E - H' \end{bmatrix} \begin{bmatrix} W_{11} & W_{12} \\ W_{21} & W_{22} \end{bmatrix} = 0. \tag{57}$$

By completing the indicated operations on the block matrices on the left side of matrix equation (57), we can replace this equation with the system of four matrix equations:

$$\begin{array}{ll} 1) & H'W_{11} + W_{11}(2\lambda_0 E + H) = 0, \\ 2) & H'W_{12} - W_{12} H = 0, \\ 3) & H'W_{21} - W_{21} H = 0, \\ 4) & H'W_{22} + W_{22}(2\lambda_0 E + H) = 0. \end{array} \right\} \tag{58}$$

[10] The factor $2i$ is again introduced for convenience.

The equation $AX - XB = 0$, where A and B are square matrices without common characteristic numbers, has only the zero solution $X = 0$.[11] Therefore the first and fourth equations (58) give: $W_{11} = W_{22} = 0$.[12] Concerning the second of these equations, as we saw in the proof of Theorem 5, this equation can be satisfied by taking

$$W_{12} = V = \begin{bmatrix} 0 & \ldots & 0 & 1 \\ 0 & \ldots & 1 & 0 \\ \cdot & \cdot & \cdot & \cdot \\ 1 & \ldots & 0 & 0 \end{bmatrix}, \tag{59}$$

(by virtue of (36)):

$$VH - H'V = 0.$$

From the symmetry of matrices W and V, it follows that

$$W_{21} = W'_{12} = V.$$

Then equation 3 is also satisfied automatically.
Thus,

$$W = \begin{pmatrix} 0 & V \\ V & 0 \end{pmatrix} = V^{(2p)}. \tag{60}$$

But then, as was explained on p. 12, equation (56) will be satisfied, by placing:

$$T = E^{(2p)} - iV^{(2p)}. \tag{61}$$

Further,

$$T^{-1} = \tfrac{1}{2}(E^{(2p)} + iV^{(2p)}). \tag{62}$$

Consequently, the antisymmetric matrix being sought will be found by the formula [13]

---

[11] The equation $AX = XB$ can be written $A_1Y = YB_1$, with $Y = S^{-1}XT$, $A_1 = S^{-1}AS$, $B_1 = T^{-1}BT$. With A_1, B_1 in Jordan normal form, the conclusion follows in an elementary way from a detailed consideration of the relation $A_1Y = YB_1$.

[12] With $\lambda_0 \neq 0$, equations (1) and (4) have no solutions other than zero solutions. With $\lambda_0 = 0$, other solutions exist, but we are selecting only the zero solutions.

[13] Here we apply equalities (55) and (60). It follows from these equalities that $V^{(2p)}J_{\lambda_0}^{(pp)}V^{(2p)} = -J_{\lambda_0}^{(pp)}$.

$$K_{\lambda_0}^{(pp)} = \tfrac{1}{2}[E^{(2p)} - iV^{(2p)}] J_{\lambda_0}^{(pp)}[E^{(2p)} + iV^{(2p)}]$$
$$= \tfrac{1}{2}[J_{\lambda_0}^{(pp)} - J_{\lambda_0}^{(pp)\prime} + i(J_{\lambda_0}^{(pp)}V^{(2p)} - V^{(2p)}J_{\lambda_0}^{(pp)})]. \quad (63)$$

Substituting in place of $J_{\lambda_0}^{(pp)}$ and $V^{(2p)}$ the corresponding block matrices from (54) and (60), we find:

$$K_{\lambda_0}^{(pp)} = \frac{1}{2}\left\{ \begin{bmatrix} H-H' & 0 \\ 0 & H'-H \end{bmatrix} + i \begin{bmatrix} \lambda_0 E+H & 0 \\ 0 & -\lambda_0 E-H \end{bmatrix} \begin{bmatrix} 0 & V \\ V & 0 \end{bmatrix} \right.$$
$$\left. - i \begin{bmatrix} 0 & V \\ V & 0 \end{bmatrix} \begin{bmatrix} \lambda_0 E+H & 0 \\ 0 & -\lambda_0 E-H \end{bmatrix} \right\}$$
$$= \frac{1}{2}\begin{bmatrix} H-H' & i(2\lambda_0 V+HV+VH) \\ -i(2\lambda_0 V+HV+VH) & H'-H \end{bmatrix}, \quad (64)$$

i.e.,

$$K_{\lambda_0}^{(pp)} = \tfrac{1}{2} \begin{bmatrix}
0 & 1 & & & & 0 & 0 & & & & i & 2\lambda_0 \\
-1 & 0 & & & & & & & & 2\lambda_0 & i \\
& & & & & & & & & & & \\
& & & & & 1 & i & & & & \\
0 & & & -1 & 0 & 2\lambda_0, & i & & & 0 \\
\hline
0 & & & -i, & -2\lambda_0 & 0 & -1 & & & 0 \\
& & & -2\lambda_0, & -i & 1 & 0 & & \\
& & & & & & & & & -1 \\
-i & & & & & & & & \\
-2\lambda_0 & -i & & & 0 & 0 & & & 1 & 0
\end{bmatrix}. \quad (65)$$

Now let us construct an antisymmetric matrix $K^{(q)}$, of qth order, which has one elementary divisor λ^q, where q is an odd number. It is obvious that the antisymmetric matrix sought will be similar to the matrix

$$J^{(q)} = \begin{bmatrix} 0 & 1 & 0 & . & . & . & . & . & . & 0 \\ 0 & 0 & 1 & & & & & & & . \\ . & & . & . & & & & & & . \\ . & & & . & . & & & & & . \\ . & & & & . & . & & & & . \\ . & & & & & . & . & -1 & 0 & \\ . & & & & & & . & 0 & -1 & \\ 0 & & . & . & . & & & 0 & & 0 \end{bmatrix}.$$

(66)

In this matrix, all the elements are zero except those in the first superdiagonal; here, the first $\frac{1}{2}(q-1)$ elements are $+1$, and the remaining $\frac{1}{2}(q-1)$ elements are -1. If we set

$$K^{(q)} = T J^{(q)} T^{-1},$$

(67)

we find from the condition of antisymmetry

$$W_1 J^{(q)} + J^{(q)\prime} W_1 = 0,$$

(68)

where

$$T'T = -2iW_1.$$

(69)

By direct calculation we can demonstrate that the matrix

$$W_1 = V^{(q)} = \begin{bmatrix} 0 & . . . & 0 & 1 \\ 0 & . . . & 1 & 0 \\ . & . . . . . \\ 1 & . . . & 0 & 0 \end{bmatrix}$$

satisfies equation (68). Taking this value for W_1, we find from (69), as before:

$$T = E^{(q)} - iV^{(q)}, \quad T^{-1} = \tfrac{1}{2}[E^{(q)} + iV^{(q)}],$$

(70)

$$K^{(q)} = \tfrac{1}{2}[E^{(q)} - iV^{(q)}]J^{(q)}[E^{(q)} + iV^{(q)}]$$
$$= \tfrac{1}{2}[J^{(q)} - J^{(q)\prime} + i(J^{(q)}V^{(q)} - V^{(q)}J^{(q)})].$$

(71)

Performing the corresponding computations, we find:

$$K^{(q)} = \begin{bmatrix} 0 & 1 & & & & & 0 \\ -1 & 0 & \cdot & & & & \\ & \cdot & \cdot & \cdot & & & \\ & & \cdot & \cdot & \cdot & & \\ & & & \cdot & \cdot & \cdot & \\ & & & & \cdot & \cdot & -1 \\ 0 & & & & & 1 & 0 \end{bmatrix} + i \begin{bmatrix} 0 & & & & & 1 & 0 \\ & & & & & & 1 \\ & & & & \cdot & \cdot & \\ & & & \cdot & \cdot & & \\ & & \cdot & \cdot & & & \\ -1 & \cdot & \cdot & & & & \\ 0 & -1 & & \cdots & & & 0 \end{bmatrix} . \quad (72)$$

Let arbitrary elementary divisors which satisfy the conditions of Theorem 7 be given:[14]

$$(\lambda - \lambda_j)^{p_j}, \quad (\lambda + \lambda_j)^{p_j} \qquad (j = 1, 2, \ldots, u), \\ \lambda^{q_k}(k = 1, 2, \ldots, v; \; q_1, q_2, \ldots, q_v, \text{ odd numbers.}) \quad (73)$$

Then the block diagonal antisymmetric matrix

$$\tilde{K} = \{ K_{\lambda_1}^{(p_1 p_1)}, \ldots, K_{\lambda_u}^{(p_u p_u)}; \; K^{(q_1)}, \ldots, K^{(q_v)} \} \quad (74)$$

has the elementary divisors (73).
The theorem is proved.

COROLLARY. *An arbitrary complex antisymmetric matrix K is orthogonally-similar to an antisymmetric matrix which has the normal form $\tilde{K}$ which is defined by* (74), (65), (72), *i.e., there exists a (complex) orthogonal matrix O such that*

$$K = O\tilde{K}O^{-1}. \quad (75)$$

REMARK. If K is a real antisymmetric matrix, then it has linear elementary divisors.

$$\lambda - i\varphi_1, \; \lambda + i\varphi_1, \ldots, \lambda - i\varphi_u, \; \lambda + i\varphi_u, \; \underbrace{\lambda, \ldots, \lambda}_{v \text{ times}}$$

In this case, if we set all $p_j = 1$ and all $q_k = 1$, in (74), we obtain

---

[14] Some of the numbers, $\lambda_1, \lambda_2, \ldots, \lambda_u$ may also be equal to zero. In addition, one of the numbers u and v may be equal to zero, i.e., in a special case there may be only elementary divisors of one type.

the normal form of a real antisymmetric matrix

$$\tilde{K} = \left\{ \begin{bmatrix} 0 & \varphi_1 \\ -\varphi_1 & 0 \end{bmatrix}, \ldots, \begin{bmatrix} 0 & \varphi_u \\ -\varphi_u & 0 \end{bmatrix}, 0, \ldots, 0 \right\}.$$

In this case, moreover, the transforming matrix can be taken as real (as is well known in view of the remark that an anti-symmetric operator is normal).

§ 5. Normal form of a complex orthogonal matrix

We begin by expounding the following theorem, which specifies the types of elementary divisors which an orthogonal matrix can have.

THEOREM 9. *1. If λ_0 ($\lambda_0^2 \neq 1$) is a characteristic number of the orthogonal matrix O, and to this characteristic number correspond the elementary divisors*

$$(\lambda - \lambda_0)^{f_1}, \ (\lambda - \lambda_0)^{f_2}, \ldots, (\lambda - \lambda_0)^{f_t},$$

than $1/\lambda_0$ is also a characteristic number of matrix O, and to this characteristic number correspond the particular elementary divisors:

$$(\lambda - \lambda_0^{-1})^{f_1}, \ (\lambda - \lambda_0^{-1})^{f_2}, \ldots, (\lambda - \lambda_0^{-1})^{f_t}.$$

2. If $\lambda_0 = \pm 1$ is a characteristic number of the orthogonal matrix 0, then the elementary divisors of even degree which correspond to this characteristic number λ_0 are repeated an even number of times.

Proof. *1.* If O is any nonsingular matrix, then to each elementary divisor $(\lambda - \lambda_0)^f$ of O there corresponds the elementary divisor $(\lambda - \lambda_0^{-1})^f$ of O^{-1}. [15] On the other hand, the matrices O and O' always have the same elementary divisors. Therefore, from the condition of orthogonality: $O' = O^{-1}$, the first part of our theorem follows at once.

[15] Let $H^{(p)}$ be the $p \times p$ matrix with 1's in the super-diagonal and 0's elsewhere. A canonical matrix with elementary divisor $(x - x_0)^p$ is $x_0E - x_0^2H^{(p)}$. The inverse matrix $x_0^{-1}E + H^{(p)} + x_0H^{(p)} + \ldots$ has a $(p-1) \times (p-1)$ minor of determinant 1, so its elementary divisor is $(x - x_0^{-1})^p$ (see Bôcher [6]).

2. Suppose that the number 1 is a characteristic number of the matrix O, and that the number -1 is not: $\det(E - O) = 0 \neq \det(E + O)$. Then we will make use of Cayley's formulas valid for real or complex matrices. We define the matrix K by the equality

$$K = (E - O)(E + O)^{-1} = (E + O)^{-1}(E - O). \quad O' = O^{-1}. \quad (76)$$

We compute $(E + O)[K + K'](E + O') = 0$, showing $K' = -K$, i.e., that K is an antisymmetric matrix. To solve equation (76) for O, we note first

$$E + K = [(E + O) + (E - O)](E + O)^{-1} = [2E](E + O)^{-1};$$

thus $E + K$ is invertible:

$$O = (E - K)(E + K)^{-1}.$$

If we set

$$f(\lambda) = \frac{1 - \lambda}{1 + \lambda},$$

we have

$$f'(\lambda) = -\frac{2}{(1 + \lambda)^2} \neq 0.$$

Consequently, in the matrix $O = f(K)$, the elementary divisors of K do not split.[16] Therefore, those elementary divisors of the matrix O, which have the form $(\lambda - 1)^{2p}$ are repeated an even number of times, since this holds for the corresponding elementary divisors λ^{2p} of the matrix K (see Theorem 7).

The case in which the orthogonal matrix O has -1 but not $+1$ as a characteristic number can be reduced to the case discussed above by replacing O by $-O$ in the above argument.

Now let us consider the general case, in which the matrix O has both $+1$ and -1 as characteristic numbers. Let us denote the minimum polynomial (of degree m) of matrix O by $\psi(\lambda)$.

[16] The argument is similar to that of the preceding footnote (in which $f(x)$ was just $1/x$). In fact, we consider $f(x_0E + H) = f(x_0)E + f'(x_0)H + \frac{1}{2}f''(x_0)H^2 + \ldots$.

Applying the part of the theorem already proved, we can write $\psi(\lambda)$ in the form

$$\psi(\lambda) = (\lambda - 1)^{m_1} (\lambda + 1)^{m_2} \prod_{j=1}^{u} (\lambda - \lambda_j)^{p_j} (\lambda - \lambda_j^{-1})^{p_j}$$

$$(\lambda_j^2 \neq 1;\ j = 1, 2, \ldots, u).$$

Let us consider the polynomial $g(\lambda)$ of degree $< m = \deg \psi(\lambda)$ for which $g(1) = 1$, and all the remaining $m - 1$ values on the spectrum of matrix O are equal to zero, and let us set:[17]

$$P = g(O). \tag{77}$$

Let us note that the functions $[g(\lambda)]^2$ and $g(1/\lambda)$ assume the same values on the spectrum of matrix O as the function $g(\lambda)$. Therefore,

$$P^2 = P,\ P' = g(O') = g(O^{-1}) = P \tag{78}$$

i.e., P is a symmetric projection matrix.[18]

Let us define the polynomial $h(\lambda)$ and the matrix Q by the equalities

$$h(x) = (x - 1)g(x), \tag{79}$$

$$Q = h(O) = (O - E)P. \tag{80}$$

Since the m_1th power of $h(x)$ becomes zero on the spectrum of matrix O, this power is divisible by $\psi(\lambda)$. Hence it follows that:

$$Q^{m_1} = 0,$$

i.e., Q is a nilpotent matrix with index of nilpotency m_1.

---

[17] From the basic formula (see Appendix II)

$$g(A) = \sum_{k=1}^{s} [g(\lambda_k)Z_{k1} + g'(\lambda_k)Z_{k2} + \ldots]$$

it follows that

$$P = Z_{11}.$$

[18] The operator P is called a projection, if $P^2 = P$. Thus a matrix P, such that $P^2 = P$, is called a *projection* matrix. A projection P in a unitary space R is an operator which projects the vector $x \in R$ orthogonally into a subspace $S = PR$, i.e., $Px = x_s$, where $x_s \in S$ and $(x - x_s) \perp S$.

From (80) we find [19]

$$Q' = (O' - E)P. \tag{81}$$

Let us consider the matrix

$$R = Q(Q' + 2E). \tag{82}$$

From (78), (80), (81), $OO' = E$, it follows that:

$$R = QQ' + 2Q = (O - O')P.$$

From this representation of the matrix R, it is seen that R *is an antisymmetric matrix.*

On the other hand, from (82)

$$R^k = Q^k(Q + 2E)^k \qquad (k = 1, 2, \ldots). \tag{83}$$

But with Q, Q' is a nilpotent matrix and, consequently, $Q' + 2E$ is nonsingular; indeed $[E + \frac{1}{2}Q']^{-1}$ is a polynomial $E - \frac{1}{2}Q' + \frac{1}{4}Q'^2 - \ldots$ in Q'. Therefore, from (83) it follows that, for any k, the matrices R^k and Q^k have the same rank.

But if k is odd, the matrix R^k is antisymmetric, and therefore (see p. 14) has even rank. Consequently, each of the matrices

$$Q, Q^3, Q^5, \ldots$$

has an odd rank.

Therefore, arguing with the matrix Q in exactly the same manner as we argued on p. 16 with the matrix K, we can state that of the elementary divisors of matrix Q, those divisors which have the form λ^{2p} are repeated an even number of times. But to each elementary divisor λ^{2p} of the matrix Q there corresponds an elementary divisor $(\lambda - 1)^{2p}$ of the matrix O, and vice versa.[20] Hence it follows that of the elementary divisors of the matrix O, those divisors which have the form $(\lambda - 1)^{2p}$ are repeated an even number of times.

[19] All the matrices $P, Q, Q', O' = O^{-1}$ which play a part here are permutatable with one other and with O, since they are all functions of O.

[20] Since $h(1) = 0$, $h'(1) \neq 0$, then in forming the matrix $Q = h(O)$ from the matrix O, the elementary divisors of form $(\lambda - 1)^{2p}$ of the matrix O do not split, and are replaced by the elementary divisors λ^{2p}.

We can make the corresponding assertion for the divisors of the form $(\lambda + 1)^{2p}$ by arguing as above with the matrix $-C$ in place of O. Thus, the theorem is completely proved. Let us now prove the converse theorem.

THEOREM 10. *Any system of powers of the form*

$$
\left.
\begin{array}{l}
(\lambda - \lambda_j)^{p_j}, \ (\lambda - \lambda_j^{-1})^{p_j} \quad (\lambda_j \neq 0; \ j = 1, 2, \ldots, u), \\
(\lambda - 1)^{q_1}, \ (\lambda - 1)^{q_2}, \ldots, (\lambda - 1)^{q_v}, \\
(\lambda + 1)^{t_1}, \ (\lambda + 1)^{t_2}, \ldots, (\lambda + 1)^{t_w} \\
(q_1, \ldots, q_v, \ t_1, \ldots, t_w, \ \text{odd numbers}
\end{array}
\right\}
\quad (84)
$$

is a system of elementary divisors of a certain complex orthogonal matrix O.[21]

Proof. Let us designate by μ_j numbers which are related to the numbers λ_j $(j = 1, 2, \ldots, u)$ by the equalities

$$
\lambda_j = e^{\mu_j} \quad (j = 1, 2, \ldots, u).
$$

Let us introduce into the discussion "canonical" antisymmetric matrices (see the preceding section)

$$
K_{\mu_j}^{(p_j p_j)} \quad (j = 1, 2, \ldots, u); \ K^{(q_1)}, \ldots, K^{(q_v)}; \ K^{(t_1)}, \ldots, K^{(t_w)},
$$

which have respectively the following elementary divisors

$$
(\lambda - \mu_j)^{p_j}, \ (\lambda + \mu_j)^{p_j} \quad (j = 1, 2, \ldots, u); \ \lambda^{q_1}, \ldots, \lambda^{q_v}; \ \lambda^{t_1}, \ldots, \lambda^{t_w}.
$$

If K is an antisymmetric matrix, then $O = e^K$ is orthogonal $(O' = e^{K'} = e^{-K} = O^{-1})$. Also, to each elementary divisor $(\lambda - \mu)^p$ of matrix K there corresponds the elementary divisor $(\lambda - e^\mu)^p$ of matrix O.[22]

Therefore, the block diagonal matrix

$$
\tilde{O} = \left\{ e^{K_{\mu_1}^{(p_1 p_1)}}, \ldots, e^{K_{\mu_u}^{(p_u p_u)}}; \ e^{K^{(q_1)}}, \ldots, e^{K^{(q_v)}}; \ -e^{K^{(t_1)}}, \ldots, -e^{K^{(t_w)}} \right\} \quad (85)
$$

[21] Certain (or even all) of the numbers λ_j may be equal to ± 1. One or two of the three numbers u, v, w may be equal to zero. Then the elementary divisors of corresponding matrix O are absent.

[22] This follows from the fact that with $f(\lambda) = e^\lambda$ we have: $f'(\lambda) = e^\lambda \neq 0$ for any λ.

s orthogonal and has the elementary divisors (84). The theorem
s proved.

From Theorems 4, 9 and 10, there follows the

COROLLARY. *An arbitrary (complex) orthogonal matrix O is
always orthogonally similar to an orthogonal matrix which has the
normal form $\tilde{O}$ above, i.e., there exists an orthogonal matrix O_1,
such that*

$$O = O_1 \tilde{O} O_1^{-1}. \tag{86}$$

Note: It is possible to give a precise picture of the form of the
diagonal cells or blocks in the normal form $\tilde{O}$, as was done for the
antisymmetric matrix $\tilde{K}$.[23]

For further researches in this subject, see [48], which gives
decomposition theorems for matrices which are orthogonal in
the extended sense (i.e., $OGO' = G$ for some fixed invertible G).

---

[23] See [71].

CHAPTER II

Singular Bundles of Matrices

§ 1. Introduction

1. This chapter deals with the following problem:

Given four matrices A, B, A_1, B_1 of the same dimensions $m \times n$ with elements from the field K. It is required to find the conditions under which there exist two square nonsingular matrices P and Q respectively of orders m and n, such that the following relationships hold simultaneously [1]

$$PAQ = A_1, \quad PBQ = B_1. \tag{1}$$

By introducing the pencils of matrices $A + \lambda B$ and $A_1 + \lambda B_1$, the two matrix equalities (1) may be replaced by one equality:

$$P(A + \lambda B)Q = A_1 + \lambda B_1. \tag{2}$$

DEFINITION 1. *Two pencils of rectangular matrices $A + \lambda B$ and $A_1 + \lambda B_1$ of the same dimensions $m \times n$, which are connected by equality* (2), *and in which P and Q are moreover constant (i.e., independent of λ) square nonsingular matrices of respective dimensions m and n will be called by us* strictly equivalent.

According to the general definition of equivalence of λ-matrices, the pencils $A + \lambda B$ and $A_1 + \lambda B_1$ are equivalent if an equality of the form (2) holds, in which P and Q are two square λ-matrices with determinants which are constant and different from zero.

---

[1] If such matrices P and Q exist in a superfield, their elements can be assumed to be in the field K. This follows from the fact that the relations (1) can be written in the form

$$PA = A_1 Q^{-1}, \quad PB = B_1 Q^{-1},$$

and hence can be thought of as a system of linear homogeneous equations in the elements of P and Q^{-1}, with coefficients in K.

For strict equivalence, it is also required that the matrices P and Q be independent of λ.[2]

The criterion of (general) equivalence of the pencils $A + \lambda B$ and $A_1 + \lambda B_1$ follows from the general criterion of equivalence of λ-matrices and is that the invariant polynomials, or, equivalently the elementary divisors of the pencils $A + \lambda B$ and $A_1 + \lambda B_1$ be the same.

In this chapter, a criterion for strict equivalence of two pencils of matrices will be established, and for each pencil there will be determined a canonical form which is strictly equivalent to it.

2. The problem stated permits of a natural geometrical interpretation. Consider the pencil of linear operators $\boldsymbol{A} + \lambda \boldsymbol{B}$, which maps $\boldsymbol{R}_n$ into $\boldsymbol{R}_m$. With a definite selection of bases in these spaces, to the pencil of operators $\boldsymbol{A} + \lambda \boldsymbol{B}$ there corresponds the pencil of rectangular matrices $A + \lambda B$ (of dimension $m \times n$); if there is a change of bases in $\boldsymbol{R}_n$ and $\boldsymbol{R}_m$, the pencil $A + \lambda B$ is replaced by the strictly equivalent pencil $P(A + \lambda B)Q$, where P and Q are square nonsingular matrices of the orders m and n. Thus, the problem of strict equivalence is to pick out those properties of a pencil of matrices $A + \lambda B$ (of dimension $m \times n$), which describe a fixed pencil of operators $\boldsymbol{A} + \lambda \boldsymbol{B}$, mapping $\boldsymbol{R}_n$ into $\boldsymbol{R}_m$, independent of the selection of bases in these spaces.

To obtain the canonical form of a pencil, we find the bases in $\boldsymbol{R}_n$ and $\boldsymbol{R}_m$, for which the pencil of operators $\boldsymbol{A} + \lambda \boldsymbol{B}$ is described by a matrix of simplest possible form.

Since the pencil of operators is determined by the two operators $\boldsymbol{A}$ and $\boldsymbol{B}$, it is also possible to state that *this chapter is concerned with the simultaneous study of two operators $\boldsymbol{A}$ and $\boldsymbol{B}$, which map $\boldsymbol{R}_n$ into $\boldsymbol{R}_m$.*

3. Pencils of matrices $A + \lambda B$ of dimension $m \times n$ are classified into two fundamental types: *regular* and *singular* pencils.

DEFINITION 2. *A pencil of matrices $A + \lambda B$ is called* regular *if 1. A and B are square matrices of the same order n and 2*

---

[2] We have used the term "strictly equivalent" in order to emphasize the fact that the term "equivalent" used in the literature allows (more generally) that the elements of P and Q be functions of λ.

he determinant det $(A + \lambda B)$ is not identically equal to zero in λ). In any other cases ($m \neq n$ or $m = n$, but det $(A + \lambda B) \equiv 0$) he pencil is called *singular*.

The criterion of strict equivalence, and also the canonical form or regular pencils of matrices were established by K. Weierstrass n 1867 [70] on the basis of his theory of elementary divisors. Similar problems for singular pencils were solved later, in 1890, n the investigations of L. Kronecker [36].[3] The results of Kronecker comprise the main contents of this chapter. For an elementary exposition of the Weierstrass theory, see [6].

§ 2. Regular pencils of matrices

1. Let us consider the special case where the pencils $A + \lambda B$ and $A_1 + \lambda B_1$ consist of square matrices $(m = n)$ and let $B \neq 0$, det $B_1 \neq 0$. In this case, as proved in [6, p. 279], the two concepts "equivalence" and "strict equivalence" of pencils coincide.[3a] Therefore, applying to the pencils the general criterion of equivalency of λ-matrices, we arrive at the theorem:

THEOREM 1. *Two pencils of square matrices of the same order* $A + \lambda B$ *and* $A_1 + \lambda B_1$, *in which* det $B \neq 0$ *and* det $B_1 \neq 0$, *are strictly equivalent only in case these pencils have the same elementary divisors in the field K.*

A pencil $A + \lambda B$ of square matrices with det $B \neq 0$ is called regular, since it is a special case of a regular matrix polynomial in λ. In the preceding section of this chapter, we used the term "regular" for a wider class of pencils. According to this definition, in the regular pencil it is possible to have the equality det $B = 0$ (and even det $A = $ det $B = 0$).

To ascertain whether Theorem 1 will apply also to regular pencils (in the extended Definition 1), let us consider the following example:

---

[3] Further literature employing a different point of view is found in [35a, 39, 65].

[3a] If equation (2) holds for some matrices P, Q whose elements are polynomials, then it holds also for some matrices P_1, Q_1 with constant elements. See [6, p. 279].

$$A + \lambda B = \begin{bmatrix} 2 & 1 & 3 \\ 3 & 2 & 5 \\ 3 & 2 & 6 \end{bmatrix} + \lambda \begin{bmatrix} 1 & 1 & 2 \\ 1 & 1 & 2 \\ 1 & 1 & 3 \end{bmatrix}, \quad A_1 + \lambda B_1 = \begin{bmatrix} 2 & 1 & 1 \\ 1 & 2 & 1 \\ 1 & 1 & 1 \end{bmatrix} + \lambda \begin{bmatrix} 1 & 1 & 1 \\ 1 & 1 & 1 \\ 1 & 1 & 1 \end{bmatrix}$$

It is easily seen that here each of the pencils $A + \lambda B$ and $A_1 + \lambda B_1$ has only one elementary divisor $\lambda + 1$. At the same time, these pencils are not strictly equivalent, since the matrices B and B_1 have ranks 2 and 1 respectively; but equality (2) would imply that the ranks of matrices B and B_1 are equal. Also, pencils (3) are regular, according to definition 1, since

$$\det (A + \lambda B) = \det (A_1 + \lambda B_1) = \lambda + 1.$$

The above example indicates that Theorem 1 is not true for the extended definition of a regular pencil.

2. For Theorem 1 to retain its validity, we must introduce the concept of "infinite" elementary divisors of a pencil. We define the pencil $A + \lambda B$ by means of "homogeneous" parameters λ, μ; $\mu A + \lambda B$. Then the determinant $\Delta(\lambda, \mu) \equiv \det (\mu A + \lambda B)$ will be a homogeneous function of λ, μ. We denote the greatest common divisor of all $k \times k$ minors of the matrix $\mu A + \lambda B$ $(k = 1, 2, \ldots, n)$ by $D_k(\lambda, \mu)$, and we obtain invariant polynomials by the well-known formulas

$$i_1(\lambda, \mu) = \frac{D_n(\lambda, \mu)}{D_{n-1}(\lambda, \mu)}, \quad i_2(\lambda, \mu) = \frac{D_{n-1}(\lambda, \mu)}{D_{n-2}(\lambda, \mu)}, \ldots;$$

here, all $D_k(\lambda, \mu)$ and $i_j(\lambda, \mu)$ are homogeneous polynomials in λ and μ. By factoring the invariant polynomials into powers of homogeneous irreducible polynomials in the field K, we obtain the elementary divisors $e_2(\lambda, \mu)$ $(\alpha = 1, 2, \ldots)$ of the pencil $\mu A + \lambda B$ in the field K.

It is quite obvious that by placing $\mu = 1$ in $e_2(\lambda, \mu)$, we will obtain again the elementary divisors $e_\alpha(\lambda)$ of pencil $A + \lambda B$. Conversely, from each elementary divisor $e_\alpha(\lambda)$ of power q of pencil $A + \lambda B$ we will obtain the corresponding elementary divisor $e_\alpha(\lambda, \mu)$ by the formula $e_\alpha(\lambda, \mu) = \mu^q e_\alpha(\lambda/\mu)$. All the elementary divisors of the pencil $\mu A + \lambda B$ with the exception of elementary divisors of the form μ^q, can be obtained in this manner.

Elementary divisors of the form μ^q exist only in case det $B = 0$, and are called "infinite" elementary divisors for the $A + \lambda B$. Since from the strict equivalence of the pencils $A + \lambda B$ and $A_1 + \lambda B_1$ there follows the strict equivalence of the pencils $\mu A + \lambda B$ and $\mu A_1 + \lambda B_1$, then in the strictly equivalent pencils $A + \lambda B$ and $A_1 + \lambda B_1$ not only the "finite," but also the "infinite" elementary divisors should coincide.

Let there now be given two regular pencils $A + \lambda B$ and $A_1 + \lambda B_1$, of which all the elementary divisors (including the infinite elementary divisors) coincide. Let us introduce homogeneous parameters: $\mu A + \lambda B$, $\mu A_1 + \lambda B_1$. We transform the parameters:

$$\lambda = \alpha_1 \tilde{\lambda} + \alpha_2 \tilde{\mu},$$
$$\mu = \beta_1 \tilde{\lambda} + \beta_2 \tilde{\mu} \qquad (\alpha_1 \beta_2 - \alpha_2 \beta_1 \neq 0).$$

In the new parameters, the pencils are written down as follows: $\tilde{\mu}\tilde{A} + \tilde{\lambda}\tilde{B}$, $\tilde{\mu}\tilde{A}_1 + \tilde{\lambda}\tilde{B}_1$, where $\tilde{B} = \beta_1 A + \alpha_1 B$, $\tilde{B}_1 = \beta_1 A_1 + \alpha_1 B_1$. From the regularity of the pencils $\mu A + \lambda B$, and $\mu A_1 + \lambda B_1$, it follows that the numbers α_1 and β_1 may be selected so that det $\tilde{B} \neq 0$ and det $\tilde{B}_1 \neq 0$.

Therefore, according to Theorem 1, the pencils $\tilde{\mu}\tilde{A} + \tilde{\lambda}\tilde{B}$ and $\tilde{\mu}\tilde{A}_1 + \tilde{\lambda}\tilde{B}_1$, and, consequently, the original pencils $\mu A + \lambda B$ and $\mu A_1 + \lambda B_1$ (or, what is the same, $A + \lambda B$ and $A_1 + \lambda B_1$) are strictly equivalent. Thus, we arrived at the following generalization of Theorem 1.

THEOREM 2. *In order that the two regular pencils $A + \lambda B$ and $A_1 + \lambda B_1$ be strictly equivalent, it is necessary and sufficient that these pencils have the same ("finite" and "infinite") elementary divisors.*

In the preceding example, pencils (3) had the same "finite" elementary divisor $\lambda + 1$, but different "infinite" elementary divisors (the first pencil has one "infinite" elementary divisor μ^2 and the second has two: μ, μ). Therefore, these pencils are not strictly equivalent.

3. Let there now be given an arbitrary regular pencil $A + \lambda B$. Then there exists a number c, such that $\det (A + cB) \neq 0$. The given pencil can be represented in the form $A_1 + (\lambda - c)B$, where $A_1 = A + cB$, and therefore $\det A_1 \neq 0$. Multiply the pencil on the left by A_1^{-1}; obtaining $E + (\lambda - c)A_1^{-1}B$. By a similarity transformation we can reduce this pencil to the form [4]

$$E + (\lambda - c)\{J_0, \ J_1\} = \{E - cJ_0 + \lambda J_0, \ E - cJ_1 + \lambda J_1\}, \quad (4)$$

where $\{J_0, \ J_1\}$ is the block diagonal normal form of the matrix $A_1^{-1}B$, J_0 a Jordan nilpotent matrix,[5] and $\det J_1 \neq 0$.

Let us multiply the first diagonal block of the right member of (4) by $(E - cJ_0)^{-1}$. We obtain: $E + \lambda(E - cJ_0)^{-1}J_0$. Here the coefficient of λ is a nilpotent matrix.[6] Therefore, by a similarity transformation this pencil can be reduced to the form [7]

$$E + \lambda \hat{J}_0 = \{N^{(u_1)}, \ N^{(u_2)}, \ldots, N^{(u_s)}\}$$
$$(N^{(u)} = E^{(u)} + \lambda H^{(u)}). \quad (5)$$

If we multiply the second diagonal block in the right member of (4) by J_1^{-1}, and then perform a similarity transformation, the second diagonal block can be reduced to the form $J + \lambda E$, where J is a matrix in normal form,[8] and E is the identity matrix. We have established the following theorem:

THEOREM 3. *An arbitrary regular pencil $A + \lambda B$ can be reduced to the (strictly equivalent) canonical quasi-diagonal form*

---

[4] The identity matrices E in the diagonal blocks of the right member of (4) have the same orders as J_0 and J_1 respectively.

[5] "Nilpotent" means that there is an integer $l > 0$ such that $J_0^l = 0$.

[6] From $J_0^l = 0$ the relation $[(E - cJ_0)^{-1}J_0]^l = 0$ follows.

[7] Here, $E^{(u)}$ is the identity matrix of order u, and $H^{(u)}$ is the matrix of order u in which the elements of the first superdiagonal are all unity, and the remaining elements are zero.

[8] Since the matrix J can be replaced by any matrix which is similar to it, it can be assumed that J is in canonical form (for example, in rational canonical form of the first or second kind, or Jordan form; see Appendices I, II.)

$$\{N^{(u_1)}, N^{(u_2)}, \ldots, N^{(u_s)}, J + \lambda E\}$$
$$(N^{(u)} = E^{(u)} + \lambda H^{(u)}), \tag{6}$$

where the first s diagonal blocks correspond to the infinite elementary divisors $\mu^{u_1}, \mu^{u_2}, \ldots, \mu^{u_s}$ *of the pencil* $A + \lambda B$, *and the normal form of the last diagonal block* $J + \lambda E$ *is uniquely determined by the finite elementary divisors of the given pencil.*

§ 3. Singular pencils. Theorem on reduction

Now let us consider a singular pencil $A + \lambda B$ of $m \times n$ matrices. Let us designate by r the *rank of the pencil,* i.e., the maximum order of a minor, the determinant of which is not identically equal to zero. From the singularity of the pencil, it follows that at least one of the inequalities $r < n$ or $r < m$ always holds. Let $r < n$. Then the columns of the λ-matrix $A + \lambda B$ are linearly dependent, i.e., the equation

$$(A + \lambda B)x = 0 \tag{7}$$

holds, where x is some nonzero column vector. Each nonzero solution x of this equation determines a certain linear dependence among the columns of the λ-matrix $A + \lambda B$. We will limit our discussion to those solutions $x(\lambda)$ of equation (7), which are polynomials in λ,[9] and among these solutions we will take a solution of minimum degree ε

$$x(\lambda) = x_0 - \lambda x_1 + \lambda^2 x_2 - \ldots + (-1)^\varepsilon \lambda^\varepsilon x_\varepsilon \quad (x_\varepsilon \neq 0). \tag{8}$$

On substituting this solution in (7) and separating powers of λ, we obtain:

$$Ax_0 = 0, \quad Bx_0 - Ax_1 = 0, \quad Bx_1 - Ax_2 = 0, \ldots,$$
$$Bx_{\varepsilon-1} - Ax_\varepsilon - 0, \quad Bx_\varepsilon = 0. \tag{9}$$

By considering this system of equalities as a system of linear

[9] In order to determine the elements of the column x satisfying equation (7), it is necessary to solve a system of linear homogeneous equations in which the coefficients of the unknowns are linear in λ. The fundamental linearly independent solutions x can always be selected so that their elements are polynomials in λ.

homogeneous equations in the elements of the columns $x_0,\ -x_1,$ $+x_2,\ \ldots,\ (-1)^\varepsilon x_\varepsilon$, we see that the matrix of the coefficients

$$M_\varepsilon = M_\varepsilon[A + \lambda B] = \overbrace{\begin{bmatrix} A & 0 & \cdots & & 0 \\ B & A & & & \\ 0 & B & \cdot & & \vdots \\ \cdot & & \cdot & \cdot & \vdots \\ \cdot & & & \cdot & \cdot & A \\ 0 & 0 & \cdots & & B \end{bmatrix}}^{\varepsilon+1} \qquad (10)$$

of this system has rank $\rho_\varepsilon < (\varepsilon + 1)n$. At the same time, because of the minimum property of the number ε, the ranks $\rho_1,\ \ldots,\ \rho_{\varepsilon-1}$ of the matrices

$$M_0 = \begin{bmatrix} A \\ B \end{bmatrix}, \quad M_1 = \begin{bmatrix} A & 0 \\ B & A \\ 0 & B \end{bmatrix}, \ldots, M_{\varepsilon-1} = \overbrace{\begin{bmatrix} A & 0 & \cdots & 0 \\ B & A & & \cdot \\ \cdot & \cdot & \cdot & \vdots \\ \cdot & & \cdot & \cdot \\ \cdot & & & \cdot & A \\ 0 & & & \cdots & B \end{bmatrix}}^{\varepsilon} \qquad (10')$$

satisfy the equalities $\rho_0 = n,\ \rho_1 = 2n,\ \ldots,\ \rho_{\varepsilon-1} = \varepsilon n$.

Thus, *the number ε is the smallest value of k, for which the sign "$<$" holds in the relationship* $\rho_k \leqq (k+1)n$.

Let us now formulate and prove the following fundamental theorem:

THEOREM 4. *If equation* (7) *has a solution of minimum degree ε and $\varepsilon > 0$, then the given pencil $A + \lambda B$ is strictly equivalent to a pencil of the form*

$$\begin{bmatrix} L_\varepsilon & 0 \\ 0 & \hat{A} + \lambda \hat{B} \end{bmatrix} \qquad (11)$$

where

$$L_\varepsilon = \overbrace{\begin{bmatrix} \lambda & 1 & 0 & \ldots & 0 & 0 \\ 0 & \lambda & 1 & & \cdot & \cdot \\ \cdot & \cdot & & \cdot & & \cdot \\ \cdot & & & & & \cdot \\ \cdot & & & & & \cdot \\ 0 & 0 & & \ldots & \lambda & 1 \end{bmatrix}}^{\varepsilon+1} \Big\}\varepsilon, \tag{12}$$

and $\hat{A} + \lambda\hat{B}$ is a pencil of matrices for which an equation similar to (7) does not have solutions of degree $< \varepsilon$.

We will divide the proof of the theorem into three parts. First we will prove that the given pencil $A + \lambda B$ is strictly equivalent to a pencil of the form

$$\begin{bmatrix} L_\varepsilon & D + \lambda F \\ 0 & \hat{A} + \lambda\hat{B} \end{bmatrix}, \tag{13}$$

where D, F, $\hat{A}$, $\hat{B}$ are constant rectangular matrices, of dimensions indicated in (12). Then we will establish that the equation $(\hat{A} + \lambda\hat{B})\hat{x} = 0$ does not have solutions $\hat{x}(\lambda)$ of degree $< \varepsilon$. After that we will show that by repeated transformations, the pencil (13) can be reduced to quasidiagonal form (11).

1. We will rephrase the first part of the proof in geometric form. In place of the pencil $A + \lambda B$ of matrices, we will consider the pencil $\boldsymbol{A} + \lambda\boldsymbol{B}$ of operators, which map $\boldsymbol{R}_n$ into $\boldsymbol{R}_m$, and we will show that with suitable selection of bases in these spaces the matrix which corresponds to operator $\boldsymbol{A} + \lambda\boldsymbol{B}$ will have the form (13).

In place of equation (7), let us take the vector equation

$$(\boldsymbol{A} + \lambda\boldsymbol{B})\boldsymbol{x} = 0 \tag{14}$$

with the vector solution

$$\boldsymbol{x}(\lambda) = \boldsymbol{x}_0 - \lambda\boldsymbol{x}_1 + \lambda^2\boldsymbol{x}_2 - \ldots + (-1)^\varepsilon \lambda^\varepsilon \boldsymbol{x}_\varepsilon; \tag{15}$$

equalities (9) are replaced by the vector equalities

$$\boldsymbol{A}\boldsymbol{x}_0 = 0, \boldsymbol{A}\boldsymbol{x}_1 = \boldsymbol{B}\boldsymbol{x}_0, \boldsymbol{A}\boldsymbol{x}_2 = \boldsymbol{B}\boldsymbol{x}_1, \ldots, \boldsymbol{A}\boldsymbol{x}_\varepsilon = \boldsymbol{B}\boldsymbol{x}_{\varepsilon-1}, \boldsymbol{B}\boldsymbol{x}_\varepsilon = 0. \tag{16}$$

We will prove below that the vectors

$$Ax_1, \; Ax_2, \ldots, Ax_\varepsilon \tag{17}$$

are linearly independent. From this the linear independence of the vectors

$$x_0, \; x_1, \ldots, x_\varepsilon \tag{18}$$

easily follows.

Indeed, since $Ax_0 = 0$, if $\alpha_0 x_0 + \alpha_1 x_1 + \ldots + \alpha_s x_s = 0$ should hold, we would obtain $\alpha_1 Ax_1 + \ldots + \alpha_\varepsilon Ax_\varepsilon = 0$; but since (17) are linearly independent, $\alpha_1 = \alpha_2 = \ldots = \alpha_\varepsilon = 0$. But $x_0 \neq 0$ since in the opposite case $x(\lambda)/\lambda$ would be a solution of equation (14) of degree $\varepsilon - 1$, which is impossible. Therefore, $\alpha_0 = 0$.

If vectors (17) and (18) respectively are now taken as initial base vectors for new bases in R_m and R_n then by (16), the matrices which correspond to the operators A, B with respect to these new bases will be

$$
\tilde{A} =
\overbrace{
\begin{bmatrix}
0 & 1 & & \ldots 0 & * \ldots * \\
0 & 0 & 1 & \ldots 0 & * \ldots * \\
\cdot & \cdot & & \cdot & \\
\cdot & \cdot & & \cdot & \ldots \\
\cdot & \cdot & & \cdot & \\
0 & 0 & & \ldots 1 & * \ldots * \\
0 & 0 & & \ldots 0 & * \ldots * \\
\cdot & \cdot & \cdot & \cdot & \cdot \\
0 & 0 & & \ldots 0 & * \ldots *
\end{bmatrix}}^{\varepsilon+1},
\quad
\tilde{B} =
\begin{bmatrix}
1 & 0 & \ldots 0 & 0 & * \ldots * \\
0 & 1 & \ldots 0 & 0 & * \ldots * \\
\cdot & & \cdot & \cdot & \\
\cdot & & \cdot & \cdot & \ldots \\
0 & 0 & \ldots 1 & 0 & * \ldots * \\
0 & 0 & \ldots 0 & 0 & * \ldots * \\
\cdot & \cdot & \cdot 0 & \cdot 0 & \cdot * \ldots * \\
0 & 0 & \ldots 0 & 0 & * \ldots *
\end{bmatrix}
$$

and the λ-matrix $\tilde{A} + \lambda\tilde{B}$ will have the form (13). To complete this part of the proof we must show that the vectors (17) are linearly independent. Let us assume the opposite, and let $Ax_h (h \geqq 1)$ be the first vector in (17), which is linearly dependent upon the preceding vectors:

$$Ax_h = \alpha_1 Ax_{h-1} + \alpha_2 Ax_{h-2} + \ldots + \alpha_{h-1} Ax_1.$$

In view of (16), this equality may be rewritten as follows:

$$Bx_{h-1} = \alpha_1 Bx_{h-2} + \alpha_2 Bx_{h-3} + \ldots + \alpha_{h-1} Bx_0,$$

e.,

$$Bx^*_{h-1} = 0,$$

with

$$x^*_{h-1} = x_{h-1} - \alpha_1 x_{h-2} - \alpha_2 x_{h-3} - \ldots - \alpha_{h-1} x_0.$$

Further, from (16),

$$Ax^*_{h-1} = B(x_{h-2} - \alpha_1 x_{h-3} - \ldots - \alpha_{h-2} x_0) = Bx^*_{h-2},$$

where

$$x^*_{h-2} = x_{h-2} - \alpha_1 x_{h-3} - \ldots - \alpha_{h-2} x_0.$$

Continuing this process further and introducing the vectors

$$x^*_{h-3} = x_{h-3} - \alpha_1 x_{h-4} - \ldots - \alpha_{h-3} x_0, \ldots, x^*_1 = x_1 - \alpha_1 x_0, \ x^*_0 = x_0,$$

we will obtain the chain of equalities

$$Bx^*_{h-1} = 0, \quad Ax^*_{h-1} = Bx^*_{h-2}, \ldots, Ax^*_1 = Bx^*_0, \quad Ax^*_0 = 0. \quad (19)$$

From (19) it follows that

$$x^*(\lambda) = x^*_0 - \lambda x^*_1 + \ldots + (-1)^{h-1}\lambda^{k-1} x^*_{h-1} \quad (x^*_0 = x_0 \neq 0)$$

is a nonzero solution of equation (14) of degree $\leq h - 1 < \varepsilon$, which is impossible. Thus, vectors (17) are linearly independent.

2. Let us now prove that the equation $(\hat{A} + \lambda\hat{B})\hat{x} = 0$ does not have solutions of degree $< \varepsilon$. First let us note that the equation $L_\varepsilon y = 0$ has a nonzero solution of minimum degree ε just as equation (7) has. This can be shown directly, if the matrix equation $L_\varepsilon y = 0$ is replaced by the system of ordinary equations

$$\lambda y_1 + y_2 = 0, \quad \lambda y_2 + y_3 = 0, \ldots, \lambda y_\varepsilon + y_{\varepsilon+1} = 0,$$

$[y = (y_1, y_2, \ldots, y_{\varepsilon+1})]$, hence $y_k = (-1)^{k-1} y_1 \lambda^{k-1} (k = 1, 2, \ldots, \varepsilon+1)$.

On the other hand, if the pencil has the "triangular" form (13), then the matrices M_k $(k = 0, 1, \ldots, \varepsilon)$ which correspond to this pencil (see (10) and (10′) on p. 36) can also be reduced, after a suitable permutation of rows and columns, to the triangular form

$$\begin{pmatrix} M_k[L_\varepsilon] & M_k[D + \lambda F] \\ 0 & M_k[\hat{A} + \lambda \hat{B}] \end{pmatrix}. \tag{20}$$

For $k = \varepsilon - 1$, all the columns of this matrix are linearly independent[10] since this is true for the columns of the matrix $M_{\varepsilon-1}[L_\varepsilon]$. But $M_{\varepsilon-1}[L_\varepsilon]$ is a square matrix of the order $\varepsilon(\varepsilon + 1)$. Therefore, the columns of the matrix $M_{\varepsilon-1}[\hat{A} + \lambda \hat{B}]$ are also linearly independent, and this means, as was shown in the beginning of this section, that the equation $(\hat{A} + \lambda \hat{B})\hat{x} = 0$ does not have a solution of degree $\leq \varepsilon - 1$, as was to be proved.

3. Let us replace pencil (13) by the pencil

$$\begin{bmatrix} E_1 & Y \\ 0 & E_2 \end{bmatrix} \begin{bmatrix} L_\varepsilon & D+\lambda F \\ 0 & \hat{A}+\lambda \hat{B} \end{bmatrix} \begin{bmatrix} E_3 & -X \\ 0 & E_4 \end{bmatrix} = \begin{bmatrix} L_\varepsilon & D+\lambda F+Y(\hat{A}+\lambda \hat{B})-L_\varepsilon X \\ 0 & \hat{A}+\lambda \hat{B} \end{bmatrix} \tag{21}$$

which is strictly equivalent to it; here E_1, E_2, E_3, E_4 are square identity matrices of the respective orders ε, $m - \varepsilon$, $\varepsilon + 1$ and $n - \varepsilon - 1$, and X, Y are arbitrary constant rectangular matrices of the corresponding dimensions. Our theorem will be completely proved if we show that the matrices X and Y can be selected so that the following matrix equality holds:

$$L_\varepsilon X = D + \lambda F + Y(\hat{A} + \lambda \hat{B}). \tag{22}$$

Let us introduce symbols for the elements of the matrices D, F, X, and also symbols for the rows of matrix Y, and for the columns of matrices $\hat{A}$, $\hat{B}$:

$$D = (d_{ik}), \quad F = (f_{ik}), \quad X = (x_{jk})$$

$$(i = 1, 2, \ldots, \varepsilon; \quad k = 1, 2, \ldots, n - \varepsilon - 1; \quad j = 1, 2, \ldots, \varepsilon + 1),$$

$$Y = \begin{bmatrix} y_1 \\ y_2 \\ \vdots \\ y_\varepsilon \end{bmatrix}, \quad \hat{A} = (a_1, a_2, \ldots, a_{n-\varepsilon-1}), \quad \hat{B} = (b_1, b_2, \ldots, b_{n-\varepsilon-1}).$$

Then matrix equation (22) can be replaced by a system of scalar

---

[10] This follows from the fact that, for $k = \varepsilon - 1$, the rank of the matrix (20) is εn; similarly for the rank of the matrix $M_{\varepsilon-1}[L_\varepsilon]$.

equations, obtained by equating the elements of the kth column in the left and right members of (22) ($k = 1, 2, \ldots, n - \varepsilon - 1$):

$$x_{2k} + \lambda x_{1k} = d_{1k} + \lambda f_{1k} + y_1 a_k + \lambda y_1 b_k ,$$
$$x_{3k} + \lambda x_{2k} = d_{2k} + \lambda f_{2k} + y_2 a_k + \lambda y_2 b_k ,$$
$$x_{4k} + \lambda x_{3k} = d_{3k} + \lambda f_{3k} + y_3 a_k + \lambda y_3 b_k , \qquad (23)$$
$$\cdots \cdots \cdots \cdots \cdots \cdots$$
$$x_{\varepsilon+1, k} + \lambda x_{\varepsilon k} = d_{\varepsilon k} + \lambda f_{\varepsilon k} + y_\varepsilon a_k + \lambda y_\varepsilon b_k$$
$$(k = 1, 2, \ldots, n - \varepsilon - 1).$$

The left members of these equalities are binomials linear with respect to λ. The constant member of each of the first $\varepsilon - 1$ of these binomials is equal to the coefficient of λ in the following binomial. But then the right members must also satisfy this condition. Therefore

$$y_1 a_k - y_2 b_k = f_{2k} - d_{1k},$$
$$y_2 a_k - y_3 b_k = f_{3k} - d_{2k}, \qquad (24)$$
$$\cdots \cdots \cdots \cdots$$
$$y_{\varepsilon-1} a_k - y_\varepsilon b_k = f_{\varepsilon k} - d_{\varepsilon-1, k}$$
$$(k = 1, 2, \ldots, n - \varepsilon - 1).$$

If equalities (24) hold, then, obviously, from (23) it is possible to determine the elements of matrix X being sought.

It now remains to show that the system of equations (24) in which the elements of matrix Y are unknown has a solution for any d_{ik} and f_{ik} ($i = 1, 2, \ldots, \varepsilon; k = 1, 2, \ldots, n - \varepsilon - 1$). Now the matrix of the coefficients of the unknown elements (viz., the rows $y_1, -y_2, y_3, -y_4, \ldots,$) has (after transposition) essentially the form

$$\overbrace{\begin{bmatrix} \hat{A} & 0 & \cdots & & 0 \\ \hat{B} & \hat{A} & & & \cdot \\ 0 & \hat{B} & \cdot & & \cdot \\ \cdot & & \cdot & \cdot & \cdot \\ \cdot & & & \cdot & \hat{A} \\ 0 & 0 & \cdots & & \hat{B} \end{bmatrix}}^{\varepsilon-1}.$$

But this matrix is the matrix $M_{\varepsilon-2}$ for the pencil of rectangular matrices $\hat{A} + \lambda\hat{B}$ [see (10') on p. 36]. The rank of this matrix is equal to $(\varepsilon - 1)(n - \varepsilon - 1)$, since as previously proved the equation $(\hat{A} + \lambda\hat{B})\hat{x} = 0$ does not have solutions of degree $< \varepsilon$. Thus, the rank of the system of equations (24) is equal to the number of equations, and such a system is always uniquely solvable. The theorem is completely proved.

§ 4. Canonical form of a singular pencil of matrices

Let a singular pencil $A + \lambda B$ of $m \times n$ matrices be given. First let us assume that there is no linear relation with constant coefficients among either the rows or the columns.

Let $r < n$, where r is the rank of the pencil, i.e., the columns of the pencil $A + \lambda B$ are linearly dependent. In this case, the equation $(A + \lambda B)x = 0$ has a nonzero solution of minimal degree ε_1. From the restriction imposed in the preceding paragraph, it follows that $\varepsilon_1 > 0$. Therefore, according to Theorem 4 the given pencil can be transformed to the form

$$\begin{bmatrix} L_{\varepsilon_1} & 0 \\ 0 & A_1 + \lambda B_1 \end{bmatrix},$$

where the equation $(A_1 + \lambda B_1)x^{(1)} = 0$ does not have solutions $x^{(1)}$ of degree $< \varepsilon_1$.

If this equation has a nonzero solution of minimal degree ε_2 (and also $\varepsilon_2 \geq \varepsilon_1$), then, applying Theorem 4 to pencil $A_1 + \lambda B_1$, we transform the given pencil to the form

$$\begin{bmatrix} L_{\varepsilon_1} & 0 & 0 \\ 0 & L_{\varepsilon_2} & 0 \\ 0 & 0 & A_2 + \lambda B_2 \end{bmatrix}.$$

Continuing this process, we can reduce the given pencil to the block diagonal form

$$\begin{bmatrix} L_{\varepsilon_1} & & & & 0 \\ & L_{\varepsilon_2} & & & \\ & & \cdot & & \\ & & & \cdot & \\ & & & & L_{\varepsilon_p} \\ & & & & & A_p + \lambda B_p \end{bmatrix}, \qquad (25)$$

where $0 < \varepsilon_1 \leqq \varepsilon_2 \leqq \ldots \leqq \varepsilon_p$, and the equation $(A_p + \lambda B_p)x^{(p)} = 0$ does not have nonzero solutions, i.e., the columns of matrix $A_p + \lambda B_p$ are linearly independent.[11]

If the rows of pencil $A_p + \lambda B_p$ are linearly dependent, then the transposed pencil $A'_p + \lambda B'_p$ can be reduced to the form (25), where the numbers [12] $(0 <)\eta_1 \leqq \eta_2 \leqq \ldots \leqq \eta_q$ play a role corresponding to that of the numbers $\varepsilon_1, \varepsilon_2, \ldots, \varepsilon_p$. Thus the given pencil $A + \lambda B$ will be transformed into the block diagonal form

$$
\begin{bmatrix}
L_{\varepsilon_1} & & & & & & & 0 \\
& L_{\varepsilon_2} & & & & & & \\
& & \ddots & & & & & \\
& & & L_{\varepsilon_p} & & & & \\
& & & & L'_{\eta_1} & & & \\
& & & & & L'_{\eta_2} & & \\
& & & & & & \ddots & \\
& & & & & & & L'_{\eta_q} \\
& & & & & & & A_0 + \lambda B_0
\end{bmatrix}
\tag{26}
$$

$$(0 < \varepsilon_1 \leqq \varepsilon_2 \leqq \ldots \leqq \varepsilon_p, \quad 0 < \eta_1 \leqq \eta_2 \leqq \ldots \leqq \eta_q),$$

where both the columns and the rows of pencil $A_0 + \lambda B_0$ are linearly independent, i.e., $A_0 + \lambda B_0$ is a regular pencil.[13]

Let us now consider the general case, in which the rows and columns of the given pencil may be connected by linear relations with constant coefficients. Let us designate the maximum number of constant independent solutions of the equations

[11] In the special case $\varepsilon_1 + \varepsilon_2 + \ldots + \varepsilon_p = m$, the block $A_p + \lambda B_p$ will be absent.

[12] Since there is no linear relation with constant coefficients among the rows of the pencil $A + \lambda B$, and a fortiori of the pencil $A_p + \lambda B_p$, it follows that $\eta_1 > 0$.

[13] In the given pencil, if $r = n$, that is, if the columns of the pencil are linearly independent, the first p diagonal blocks of the form L_ε ($p = 0$) will be absent in (26). The corresponding remark holds for $r = m$, i.e. when the row in $A + \lambda B$ are linearly independent, the diagonal blocks of the form L'_η ($q = 0$) will be absent in (26).

$$(A + \lambda B)x = 0 \quad \text{and} \quad (A' + \lambda B')y = 0$$

by g and h, respectively. As we did in the proof of Theorem 4, let us consider the vector equation $(\boldsymbol{A} + \lambda \boldsymbol{B})\boldsymbol{x} = 0$ corresponding to the first of these equations. ($\boldsymbol{A}$ and $\boldsymbol{B}$ are operators which map $\boldsymbol{R}_n$ into $\boldsymbol{R}_m$.) Let us designate the linearly independent constant solutions of this equation by $e_1, e_2, \ldots, e_g$, and take them for initial basis vectors of $\boldsymbol{R}_n$. Then in the corresponding matrix $\tilde{A} + \lambda \tilde{B}$ the first g columns will consist of zeros

$$\tilde{A} + \lambda \tilde{B} = (\overset{g}{\overline{0,}}\ \tilde{A}_1 + \lambda \tilde{B}_1). \tag{27}$$

In exactly the same manner, the first h rows in the pencil $\tilde{A}_1 + \lambda \tilde{B}_1$ can be made zero. Then the given pencil will assume the form

$$\begin{pmatrix} h \overset{g}{\overline{\lceil 0,}} & 0 \\ 0, & A^0 + \lambda B^0 \end{pmatrix}, \tag{28}$$

where the rows and columns of the pencil $A^0 + \lambda B^0$ are not connected by any linear relation with constant coefficients. The pencil $A^0 + \lambda B^0$ can be transformed into the form (26). Thus, in the most general case the pencil $A + \lambda B$ can always be reduced to the canonical block diagonal form

$$\text{diag}\ \{h \overset{g}{\overline{\lceil 0,}}\ L_{\varepsilon_{g+1}}, \ldots, L_{\varepsilon_p}, L'_{\eta_{h+1}}, \ldots, L'_{\eta_q}, A_0 + \lambda B_0\}. \tag{29}$$

The subscripts written in formula (29) are consonant with the convention $\varepsilon_1 = \varepsilon_2 = \ldots = \varepsilon_g = 0$ and $\eta_1 = \eta_2 = \ldots = \eta_h = 0$.

Substituting for the regular pencil $A_0 + \lambda B_0$ in (29) its canonical form (6) (see Section 2, p. 35), we obtain finally the following block diagonal matrix:

$$\{n \overset{g}{\overline{\lceil 0}};\ L_{\varepsilon_{g+1}}, \ldots, L_{\varepsilon_p};\ L'_{\eta_{h+1}}, \ldots, L'_{\eta_q};\ N^{(u_1)}, \ldots, N^{(u_s)};\ J + \lambda E\}, \tag{30}$$

where the matrix J has Jordan or rational canonical form, and $N^{(u)} = E^{(u)} + \lambda H^{(u)}$.

Matrix (30) *is a canonical form for the pencil* $A + \lambda B$ *in the most general case.* In the following section, we shall introduce the concept (due to Kronecker) of minimal indices of the pencil, and thus determine the canonical form (30) directly from the given pencil, without having to carry out the successive steps in the process of reduction.

§ 5. Minimal index of a pencil: criterion for row equivalence of pencils

Let there be given an arbitrary singular pencil of rectangular matrices $A + \lambda B$. Then k polynomial column matrices $x_1(\lambda)$, $x_2(\lambda), \ldots, x_k(\lambda)$ which are solutions of the equation

$$(A + \lambda B)x = 0, \tag{31}$$

will be linearly dependent, if the rank of the polynomial matrix, $X = [x_1(\lambda), x_2(\lambda), \ldots, x_k(\lambda)]$ formed from these columns, is less than k. In this case there are k polynomials $p_1(\lambda), p_2(\lambda), \ldots, p_k(\lambda)$, which are not identically equal to zero, and these polynomials are such that

$$p_1(\lambda)x_1(\lambda) + p_2(\lambda)x_2(\lambda) + \ldots + p_k(\lambda)x_k(\lambda) \equiv 0.$$

If the rank of matrix X is equal to k, then there is no such relation, and the solutions $x_1(\lambda), x_2(\lambda), \ldots, x_k(\lambda)$ are linearly independent.

Of all the solutions of equation (31), let us take the nonzero solution $x_1(\lambda)$ of minimum degree ε_1. Of all the solutions of the same equation which are linearly independent of $x_1(\lambda)$, let us select the solution $x_2(\lambda)$ of minimum degree ε_2. It is obvious that $\varepsilon_1 \leqq \varepsilon_2$. Let us continue this process, selecting from all the solutions which are linearly independent of $x_1(\lambda)$ and $x_2(\lambda)$ the solution $x_3(\lambda)$ of minimum degree ε_3, etc. Since the number of linearly independent solutions of equation (31) is always $\leqq n$, then this process should terminate. We will obtain a *fundamental series of solutions* of equation (31)

$$x_1(\lambda), \; x_2(\lambda), \ldots, x_p(\lambda) \tag{32}$$

of degrees

$$\varepsilon_1 \leqq \varepsilon_2 \leqq \ldots \leqq \varepsilon_p. \tag{33}$$

In general, a fundamental series of solutions is *not* uniquely determined (to within constant factors) by the given pencil $A + \lambda B$.

However, *two different fundamental series of solutions always have the same series of degrees* $\varepsilon_1, \varepsilon_2, \ldots, \varepsilon_p$. Indeed, let us consider together with (32) the fundamental series of solutions $\tilde{x}_1(\lambda)$, $\tilde{x}_2(\lambda), \ldots$ of degrees $\tilde{\varepsilon}_1, \tilde{\varepsilon}_2, \ldots$. Let the following relations connect the degrees (33)

$$\varepsilon_1 = \ldots = \varepsilon_{n_1} < \varepsilon_{n_1+1} = \ldots = \varepsilon_{n_2} < \ldots$$

and, similarly, for the degrees $\tilde{\varepsilon}_1, \tilde{\varepsilon}_2, \ldots$,

$$\tilde{\varepsilon}_1 = \ldots = \tilde{\varepsilon}_{\tilde{n}_1} < \tilde{\varepsilon}_{\tilde{n}_1+1} = \ldots = \tilde{\varepsilon}_{\tilde{n}_2} < \ldots$$

it is obvious that $\varepsilon_1 = \tilde{\varepsilon}_1$. Any column $\tilde{x}_i(\lambda)$ $(i = 1, 2, \ldots, \tilde{n}_1)$ is a linear combination of the columns $x_1(\lambda), x_2(\lambda), \ldots, x_{n_1}(\lambda)$, since otherwise, in (32) the solution $x_{n_1+1}(\lambda)$ could be replaced by the solution $\tilde{x}_i(\lambda)$ of lower degree. On the other hand, it is obvious that any column $x_i(\lambda)$ $(i = 1, 2, \ldots, n_1)$ is a linear combination of the columns $\tilde{x}_1(\lambda), \tilde{x}_2(\lambda), \ldots, \tilde{x}_{\tilde{n}_1}(\lambda)$. Therefore, $n_1 = \tilde{n}_1$ and $\varepsilon_{n_1+1} = \tilde{\varepsilon}_{\tilde{n}_1+1}$. Similarly, we see that $n_2 = \tilde{n}_2$ and $\varepsilon_{n_2} = \tilde{\varepsilon}_{\tilde{n}_2}$, etc.

Each solution $x_k(\lambda)$ in the fundamental series (32) gives a linear relation of degree ε_k among the columns of matrix $A + \lambda B$ $(k = 1, 2, \ldots, p)$. Therefore the numbers $\varepsilon_1, \varepsilon_2, \ldots, \varepsilon_p$ are called *the minimal indices for the columns* of pencil $A + \lambda B$.

The minimal indices $\eta_1, \eta_2, \ldots, \eta_q$ *for the rows of pencil* $A + \lambda B$ are defined in a similar manner. In this connection, the equation $(A + \lambda B)x = 0$ is replaced by the equation $(A' + \lambda B')y = 0$ and the numbers $\eta_1, \eta_2, \ldots, \eta_q$ are determined as the minimal indices for the columns of the transposed equation $A' + \lambda B'$.

Strictly equivalent pencils have one and the same minimal indices. In fact, let there be given two such pencils: $A + \lambda B$ and $P(A + \lambda B)Q$ (P and Q are square nonsingular matrices). Then equation (31) for the first pencil, after multiplication of each term from the left by P may be written:

$$P(A + \lambda B)Q \cdot Q^{-1}x = 0.$$

Hence it is seen that all the solutions of equation (31), after multiplication from the left by Q^{-1}, give a complete system of solutions of the equation

$$P(A + \lambda B)Qz = 0.$$

Therefore, the pencils $A + \lambda B$ and $P(A + \lambda B)Q$ have the same minimal indices for the columns. Equality of the minimal indices for the rows is established by considering the transposed pencils. Let us compute the minimal indices for the canonical quasi-diagonal matrix

$$\text{diag} \{ \overset{g}{_h\overline{[0}},\ L_{\varepsilon_{g+1}}, \ldots, L_{\varepsilon_p};\ L'_{\eta_{h+1}}, \ldots, L'_{\eta_q},\ A_0 + \lambda B_0 \} \quad (34)$$

$[A_0 + \lambda B_0$ is a regular pencil which has the normal form (6)].

First let us note that *the complete system of minimal indices for the columns (rows) of a quasidiagonal matrix is the same as the collection of the systems of minimal indices of the individual diagonal blocks*. The matrix L_ε has the one index ε for the columns, and the rows of this matrix are linearly independent. In exactly the same manner, the matrix L'_η has only the one index η for the rows, and the columns of this matrix are linearly independent. The regular pencil $A_0 + \lambda B_0$ has no minimal indices at all. Therefore, matrix (34) has for minimal indices of the columns

$$\varepsilon_1 = \ldots = \varepsilon_g = 0, \quad \varepsilon_{g+1}, \ldots, \varepsilon_p,$$

and for the rows

$$\eta_1 = \ldots = \eta_h = 0, \quad \eta_{h+1}, \ldots, \eta_q.$$

Let us note further that matrix L_ε has no elementary divisors, since among its minors of maximum order ε there is a minor which is equal to unity, and a minor equal to $\lambda\varepsilon$. It is clear that the same holds for the transposed matrix L'_ε. Since the elementary divisors of the quasidiagonal matrix are obtained by combining the elementary divisors of the individual diagonal blocks (this is clear because of the invariantive definition of the elementary divisors in terms of the invariant factors), then *the elementary divisors of the λ-matrix* (34) *coincide with the elementary divisors of its regular "nucleus"* $A_0 + \lambda B_0$.

The canonical form of pencil (34) *is completely determined by the minimal indices* $\varepsilon_1, \ldots, \varepsilon_p, \eta_1, \ldots, \eta_q$ *and the elementary divisors of this pencil or* (*what is the same thing*) *of the pencil* $A + \lambda B$ *which is strictly equivalent to it.* Since two pencils which have one and the same canonical form are strictly equivalent to each other, we have proved the following theorem:

THEOREM 5. (Kronecker). *In order that two arbitrary pencils of rectangular matrices* $A + \lambda B$ *and* $A_1 + \lambda B_1$ *of the same dimensions* $m \times n$ *be strictly equivalent, it is necessary and sufficient that these pencils have the same minimal indices and the same* ("*finite*" *and* "*infinite*") *elementary divisors.*

In conclusion, we exhibit the canonical form of the pencil $A + \lambda B$, which has for minimal indices $\varepsilon_1 = 0$, $\varepsilon_2 = 1$, $\varepsilon_3 = 2$, $\eta_1 = 0$, $\eta_2 = 0$, $\eta_3 = 2$ and [14] elementary divisors λ^2, $(\lambda + 2)^2$, μ^3:

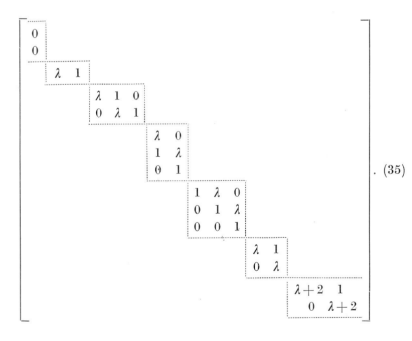

$$. \quad (35)$$

[14] Blanks in this scheme denote zero elements.

§ 6. Singular pencils of quadratic and Hermitian forms

Let there be given the two complex quadratic forms:

$$A(x, x) = \sum_{i, k=1}^{n} a_{ik} x_i x_k, \qquad B(x, x) = \sum_{i, k=1}^{n} b_{ik} x_i x_k;$$

they generate a pencil of quadratic forms $A(x, x) + \lambda B(x, x)$. To this pencil of forms corresponds the pencil of symmetric matrices $A + \lambda B$ $(A' = A, B' = B)$. If the variables in the pencil of forms $A(x, x) + \lambda B(x, x)$ undergo a nonsingular linear transformation $x = Tz$ $(\det T \neq 0)$, then the pencil of matrices

$$\tilde{A} + \lambda \tilde{B} = T'(A + \lambda B)T \tag{36}$$

will correspond to the transformed pencil of forms $\tilde{A}(z, z) + \lambda \tilde{B}(z, z)$; here T is a constant (i.e., independent of λ) nonsingular square matrix of nth order.

Two pencils of matrices $A + \lambda B$ and $\tilde{A} + \lambda \tilde{B}$, which are connected by identity (36), are called *congruent* (or *conjunctively equivalent*).

If in place of the pencil of quadratic forms we consider a pencil of Hermitian forms

$$A(x, x) + \lambda B(x, x) \ [A(x, x) = \sum_{i, k=1}^{n} a_{ik} x_i \bar{x}_k, \ B(x, x) = \sum_{i, k=1}^{n} b_{ik} x_i \bar{x}_k],$$

then to this pencil of forms there will correspond the pencil of Hermitian matrices $A + \lambda B$ $(A^* = A, B^* = B)$.[15] If the variables undergo the transformation $x = \bar{T}z$ $(\det T \neq 0)$, then the transformed pencil of forms will possess the pencil

$$\tilde{A} + \lambda \tilde{B} = T^*(A + \lambda B)T \quad (\det T \neq 0) \tag{37}$$

of Hermitian matrices.

We will call two pencils of matrices $A + \lambda B$ and $\tilde{A} + \lambda \tilde{B}$ which are connected by means of identity (37) *conjunctively equivalent*.

---

[15] In this section, a superior asterisk denotes the conjugate of the transposed matrix: $A^* = \bar{A}'$.

It is obvious that pencils of matrices which are congruent or conjunctively equivalent are *a fortiori* equivalent. Indeed, it turns out that if two pencils of symmetric (or antisymmetric) matrices are under consideration, the concepts of equivalence and congruence coincide; similarly, for Hermitian matrices, the concepts of equivalence and conjunctive equivalence coincide. These facts are proved in Theorem 6.

THEOREM 6. *Two strictly equivalent pencils of complex symmetric (or antisymmetric) matrices are always congruent. Two strictly equivalent pencils of Hermitian matrices are always conjunctively equivalent.*

Proof. *1.* Let the two strictly equivalent pencils of symmetric (antisymmetric) matrices $\Lambda \equiv A + \lambda B$ and $\tilde{\Lambda} \equiv \tilde{A} + \lambda \tilde{B}$ be given:

$$\tilde{\Lambda} = P\Lambda Q \quad (\Lambda' = \pm \Lambda,\ \tilde{\Lambda}' = \pm \tilde{\Lambda};\ \det P \neq 0, \det Q \neq 0). \quad (38)$$

Taking the transpose of (38), we obtain:

$$\tilde{\Lambda} = Q'\Lambda P'. \quad (39)$$

From (38) and (39) we find:

$$\Lambda Q P'^{-1} = P^{-1} Q' \Lambda. \quad (40)$$

If we set

$$U = Q P'^{-1}, \quad (41)$$

we can rewrite equality (40) as follows:

$$\Lambda U = U' \Lambda. \quad (42)$$

It easily follows from (42) that:

$$\Lambda U^k = U'^k \Lambda \quad (k = 0,\ 1,\ 2,\ \ldots),$$

and, in general,

$$\Lambda S = S' \Lambda, \quad (43)$$

where

$$S = f(U), \quad (44)$$

and $f(\lambda)$ is an arbitrary polynomial in λ. Let us assume that this polynomial is so chosen that det $S \neq 0$. Then from (43) we find:

$$\Lambda = S'\Lambda S^{-1}. \tag{45}$$

Substituting the expression obtained for Λ in (38), we obtain:

$$\tilde{\Lambda} = PS'\Lambda S^{-1}Q. \tag{46}$$

In order for this relation to be a congruence, it is necessary that the equality

$$(PS')' = S^{-1}Q$$

be satisfied; this equality may be rewritten as follows:

$$S^2 = QP'^{-1} = U.$$

But the matrix $S = f(U)$ will satisfy this condition, if $f(\lambda)$ is some interpolation polynomial for $\sqrt{\lambda}$ on the spectrum of the matrix U. This can be arranged, since the many-valued function $\sqrt{\lambda}$ has a single-valued branch, uniquely defined on the spectrum of the matrix U, since det $U \neq 0$.

Then equality (46) becomes

$$\tilde{\Lambda} = T'\Lambda T \quad (T = SQ = \sqrt{QP'^{-1}}Q), \tag{47}$$

which is, by definition, the condition that the pencils be congruent.

2. The proof for the case of Hermitian forms differs from the above proof only in that the symbol * is written in place of the symbol '.

From the proved theorem and Theorem 5 follows the subsequent corollary.

COROLLARY. *Two pencils of quadratic (Hermitian) forms*

$$A(x, x) + \lambda B(x, x) \text{ and } \tilde{A}(z, z) + \lambda \tilde{B}(z, z)$$

can be transformed one into the other by the transformation $x = Tz$ (det $T \neq 0$) if and only if the pencils of symmetric (Hermitian) matrices $A + \lambda B$ and $\tilde{A} + \lambda \tilde{B}$ have the same elementary divisors ("finite" and "infinite") and the same minimal indices.

Note. In the case of a pencil of symmetric or Hermitian matrices, the rows and columns have the same minimal indices:

$$p = q; \quad \varepsilon_1 = \eta_1, \ldots, \varepsilon_p = \eta_p. \tag{48}$$

Let us consider the following problem. *Given two arbitrary complex quadratic forms*

$$A(x, x) = \sum_{i,\,k=1}^{n} a_{ik} x_i x_k, \quad B(x, x) = \sum_{i,\,k=1}^{n} b_{ik} x_i x_k,$$

under what conditions does there exist a nonsingular transformation of the variables $x = Tz$ (det $T \neq 0$) which will simultaneously reduce both forms to sums of squares

$$\sum_{i=1}^{n} a_i z^2 \quad \text{and} \quad \sum_{i=1}^{n} b_i z_i^2 ? \tag{49}$$

A similar problem arises for two Hermitian forms $A(x, x)$ and $B(x, x)$, but in this case instead of (49) we must write:

$$\sum_{i=1}^{n} a_i z_i \bar{z}_i \quad \text{and} \quad \sum_{i=1}^{n} b_i z_i \bar{z}_i, \tag{50}$$

where a_i and b_i $(i = 1, 2, \ldots, n)$ are real numbers.

Let us assume that the quadratic (Hermitian) forms $A(x, x)$ and $B(x, x)$ possess the indicated property. Then the pencil of matrices $A + \lambda B$ will be congruent (respectively conjunctively equivalent) to the pencil of diagonal matrices

$$\{a_1 + \lambda b_1,\ a_2 + \lambda b_2, \ldots, a_n + \lambda b_n\}. \tag{51}$$

Among the binomials $a_i + \lambda b_i$ in the diagonal let there be exactly $r\,(r \leq n)$ binomials which are not identically equal to zero. Without loss of generality, we may take

$$a_1 = b_1 = 0, \ldots, a_{n-r} = b_{n-r} = 0, \quad a_i + \lambda b_i \not\equiv 0$$
$$(i = n - r + 1, \ldots, n).$$

We set

$$A_0 + \lambda B_0 = \{a_{n-r+1} + \lambda b_{n-r+1}, \ldots, a_n + \lambda b_n\},$$

and represent matrix (51) in the form

$$\{\overset{n-r}{\overbrace{0,}}\ A_0 + \lambda B_0\}. \tag{52}$$

Comparing (52) with (34) (p. 47), we see that in the present case all the minimal indices are equal to zero. In addition, all the elementary divisors are linear (of first degree), and in the case of Hermitian forms are real. We have arrived at the following theorem.

THEOREM 7. *Two quadratic or Hermitian forms $A(x, x)$ and $B(x, x)$, can be simultaneously reduced to sums of squares [(49) or (50)] by a nonsingular transformation of the variables if and only if all the elementary divisors (finite and infinite) of the pencil of matrices $A + \lambda B$ are of the first degree (and are real in the case of Hermitian forms) and all the minimal indices are equal to zero.*

In the general case, a canonical form for simultaneous reduction of two quadratic or two Hermitian forms $A(x, x)$ and $B(x, x)$ is conveniently found by taking that "canonical" pencil of symmetric (or Hermitian) matrices which is strictly equivalent to the pencil $A + \lambda B$.

Let the pencil of symmetric matrices $A + \lambda B$ have minimal indices $\varepsilon_1 = \ldots = \varepsilon_g = 0$, $\varepsilon_{g+1} \neq 0, \ldots, \varepsilon_p \neq 0$; infinite elementary divisors $\mu^{u_1}, \mu^{u_2}, \ldots, \mu^{u_s}$; and finite elementary divisors $(\lambda + \lambda_1)^{c_1}, (\lambda + \lambda_2)^{c_2}, \ldots, (\lambda + \lambda_t)^{c_t}$. Then in the canonical form (30) $g = h$, $p = q$ and $\varepsilon_{g+1} = \eta_{g+1}, \ldots, \varepsilon_p = \eta_p$. In (30) let us replace each pair of diagonal blocks L_ε and L'_ε by the one diagonal block

$$\begin{bmatrix} 0 & L'_\varepsilon \\ L_\varepsilon & 0 \end{bmatrix},$$

and let us replace each block $N^{(u)} = E^{(u)} + \lambda H^{(u)}$ by the strictly equivalent symmetric block

$$\tilde{N}^{(u)} = V^{(u)} N^{(u)} = \begin{bmatrix} 0 & 0 \ldots 0 & 1 \\ 0 & 0 \ldots 1 & \lambda \\ \cdot & \cdots \cdots & \cdot \\ 1 & \lambda \ldots 0 & 0 \end{bmatrix} \quad \left(V^{(u)} = \begin{bmatrix} 0 & 0 \ldots 0 & 1 \\ 0 & 0 \ldots 1 & 0 \\ \cdot & & \cdot & \cdot \\ \cdot & & 1 \cdot & \cdot \\ 1 & 0 \ldots 0 & 0 \end{bmatrix} \right) \quad (53)$$

In addition, in place of the regular diagonal block $J + \lambda E$ in (30) (J is a Jordan matrix)

$$J + \lambda E = \{(\lambda + \lambda_1)E^{(c_1)} + H^{(c_1)}, \ldots, (\lambda + \lambda_t)E^{(c_t)} + H^{(c_t)}\}$$

we take the strictly equivalent pencil

$$\{Z^{(c_1)}_{\lambda_1}, \ldots, Z^{(c_t)}_{\lambda_t}\},$$

where

$$Z^{(c_i)}_{\lambda_i} = V^{(c_i)}\left[(\lambda + \lambda_i)E^{(c_i)} + H^{(c_i)}\right] = \begin{bmatrix} 0 & \cdots & 0 & \lambda + \lambda_i \\ 0 & \cdots & \lambda + \lambda_i & 1 \\ & & \cdot & \cdot \\ & \cdot & \cdot & \\ & \cdot & \cdot & \\ \cdot & \cdot & & \\ \lambda + \lambda_i & 1 & \cdots & 0 \end{bmatrix}$$

$$(i = 1, 2, \ldots, t). \qquad (54)$$

The pencil $A + \lambda B$ is strictly equivalent to the symmetric pencil

$$\tilde{A} + \lambda\tilde{B}$$

$$= \left\{0, \begin{bmatrix} 0 & L'_{\varepsilon_{g+1}} \\ L_{\varepsilon_{g+1}} & 0 \end{bmatrix}, \ldots, \begin{bmatrix} 0 & L'_{\varepsilon_p} \\ L'_{\varepsilon_p} & 0 \end{bmatrix}; \tilde{N}^{(u_1)}, \ldots, \tilde{N}^{(u_s)}; Z^{(c_1)}_{\lambda_1}, \ldots, Z^{(c_t)}_{\lambda_t}\right\}.$$

$$(55)$$

The display (55) gives the canonical form $\tilde{A}(z, z)$, $\tilde{B}(z, z)$ for simultaneous reduction of two quadratic forms $A(x, x)$, $B(x, x)$ with complex coefficients, where the transformation of variables $x = Tz$ is nonsingular (det $T \neq 0$).

If $A(x, x)$ and $B(x, x)$ are Hermitian forms, then the "finite" elementary divisors of the pencil $A + \lambda B$ are either real, or else conjugate complex in pairs:

$$(\lambda + \lambda'_i)^{c_i}, \ (\lambda + \lambda_j)^{d_j}, \ (\lambda + \bar{\lambda}_j)^{d_j} \ (i = 1, 2, \ldots, v; \ j = 1, 2, \ldots, w)$$

$[\lambda'_i \ (i = 1, 2, \ldots, v)$ are real numbers]. For each pair of conjugate complex elementary divisors $(\lambda + \lambda_j)^{d_j}$, $(\lambda + \bar{\lambda}_j)^{d_j}$, we take as corresponding Hermitian pencil

$$W_j = V^{(2d_j)} \{(\lambda + \lambda_j)E + H, \ (\lambda + \bar{\lambda}_j)E + H\}$$

$$= \begin{bmatrix} 0 & V \\ V & 0 \end{bmatrix} \begin{bmatrix} (\lambda + \lambda_j)E + H & 0 \\ 0 & (\lambda + \bar{\lambda}_j)E + H \end{bmatrix} = \begin{bmatrix} 0 & Z^{(d_j)}_{\bar{\lambda}_j} \\ Z^{(d_j)}_{\lambda_j} & 0 \end{bmatrix}, \quad (56)$$

$$E = E^{(d_j)}, \quad H = H^{(d_j)}, \quad V = V^{(d_j)}.$$

Thus, for Hermitian matrices, the canonical pencil corresponding to (55) is

$$\widehat{A} + \lambda \widehat{B} = \left\{ \overset{g}{[0]}_h, \ \begin{bmatrix} 0 & L'_{\varepsilon_{g+1}} \\ L_{\varepsilon_{g+1}} & 0 \end{bmatrix}, \dots, \begin{bmatrix} 0 & L'_{\varepsilon_p} \\ L_{\varepsilon_p} & 0 \end{bmatrix}, \right.$$

$$\left. N^{(u_1)}, \dots, N^{(u_s)}, \ Z^{(c_1)}_{\lambda_1}, \dots, Z^{(c_v)}_{\lambda_v}, \ W_1, \dots, W_w \right\}. \quad (57)$$

The display (57) gives the canonical form $\widehat{A}(z, z)$, $\widehat{B}(z, z)$ for simultaneous reduction of two Hermitian forms $A(x, x)$, $B(x, x)$, where the transformation of variables $x = Tz$ is nonsingular (det $T \neq 0$).

§ 7. Applications to differential equations

Let us apply the results above to the problem of integrating the following system of m ordinary linear differential equations of the first order in n unknown functions (with constant coefficients)[16]

$$\sum_{k=1}^{n} a_{ik} x_k + \sum_{k=1}^{n} b_{ik} \frac{dx_k}{dt} = f_i(t) \quad (i = 1, 2, \dots, m). \quad (58)$$

Using matrix notation, (58) can be written

$$Ax + B \frac{dx}{dt} = f(t); \quad (59)$$

here

---

[16] The special case $m = n$, $B = (b_{ij}) = $ identity matrix is classical and is treated in many texts. See e.g., Schreier-Sperner [62]. It is clear that any system of linear differential equations with constant coefficients, in which the order of the highest derivative appearing is s, can be reduced to the form (58) if the first $s - 1$ derivatives of the unknown functions are taken as additional unknown functions.

$$A = (a_{ik}), \quad B = (b_{ik}) \quad (i = 1, 2, \ldots, m; \quad k = 1, 3, \ldots, n),$$

$$x = (x_1, x_2, \ldots, x_n), \quad f = (f_1, f_2, \ldots, f_m).^{17}$$

Let us introduce new unknown functions $z_1, z_2, \ldots, z_n$, which are connected with the old functions by a linear nonsingular transformation with constant coefficients:

$$x = Qz \quad [z = (z_1, z_2, \ldots, z_n); \quad \det Q \neq 0]. \tag{60}$$

Further, it is no restriction on the problem to replace equations (58) by any m independent linear combinations of them; this is equivalent to multiplying the matrices A, B, f on the left by a square nonsingular matrix P of mth order. If we substitute Qz for x in (59) and multiply each term of (59) on the left by P, we obtain:

$$\tilde{A}z + \tilde{B}\frac{dz}{dt} = \tilde{f}(t), \tag{61}$$

where

$$\tilde{A} = PAQ, \quad \tilde{B} = PBQ, \quad \tilde{f} = Pf = (\tilde{f}_1, \tilde{f}_2, \ldots, \tilde{f}_n). \tag{62}$$

Thus, the pencils of matrices $A + \lambda B$ and $\tilde{A} + \lambda\tilde{B}$ are strictly equivalent:

$$\tilde{A} + \lambda\tilde{B} = P(A + \lambda B)Q. \tag{63}$$

We select the matrices P and Q so that the pencil $\tilde{A} + \lambda\tilde{B}$ has the canonical block diagonal form

$$\tilde{A} + \lambda\tilde{B} = \{0, L_{\varepsilon_{g+1}}, \ldots, L_{\varepsilon_p}, L'_{\eta_{h+1}}, \ldots, L'_{\eta_g},$$
$$N^{(u_1)}, \ldots, N^{(u_s)}, J + \lambda E\}. \tag{64}$$

Since the blocks in (64) are diagonal, the system of differential equations decomposes to $\nu = p - g + q - h + s + 2$ separate systems of the form

$$0 \cdot z^{[1]} = \tilde{f}^{[1]}, \tag{65}$$

[22] The symbol $(x_1, x_2, \ldots, x_n)$ still designates a column matrix with elements $x_1, x_2, \ldots, x_n$.

$$L_{\varepsilon_{g+i}}\left(\frac{d}{dt}\right) z^{[1+i]} = \tilde{f}^{[1+i]} \qquad (i = 1, 2, \ldots, p - g), \tag{66}$$

$$L'_{\eta_{h+j}}\left(\frac{d}{dt}\right) z^{[p-g+1+j]} = \tilde{f}^{[p-g+1+j]} \qquad (j = 1, 2, \ldots, q - h), \tag{67}$$

$$N^{(u_k)}\left(\frac{d}{dt}\right) z^{[p-g+q-h+1+k]} = \tilde{f}^{[p-g+q-h+1+k]} \qquad (k = 1, 2, \ldots, s), \tag{68}$$

$$\left(J + \frac{d}{dt}\right) z^{[\nu]} = \tilde{f}^{[\nu]}, \tag{69}$$

where

$$z = \begin{bmatrix} z^{[1]} \\ z^{[2]} \\ \vdots \\ z^{[\nu]} \end{bmatrix}, \quad \tilde{f} = \begin{bmatrix} \tilde{f}^{[1]} \\ \tilde{f}^{[2]} \\ \vdots \\ \tilde{f}^{[\nu]} \end{bmatrix}, \tag{70}$$

$$z = (z_1, \ldots, z_g), \tilde{f}^{[1]} = (\tilde{f}_1, \ldots, \tilde{f}_h), z^{[2]} = (z_{g+1}, \ldots), \tilde{f}^{[2]} = (\tilde{f}_{h+1}, \ldots) \text{ etc.,} \tag{71}$$

$$\Lambda\left(\frac{d}{dt}\right) = A + B\frac{d}{dt}, \quad \text{if} \quad \Lambda(\lambda) \equiv A + \lambda B. \tag{72}$$

Thus, integration of system (59) in the most general case is reduced to integration of the special systems (65)-(69) of the same type. In these systems, the pencil of matrices $A + \lambda B$ has the forms, respectively, 0, L_ε, L'_η, $N^{(u)}$, $J + \lambda E$.

(i) In order for system (65) not to be self-contradictory, it is necessary and sufficient that

$$\tilde{f}^{[1]} \equiv 0,$$

i.e.,

$$\tilde{f}_1 \equiv 0, \ldots, \tilde{f}_h \equiv 0. \tag{73}$$

In this case, the unknown functions $z_1, z_2, \ldots, z_g$, which comprise the column $z^{[1]}$, may be taken to be arbitrary functions of t.

(ii) System (66) represents a system of the form

$$L_\varepsilon\left(\frac{d}{dt}\right) z = \tilde{f} \tag{74}$$

or, written in extended form,[18]

$$\frac{dz_1}{dt} + z_2 = \tilde{f}_1(t), \frac{dz_2}{dt} + z_3 = \tilde{f}_2(t), \ldots, \frac{dz_\varepsilon}{dt} + z_{\varepsilon+1} = \tilde{f}_{\varepsilon+1}(t). \quad (75)$$

Such a system is always a compatible system. If an arbitrary function of t is taken as $z_{\varepsilon+1}(t)$, then all the remaining unknown functions z_ε, $z_{\varepsilon-1}$, ..., z_1 will be determined by successive quadratures from (75).

(iii)   System (67) represents a system of the form

$$L'_\eta\left(\frac{d}{dt}\right) z = \tilde{f} \quad (76)$$

or, written in extended form, [19]

$$\frac{dz_1}{dt} = \tilde{f}_1(t), \frac{dz_2}{dt} + z_1 = \tilde{f}_2(t), \ldots, \frac{dz_\eta}{dt} + z_{\eta-1} = \tilde{f}_\eta(t), \ z_\eta = \tilde{f}_{\eta+1}(t).$$

$$(77)$$

From the set of equations (77), excluding the first, we determine z_η, $z_{\eta-1}$, ..., z_1 uniquely:

$$z_\eta = \tilde{f}_{\eta+1}, \ z_{\eta-1} = \tilde{f}_\eta - \frac{d\tilde{f}_{\eta+1}}{dt}, \ldots, z_1 = \tilde{f}_2 - \frac{d\tilde{f}_3}{dt}$$

$$+ \ldots + (-1)^{\eta-1}\frac{d^{-1}_\eta \tilde{f}_{\eta+1}}{dt^{\eta-1}}. \quad (78)$$

By substituting the expression obtained for z_1 in the first equation, we obtain the condition of compatibility

$$\tilde{f}_1 - \frac{d\tilde{f}_2}{dt} + \frac{d^2\tilde{f}_3}{dt^2} - \ldots + (-1)^\eta \frac{d^\eta \tilde{f}_{\eta+1}}{dt^\eta} = 0. \quad (79)$$

(iv)   System (68) represents a system of the form

[18] We have changed the indices of z and of $\tilde{f}$ in order to simplify the notation. To fit system (75) into the scheme of system (66), ε must be replaced by ε_i, each index of z must be increased by $g + \varepsilon_{g+i-1} + i - 1$, and each index of $\tilde{f}$ must be increased by $h + \varepsilon_{g+1} + \ldots + \varepsilon_{g+j-1}$.

[19] We have again changed the notation. See the preceding footnote.

$$N^{(u)}\left(\frac{d}{dt}\right)z = \tilde{f} \tag{80}$$

or, written in extended form,

$$\frac{dz_2}{dt} + z_1 = \tilde{f}_1, \frac{dz_3}{dt} + z_2 = \tilde{f}_2, \ldots, \frac{dz_u}{dt} + z_{u-1} = \tilde{f}_{u-1}, \ z_u = \tilde{f}_u. \tag{81}$$

Thus the solution of this recursion is explicitly

$$z_u = \tilde{f}_u, z_{u-1} = \tilde{f}_{u-1} - \frac{d\tilde{f}_u}{dt}, \ldots, z_1 = \tilde{f}_1 - \frac{d\tilde{f}_2}{dt} + \frac{d^2\tilde{f}_3}{dt^2} - \cdots$$

$$+ (-1)^{u-1}\frac{d^{u-1}f_u}{dt^{u-1}}. \tag{82}$$

(v)   System (69) represents a system of the classical form

$$Jz + \frac{dz}{dt} = \tilde{f}. \tag{83}$$

As is known (see footnote 16), the general solution of such a system has the form

$$z = e^{-Jt}z_0 + \int_0^t e^{-J(t-\tau)}f(\tau)d\tau; \tag{84}$$

where z_0 is a column of arbitrary constants (initial values of the unknown functions at $t = 0$).

The return from system (61) to system (59) is given by formulas (60) and (62), according to which each of the functions $x_1, \ldots, x_n$ is a linear combination of the functions $z_1, \ldots, z_n$, and each of the functions $\tilde{f}_1(t), \ldots, \tilde{f}_m(t)$ is expressed linearly (with constant coefficients) by means of the functions $f_1(t), \ldots, f_m(t)$.

The above analysis shows that *for system (58) to be compatible in the general case certain definite linear finite and differential relations (with constant coefficients) must be satisfied among the right members of the equations.*

If these conditions are satisfied, then the general solution of the system contains (in the general case) both arbitrary constants and arbitrary functions; these enter linearly in both cases.

The character of the conditions of compatibility and the character of the solutions (in particular the number of arbitrary constants and arbitrary functions) are determined by the minimal indices and the elementary divisors of the pencil $A + \lambda B$, since the canonical form of the system of differential equations (65)-(69) depends upon these indices and divisors.

CHAPTER III

Matrices with Nonnegative Elements

In this chapter, the properties of real matrices with nonnegative elements are studied. These matrices have extremely important application in the theory of probability in the investigation of Markov chains ("stochastic matrices," see [20]) and in the theory of small oscillations of elastic systems ("oscillating matrices," see [24]).

§ 1. General properties

Let us begin with a definition.

DEFINITION 1. *We will call a matrix A with real elements*

$$A = (a_{ik}) \quad (i = 1, 2, \ldots, m; \quad k = 1, 2, \ldots, n)$$

nonnegative (symbol: $A \geqq 0$) *or* positive (symbol: $A > 0$), *if all the elements of the matrix A are nonnegative (respectively positive)*: $a_{ik} \geqq 0$ *(respectively > 0)*.

DEFINITION 2. *The square matrix* $A = (a_{ik})_1^n$ *is said to be* reducible *(more explicitly: reducible by a permutation), if the indices $1, 2, \ldots, n$ can be divided into two disjoint nonempty sets $i_1, i_2, \ldots, i_\mu; k_1, k_2, \ldots, k_\nu (\mu + \nu = n)$, such that*

$$a_{i_\alpha k_\beta} = 0 \quad (\alpha = 1, 2, \ldots, \mu; \quad \beta = 1, 2, \ldots, \nu).$$

Otherwise we will say that the matrix A is irreducible.

The definition of reducible and irreducible matrices may be formulated as follows:

DEFINITION 2′. *The matrix* $A = (a_{ik})_1^n$ *is called* reducible, *if there is a permutation of the indices which reduces it to the form*

$$\tilde{A} = \begin{bmatrix} B & 0 \\ C & D \end{bmatrix},$$

61

where B and D are square matrices. Otherwise the matrix A is called irreducible.

Let the matrix $A = (a_{ik})_1^n$ correspond to the linear operator A in an n-dimensional vector space R with basis $e_1, e_2, \ldots, e_n$. A permutation of rows of the matrix A amounts to a renumbering of the basis vectors, i.e., to a change from the basis $e_1, e_2, \ldots, e_n$ to the new basis $e_1' = e_{j_1}, e_2' = e_{j_2}, \ldots, e_n' = e_{j_n}$, where $(j_1, j_2, \ldots, j_n)$ is a certain permutation of the indices $1, 2, \ldots, n$. With respect to this new basis, A possesses the matrix $\tilde{A} = T^{-1}AT$ similar to A.

By a ν-dimensional *coordinate subspace* in R we will mean any subspace in R with a basis $e_{k_1}, e_{k_2}, \ldots, e_{k_\nu}$ $(1 \leq k_1 < k_2 < \ldots < k_\nu \leq n)$. From each basis $e_1, e_2, \ldots, e_n$ of the space R we can form C_ν^n ν-dimensional coordinate subspaces. The definition of a reducible matrix can also be given in the following form:

DEFINITION 2''. *The matrix* $A = (a_{ik})_1^n$ *is called* reducible *if and only if the operator* A *corresponding to this matrix has a ν-dimensional invariant coordinate subspace with* $0 < \nu < n$.

Let us prove the following lemma:

LEMMA 1. *If* $A \geq 0$ *is an irreducible matrix and* n *is the order of matrix* A, *then*

$$(E + A)^{n-1} > 0. \tag{1}$$

Proof.   To prove the lemma, it is sufficient to show that for any vector (column)[1] $y \geq 0$ $(y \neq 0)$ the following inequality holds:

$$(E + A)^{n-1}y > 0.$$

This inequality can be established, by showing that *under the assumptions* $y \geq 0$ *and* $y \neq 0$, *the vector* $z = (E + A)y$ *always has fewer zero coordinates than vector* y. Let us assume the opposite. Then for some y, the vectors y and z have the same number

---

[1] Here and later in the chapter, we think of a vector as being a column of n numbers. In doing this, we have to keep in mind that a linear operator determines the elements of the matrix $A = (a_{ij})_{1, \ldots, n}$ which represents it only with respect to a certain basis. When the basis is changed, both the a_{ij} and the coordinates of the vector will change.

of zero coordinates.[2] Without loss of generality, it can be supposed that the columns y and z have the form [3]

$$y = \begin{pmatrix} u \\ 0 \end{pmatrix}, \qquad z = \begin{pmatrix} v \\ 0 \end{pmatrix}, \qquad u > 0, \quad v > 0,$$

where the subcolumns u and v have the same dimension.

Corresponding to this subdivision, we set

$$A = \begin{bmatrix} A_{11} & A_{12} \\ A_{21} & A_{22} \end{bmatrix},$$

and we have:

$$\begin{bmatrix} u \\ 0 \end{bmatrix} + \begin{bmatrix} A_{11} & A_{12} \\ A_{21} & A_{22} \end{bmatrix} \begin{bmatrix} u \\ 0 \end{bmatrix} = \begin{bmatrix} v \\ 0 \end{bmatrix},$$

hence

$$A_{21} u = 0.$$

Since $u > 0$, it follows that:

$$A_{21} = 0.$$

This equality contradicts the hypothesis that matrix A is irreducible. Thus, the lemma is proved.

We use the following notation for the elements of the powers of matrix A:

$$A^q = (a_{ik}^{(q)})_1^n \qquad (q = 1, 2, \ldots).$$

Then it follows from the lemma that:

COROLLARY. *If $A \geq 0$ is an irreducible matrix, then for any pair of indices $(1 \leq)i,\ k\ (\leq n)$ there exists a positive integer q such that*

$$a_{ik}^{(q)} > 0. \tag{2}$$

---

[2] Since $Ay \geq 0$, and $z = y + Ay$, any coordinate of the vector z will be positive if the corresponding coordinate of the vector y is positive.

[3] The columns y and z can be reduced to this form by renumbering their coordinates (the same renumbering being used for each).

Here the number q can always be chosen to satisfy the restrictions

$$q \leqq m - 1, \quad \text{if} \quad i \neq k,$$
$$q \leqq m, \quad \text{if} \quad i = k, \tag{3}$$

where m is the degree of the minimal polynomial $\psi(\lambda)$ of the matrix A.

Let $r(\lambda)$ be the remainder in the division of $(\lambda + 1)^{n-1}$ by $\psi(\lambda)$. By (1), $r(A) > 0$. Since the degree of $r(\lambda)$ is less than m, it follows from this inequality that for any $(1 \leqq)i$, $k(\leqq n)$ at least one of the nonnegative numbers

$$\delta_{ik}, \ a_{ik}, \ a_{ik}^{(2)}, \ \ldots, a_{ik}^{(m-1)}$$

is not equal to zero. Since $\delta_{ik} = 0$ when $i \neq k$, the first of relations (3) follows. The second relation (for $i = k$) is obtained similarly, if the inequality $r(A) > 0$ is replaced by the inequality[4] $Ar(A) > 0$.

Note: The above corollary shows that the exponent $n - 1$ in inequality (1) can be replaced by the number $m - 1$.

§ 2. Properties of the spectra of irreducible nonnegative matrices

1. In 1907 Perron established remarkable properties of the spectrum (i.e., of characteristic numbers and characteristic vectors) of positive matrices.[5]

THEOREM 1 (Perron). *A positive matrix $A = (a_{ik})_1^n$ always has a characteristic number r which is real and positive, which is a simple root of the characteristic equation, and which exceeds in modulus all other characteristic numbers. To this "dominant" characteristic number r there corresponds a characteristic vector $z = (z_1, z_2, \ldots, z_n)$ of the matrix A with positive coordinates $z_i > 0$ $(i = 1, 2, \ldots, n)$.[6]*

[4] The product of an irreducible nonnegative matrix and a positive matrix is always a positive matrix.

[5] See [55, 56] and also [24].

[6] Since the number r is a simple characteristic value, the corresponding characteristic vector z is determined to within a scalar factor. According to Perron's result, all coordinates of z are different from zero, real, and of the same sign. If the vector is multiplied by ± 1, a new eigenvector is obtained, every coordinate of which is positive. Such a vector is called a *positive vector*. This agrees with Definition 1.

A positive matrix is a special case of an irreducible nonnegative matrix. Frobenius [7] generalized the theorem of Perron in an investigation of the spectral properties of irreducible nonnegative matrices.

THEOREM 2 (Frobenius). *An irreducible nonnegative matrix $A = (a_{ik})_1^n$ always has a positive characteristic number r, which is a simple root of the characteristic equation. The moduli of all the other characteristic numbers are at most r. A characteristic vector z with positive coordinates corresponds to the "dominant" characteristic number r.*

If in addition A has precisely h characteristic numbers $\lambda_0 = r, \lambda_1, \ldots, \lambda_{h-1}$, of modulus equal to r, then these numbers are all different from each other and are roots of the equation

$$\lambda^h - r^h = 0, \tag{4}$$

and, in general, the entire spectrum $\lambda_0, \lambda_1, \ldots, \lambda_{n-1}$ of the matrix $A = (a_{ik})_1^n$, when plotted as a system of points in the complex λ-plane, is carried into itself when the plane is rotated by the angle $2\pi/h$. When $h > 1$, the matrix A may be reduced to the following "cyclic" form by a permutation of the indices.

$$A = \begin{bmatrix} 0 & A_{12} & 0 & \ldots & 0 \\ 0 & 0 & A_{23} & \ldots & 0 \\ 0 & 0 & 0 & \ldots & A_{h-1,h} \\ A_1 & 0 & 0 & \ldots & 0 \end{bmatrix}$$

where the blocks along the diagonal are square.

Since the theorem of Perron is a special case of the theorem of Frobenius, we will prove only the latter. Let us begin with certain notations.

We write:

$$C \leqq D \quad \text{or} \quad D \geqq C,$$

where C and D are real rectangular matrices of identical dimensions $m \times n$:

---

[7] See Frobenius [21, 22].

$$C = (c_{ik}), \quad D = (d_{ik}) \quad (i = 1, 2, \ldots, m; \quad k = 1, 2, \ldots, n),$$

to mean

$$c_{ik} \leqq d_{ik} \quad (i = 1, 2, \ldots, m; \quad k = 1, 2, \ldots, n). \tag{6}$$

If strict inequality holds in *all* the inequalities (6), then we will write:

$$C < D \quad \text{or} \quad D > C.$$

In particular, $C \geqq 0$ $(C > 0)$ means that all the elements of matrix C are nonnegative (respectively positive).

In addition, we will employ C^{+} to denote mod C, i.e., the matrix which is obtained from C by replacing all the elements of C by their moduli.

2. *Proof of the theorem of Frobenius.*[8] For a fixed real vector $x = (x_1, x_2, \ldots, x_n) \geqq 0$ $(x \neq 0)$ we set

$$r_x = \min_{1 \leqq i \leqq n} \frac{(Ax)_i}{x_i} \left((Ax)_i = \sum_{k=1}^{n} a_{ik} x_k; \quad i = 1, 2, \ldots, n \right);$$

in determining the minimum, those values of the index i for which $x_i = 0$, are excluded. It is obvious that $r_x \geqq 0$ and r_x is the maximum of the real numbers ρ for which the following inequality holds:

$$\rho x \leqq Ax.$$

We will prove that the function r_x attains its least upper bound r on a certain vector $z \geqq 0$:

$$r = r_z = \max_{x \geqq 0} r_x = \max_{x \geqq 0} \min_{1 \leqq i \leqq n} \frac{(Ax)_i}{x_i}. \tag{7}$$

From the definition of r_x, it follows that multiplication of the vector $x \geqq 0$ $(x \neq 0)$ by the number $\lambda > 0$ does not change the quantity r_x. Therefore, in seeking the maximum of the function r_x, we may confine our attention to the closed set M, consisting of those vectors x, for which

$$x \geqq 0, \quad (x, x) = x_1^2 + x_2^2 + \ldots + x_n^2 = 1.$$

---

[8] This proof is due to Wielandt [72].

If the function r_x were continuous on the set M, then the least upper bound would be attained. However, the function r_x is continuous in any "point" x if $x > 0$, but in the boundary points of set M, where one of the coordinates becomes zero, the function can have discontinuities. Therefore, instead of the set M we will introduce the set N, which consists of all vectors y of the form

$$y = (E + A)^{n-1}x \quad (x \in M).$$

Set N is bounded and closed since set M has these properties, and according to Lemma 1, N consists of *positive* vectors. Now if we multiply both members of the inequality

$$r_x x \leqq Ax$$

by $(E + A)^{n-1} > 0$, we obtain:

$$r_x y \leqq Ay \ [y = (E + A)^{n-1}x].$$

Hence, on the basis of the definition of r_y, we find that

$$r_x \leqq r_y.$$

Therefore, in seeking the maximum of r_x, we may replace set M by set N, which consists of only positive vectors. On the bounded closed set N the function r_x is continuous and therefore attains its maximum value on a certain vector $z > 0$.

Let us call any vector $z \geqq 0$, for which

$$r_z = r, \tag{8}$$

an extremal vector.

Let us now prove that (i) *the number r determined by equality (7) is positive and is a characteristic number of matrix A, and* (ii) *any extremal vector z is positive and is a characteristic vector of matrix A for the characteristic number r, i.e.,*

$$r > 0, \quad z > 0, \quad Az = rz. \tag{9}$$

In fact, if $u = (1, 1, \ldots, 1)$, then

$$r_u = \min_{1 \leqq i \leqq n} \sum_k a_{ik}.$$

But then $r_u > 0$, since no row of the irreducible matrix can consist only of zeros. Consequently, $r > 0$, since $r \geqq r_u$. Further, let the following relation hold:

$$x = (E + A)^{n-1}z. \tag{10}$$

Then, according to lemma 1, $x > 0$. Let us now assume that $Az - rz \neq 0$. Then from (1), (8), and (10) we obtain successively

$$Az - rz \geqq 0, \quad (E + A)^{n-1}(Az - rz) > 0, \quad Ax - rx > 0.$$

The latter inequality contradicts the definition of the number r since it would follow from this inequality that $Ax - (r+\varepsilon)x > 0$ for some sufficiently small $\varepsilon > 0$, i.e., $r_x \geqq r + \varepsilon > r$. Consequently, $Az = rz$. But then

$$0 < x = (E + A)^{n-1}z = (1 + r)^{n-1}z,$$

whence it follows that $z > 0$.

We will now show that r is an upper bound for *the moduli of all characteristic numbers*. Let the following relation hold:

$$Ay = \alpha y \quad (y \neq 0). \tag{11}$$

Taking moduli of the left and right members of equality (11), we obtain: [9]

$$|\alpha| y^+ \leqq Ay^+.$$

Hence

$$|\alpha| \leqq r_{y^+} \leqq r.$$

Let us assume that some characteristic vector y corresponds to the characteristic number r:

$$Ay = ry \quad (y \neq 0).$$

Then, setting α equal to r in (11) and (12), we conclude that y^+ is an extremal vector and, consequently, $y^+ > 0$, i.e. $y = (y_1, y_2, \ldots, y_n)$, where $y_i \neq 0$ $(i = 1, 2, \ldots, n)$. Hence it follows that *to the characteristic number r there corresponds only one characteristic direction*, since if there were two linearly independent characteristic vectors z and z_1 we would have been

---

[9] The vector y^+ is obtained from the vector y by replacing each element by its modulus.

able to select the numbers c and d such that the characteristic vector $y = cz + dz_1$ would be nonnegative and have a zero coordinate, and this has been proved impossible.

Let us consider the adjoint matrix of the characteristic matrix $\lambda E - A$:

$$B(\lambda) = (B_{ik}(\lambda))_1^n = \Delta(\lambda)(\lambda E - A)^{-1},$$

where $\Delta(\lambda)$ is the characteristic polynomial of the matrix A, and $B_{ik}(\lambda)$ is the algebraic cofactor of the element $\lambda\delta_{ki} - a_{ki}$ in the matrix $\lambda E - A$. Since only one characteristic vector

$$z = (z_1, z_2, \ldots, z_n),$$

$z_1 > 0,\ z_2 > 0, \ldots, z_n > 0$, corresponds to the characteristic number r (aside from a scalar factor), it follows that $B(r) \neq 0$ and that, in any nonzero column of the matrix $B(r)$, all the elements are different from zero and are of the same sign. The same condition holds for the rows of the matrix $B(r)$, as we see by replacing A in the discussion above by the transposed matrix A'. From these properties of the rows and columns of the matrix A, it follows that all $B_{ik}(r)$ ($i,\ k = 1, 2, \ldots, n$) are different from zero and are of the same sign σ. Therefore,

$$\sigma\Delta'(r) = \sigma \sum_{i=1}^n B_{ii}(r) > 0,$$

.e., $\Delta'(r) \neq 0$ and r *is a simple root of the characteristic equation* $\Delta(\lambda) = 0$.

Since r is the dominant root of the polynomial $\Delta(\lambda) = \lambda^n + \ldots$, hen $\Delta(\lambda)$ increases with $\lambda \geq r$. Therefore $\Delta'(r) > 0$ and $\sigma = 1$, i.e.,

$$B_{ik}(r) > 0 \quad (i,\ k = 1, 2, \ldots, n). \tag{13}$$

3. Now we turn to the proof of the second part of the theorem of Frobenius. We base the discussion on the following interesting emma:[10]

LEMMA 2. *If $A = (a_{ik})_1^n$ and $C = (c_{ik})_1^n$ are two square matrices*

[10] Also due to Wielandt [72].

of the same order n, *and if* A *is an irreducible matrix and* [11]

$$C^+ \leqq A \qquad (14)$$

then the following inequality holds between any characteristic number γ *of the matrix* C *and the maximum characteristic number* r *of the matrix* A:

$$|\gamma| \leqq r. \qquad (15)$$

In relation (15), *the sign of equality can hold only in case we have*

$$C = \exp(i\varphi)DAD^{-1}, \qquad (16)$$

where $\exp(i\varphi) = \gamma/r$, *and* D *is a diagonal matrix in which the moduli of the diagonal elements are equal to unity* $(D^+ = E)$.

Proof of the lemma. Let us denote by y a characteristic vector of the matrix C, which corresponds to the characteristic number γ:

$$Cy = \gamma y \quad (\gamma \neq 0). \qquad (17)$$

From (14) and (17) we find that:

$$|\gamma| y^+ \leqq C^+ y^+ \leqq A y^+. \qquad (18)$$

Therefore

$$|\gamma| \leqq r_y + \leqq r.$$

Let us now consider the case in which the equality $|\gamma| = r$ holds. In this case, it follows from (18) that y^+ is an extremal vector for the matrix A, and, consequently, $y^+ > 0$, and y^+ is a characteristic vector of the matrix A corresponding to the characteristic number r. Therefore, relation (18) assumes the form

$$Ay^+ = C^+ y^+ = r y^+, \quad y^+ > 0. \qquad (19)$$

Hence, by (14),

$$C^+ = A. \qquad (20)$$

Let $y = (y_1, y_2, \ldots, y_n)$, where

$$y_j = |y_j| \exp(i\psi_j) \quad (j = 1, 2, \ldots, n).$$

---

[11] C is a complex matrix, and $A \geqq 0$.

Let us define the diagonal matrix D by the equality

$$D = \{\exp{(i\psi_1)}, \exp{(i\psi_2)}, \ldots, \exp{(i\psi_n)}\}.$$

Then

$$y = Dy^+.$$

By substituting this expression for y in (17) and setting γ equal to $r \exp{(i\varphi)}$ we easily find that:

$$Fy^+ = ry^+, \tag{21}$$

where

$$F = \exp{(-i\varphi)}D^{-1}CD. \tag{22}$$

Comparing (19) with (21), we obtain:

$$Fy^+ = C^+y^+ = Ay^+. \tag{23}$$

However, by (22) and (20),

$$F^+ = C^+ = A.$$

Therefore, from (23) we find that

$$Fy^+ = F^+y^+.$$

Since $y^+ > 0$, this equality can hold only if

$$F = F^+,$$

i.e.,

$$\exp{(-i\varphi)}D^{-1}CD = A.$$

Hence

$$C = \exp{(i\varphi)}DAD^{-1}.$$

The lemma is proved.

4. Now we return to the theorem of Frobenius itself and apply the lemma we have just proved to an irreducible matrix $A \geqq 0$, which has exactly h characteristic numbers, all of modulus r, where r exceeds the moduli of the remaining characteristic roots:

$$\lambda_0 = r \exp{(i\varphi_0)}, \quad \lambda_1 = r \exp{(i\varphi_1)}, \ldots, \lambda_{h-1} = r \exp{(i\varphi_{h-1})}$$
$$(0 = \varphi_0 < \varphi_1 < \varphi_2 < \ldots < \varphi_{h-1} < 2\pi).$$

In the lemma, we set C equal to A and γ equal to λ_k. Then, for any $k = 0, 1, \ldots, h - 1$ we will have:

$$A = \exp\,(i\varphi_k)\,D_k A D_k^{-1}, \tag{24}$$

where D_k is a diagonal matrix with $D_k^+ = E$.

Again, we let z be some positive characteristic vector (of the matrix A) corresponding to the dominant real characteristic number r:

$$Az = rz. \tag{25}$$

Then, if we define $y^{(k)}$ by

$$y^{(k)} = D_k z \quad (y^{(k)+} = z > 0), \tag{26}$$

we find from (25) and (26) that:

$$Ay^{(k)} = \lambda_k y^{(k)} \quad (\lambda_k = r \exp\,(i\varphi_k),\; k = 0, 1, \ldots, h-1) \tag{27}$$

The latter equalities show that the vectors $y^{(0)}$, $y^{(1)}, \ldots, y^{(h-1)}$, as determined from (26), are characteristic vectors of the matrix A for the characteristic numbers λ_0, $\lambda_1, \ldots, \lambda_{h-1}$.

It follows from (24) not only that λ_0 is equal to r, but that each of the characteristic numbers $\lambda_1, \ldots, \lambda_{h-1}$ of the matrix A is simple. Therefore, the characteristic vectors $y^{(k)}$, i.e., the characteristic vectors of the matrix D_k $(k = 0, 1, \ldots, h - 1)$, are determined to within a scalar factor. To specify the matrices $D_0, D_1, \ldots, D_{h-1}$ uniquely, we will take the first diagonal element of each of these matrices to be unity. Then $D_0 = E$ and $y^{(0)} = z > 0$.

Further, it follows from (24) that:

$$A = \exp\,\{i(\varphi_j \pm \varphi_k)\} D_j D_k^{\pm 1} A D_1^{\mp 1} D_j^{-1} \quad (j, k = 0, 1, \ldots, h - 1).$$

Hence, as in the previous case, we conclude that the vector

$$D_j D_k^{\pm 1} z$$

is a characteristic vector of the matrix A, belonging to the characteristic number $r \exp\,\{i(\varphi_j \pm \varphi_k)\}$.

Therefore, $\exp\,\{i(\varphi_j \pm \varphi_k)\}$ coincides with one of the numbers $\exp\,(i\varphi_l)$ and the matrix $D_j D_k^{\pm 1}$ coincides with the corresponding matrix D, i.e., there exist $(0 \leqq) l_1$, $l_2 (\leqq h - 1)$ such that

$$\exp\{i(\varphi_j + \varphi_k)\} = \exp(i\varphi_l), \quad \exp\{i(\varphi_j - \varphi_k)\} = \exp(i\varphi_{l_2}),$$

$$D_j D_k = D_{l_1}, \quad D_j D_k^{-1} = D_{l_2}.$$

Thus, the numbers $\exp(i\varphi_0)$, $\exp(i\varphi_1)$, $\ldots$, $\exp(i\varphi_{h-1})$ *on the one hand and the corresponding diagonal matrices* D_0, D_1, $\ldots$, D_{h-1} *on the other hand form two isomorphic multiplicative abelian groups.*

In any finite group, consisting of exactly h distinct elements, the hth power of any element is equal to the identity of the group.[12] Therefore, $\exp(i\varphi_0)$, $\exp(i\varphi_1)$, $\ldots$, $\exp(i\varphi_{h-1})$ are hth roots of unity. Since there exist only h distinct hth roots from unity, and $\varphi_0 = 0 < \varphi_1 < \varphi_2 < \ldots < \varphi_{h-1} < 2\pi$, then

$$\varphi_k = 2k\pi/h \quad (k = 0, 1, 2, \ldots, h - 1)$$

and

$$\exp(i\varphi_k) = \varepsilon^k \quad (\varepsilon = \exp(i\varphi_1) = \exp(2\pi i/h); k = 0, 1, \ldots, h-1), \quad (28)$$

$$\lambda_k = r\varepsilon^k \quad (k = 0, 1, \ldots, h - 1). \quad (29)$$

The set of numbers λ_0, λ_1, $\ldots$, λ_{h-1} is precisely the set of roots of equation (4).

By (28) we have: [13]

$$D_k = D^k \quad (D = D_1; k = 0, 1, \ldots, h - 1). \quad (30)$$

Now equality (24) gives us (with $k = 1$):

$$A = \exp(2\pi i/h) DAD^{-1}. \quad (31)$$

Hence it follows that the product of matrix A by $\exp(2\pi i/h)$ is a matrix similar to A, and thus the entire system of n

[12] The order of every element in a finite group divides the order of the group.

[13] Here we are using the isomorphism between the multiplicative groups $\{\exp i\varphi_0, \exp i\varphi_1, \ldots, \exp i\varphi_{k-1}\}$ and $\{D_0, D_1, \ldots, D_{h-1}\}$.

characteristic numbers of the matrix A, when multiplied by exp $(2\pi i/h)$ is carried into itself.[14]

Further,

$$D^h = E;$$

therefore all the diagonal elements in D are hth roots of unity. By permuting the indices of A (and also of D) the matrix D can be brought to the following quasidiagonal form:

$$D = \{\eta_0 E_0, \eta_1 E_1, \ldots, \eta_{s-1} E_{s-1}\},$$

where $E_0, E_1, \ldots, E_{s-1}$ are identity matrices, and

$$\eta_p = \exp\,(i\psi_p),\ \psi_p = n_p\,2\pi/h$$

(n_p an integer; $p = 0, 1, \ldots, s-1$; $0 = n_0 < n_1 < \ldots < n_{s-1} < h$). It is obvious that $s \leq h$.

We write A in block form conformal with (32)

$$A = \begin{bmatrix} A_{11} & A_{12} & \ldots & A_{1s} \\ A_{21} & A_{22} & \ldots & A_{2s} \\ \cdot & \cdot & \cdot & \cdot \\ A_{s1} & A_{s2} & \ldots & A_{ss} \end{bmatrix}$$

and we replace equality (31) by the system of equalities

$$\varepsilon A_{pq} = \frac{\eta_{q-1}}{\eta_{p-1}} A_{pq} \quad (p,\,q = 1, 2, \ldots, s;\ \varepsilon = \exp\,(2\pi i/h)).$$

Hence, for any p and q, either $\eta_{q-1}/\eta_{p-1} = \varepsilon$, or $A_{pq} = 0$.

Let us suppose p is 1. Since not all the matrices $A_{12}, A_{13}, \ldots, A_{1s}$ can be zero, then one of the numbers $\eta_1/\eta_0, \eta_2/\eta_0, \ldots, (\eta_{s-1})/\eta_0$ ($\eta_0 = 1$) must be equal to ε. This is possible only if $n_1 = 1$

[14] The number h is the greatest positive number which possesses this property, since the matrix A has exactly h characteristic numbers of this maximum modulus r. In addition, it follows from (31) that the set of all the characteristic numbers of the matrix splits into subsystems (of h numbers each) of the form $\mu_0, \mu_0\varepsilon, \ldots, \mu_0\varepsilon^{h-1}$, and that in each such subsystem every characteristic number corresponds to an elementary divisor of the same degree. The roots $\lambda_0, \lambda_1, \ldots, \lambda_{h-1}$ of equation (4) form one of these subsystems.

Then $\eta_1/\eta_0 = \varepsilon$ and $A_{11} = A_{13} = \ldots = A_{1s} = 0$. Taking p equal to 2 in (34), we find similarly that $n_2 = 2$ and $A_{21} = A_{22} = A_{24} = \ldots = A_{2s} = 0$, etc. Thus we see that A must have the form

$$
A = \begin{bmatrix}
0 & A_{12} & 0 & \ldots & 0 \\
0 & 0 & A_{23} & \ldots & 0 \\
\cdots & \cdots & \cdots & \cdots & \cdots \\
0 & 0 & 0 & \ldots & A_{s-1,\,s} \\
A_{s1} & A_{s2} & A_{s3} & \ldots & A_{s,\,s}
\end{bmatrix}.
$$

Here $n_1 = 1$, $n_2 = 2, \ldots, n_{s-1} = s - 1$. But then, for $p = s$, the right side of equality (34) has the factor

$$
\frac{\eta_{q-1}}{\eta_{s-1}} = \exp\{(q - s)2\pi i/h\} \quad (q = 1, 2, \ldots, s).
$$

One of these numbers must be equal to $\varepsilon = \exp(2\pi i/h)$. This is possible only for $s = h$ and $q = 1$ and thus further $A_{s2} = \ldots = A_{ss} = 0$.

This shows that

$$
D = \{E_0,\ \varepsilon E_1,\ \varepsilon^2 E_2, \ldots, \varepsilon^{h-1}E_{h-1}\}
$$

and the matrix A has the form (5).

The theorem of Frobenius is completely proved.

. Let us make several remarks on the theorem of Frobenius.

REMARK 1. In proving the theorem of Frobenius, we also proved that if an irreducible matrix $A \geqq 0$ has dominant characteristic number r, then the adjoint matrix $B(\lambda)$ is positive for $\lambda = r$

$$
B(r) > 0, \tag{35}
$$

i.e.,

$$
B_{ik}(r) > 0 \quad (i,\, k = 1, 2, \ldots, n), \tag{35'}
$$

where $B_{ik}(r)$ is the algebraic cofactor of the element $r\delta_{ki} - a_{ki}$ in the determinant of $rE - A$.

Now let us consider the *reduced adjoint matrix*

$$
C(\lambda) = B(\lambda)/D_{n-1}(\lambda),
$$

where $D_{n-1}(\lambda)$ is the greatest common divisor of all the polynomials $B_{ik}(\lambda)$ $(i, k = 1, 2, \ldots, n)$. Note that (35') guarantees that $D_{n-1}(r) \neq 0$. All the roots of the polynomial $D_{n-1}(\lambda)$ are characteristic numbers [15] which are distinct from r. Therefore, all the roots of $D_{n-1}(\lambda)$ are either complex, or real but less than r. Hence $D_{n-1}(r) > 0$, which together with (35) gives: [16]

$$C(r) = B(r)/D_{n-1}(r) > 0. \tag{36}$$

REMARK 2. Inequalities (35') allow us to find bounds for the characteristic number r.

Let us introduce the symbols

$$s_i = \sum_{k=1}^{n} a_{ik} \quad (i = 1, 2, \ldots, n), \quad s = \min s_i, \quad S = \max s_i \ (1 \leq i \leq n).$$

Then *for an irreducible matrix $A \geq 0$*

$$s \leq r \leq S, \tag{37}$$

where the sign of equality to the left or right of r holds only when $s = S$, i.e., when all the "row sums" $s_1, s_2, \ldots, s_n$ are equal.[17]

Indeed, let us add to the last column of the characteristic determinant

$$\Delta(r) = \det \begin{bmatrix} r-a_{11}, & -a_{12}, & \ldots, & -a_{1n} \\ -a_{21}, & r-a_{22}, & \ldots, & -a_{2n} \\ \cdot & \cdot & \cdot & \cdot \\ -a_{n1}, & -a_{n2}, & \ldots, & r-a_{nn} \end{bmatrix}$$

all the preceding columns and let us then expand the determinant by minors of the elements of the last column. We obtain:

$$\sum_{k=1}^{n} (r - s_k) B_{nk}(r) = 0.$$

Hence, inequality (37) follows from (35').

[15] $D_{n-1}(\lambda)$ is a divisor of the characteristic polynomial $D_n(\lambda) \equiv \det(\lambda E - A)$
[16] In the following section it will be proved that, for an irreducible matrix, $B(\lambda) > 0$, $C(\lambda) > 0$ for any real $\lambda \geq r$.
[17] There are papers which concern themselves with establishing an interval for r which is smaller than (s, S). See [7, 38, 52].

REMARK 3. *The irreducible matrix $A \geq 0$ cannot have two linearly independent nonnegative characteristic vectors.* Suppose on the contrary that the matrix A has a characteristic vector $y \geq 0$ (which is linearly independent of z) corresponding to the characteristic number α, as well as the positive characteristic vector $z > 0$, which corresponds to the dominant characteristic number r:

$$Ay = \alpha y \quad (y \neq 0; \; y \geq 0).$$

Since r is a simple root of the characteristic equation $\det (\lambda E - A) = 0$, then

$$\alpha \neq r.$$

Let us denote by u the positive characteristic vector of the transposed matrix A' corresponding to $\lambda = r$:

$$A'u = ru \quad (u > 0).$$

Then [18]

$$r(y, u) = (y, A'u) = (Ay, u) = \alpha(y, u);$$

hence, since $\alpha \neq r$,

$$(y, u) = 0;$$

but this is impossible with $u > 0$, $y \geq 0$, $y \neq 0$.

REMARK 4. In the proof of the theorem of Frobenius, we established the following property of the dominant characteristic number r of the irreducible matrix $A \geq 0$:

$$r = \max_{(x \geq 0)} r_x,$$

where r_x is the maximum of the numbers ρ, for which the inequality $\rho x \leq Ax$ holds. In other words, since

$$r_x = \min_{1 \leq i \leq n} \frac{(Ax)_i}{x_i},$$

---

[18] Let $y = (y_1, \ldots, y_n)$, $u = (u_1, u_2, \ldots, u_n)$. The scalar product $y'u = \Sigma\, y_i u_i$ we denote by (u, u). Then $(y, A'u) = y'A'u$, and $(Ay, u) = (Ay)'u = y'A'u$.

then it is true that

$$r = \max_{(x \geq 0)} \min_{1 \leq i \leq n} \frac{(Ax)_i}{x_i}.$$

Similarly, we can define r^x for any vector $x \geq 0$ $(x \neq 0)$ as the smallest of the numbers σ, which satisfy the inequality

$$\sigma x \geq Ax,$$

i.e., we can define r^x as follows:

$$r^x = \max_{1 \leq i \leq n} \frac{(Ax)_i}{x_i}.$$

In this definition, if the relations $x_i = 0$, $(Ax)_i \neq 0$ hold for some i, then we take $r^x = + \infty$. By arguments similar to those used in discussing the function r_x, it can be proved that the function r^x attains its minimum value $\hat{r}$ on a certain vector $v > 0$.

Let us show that the number $\hat{r}$, as determined by the equality

$$\hat{r} = \min_{x \geq 0} r^x = \min_{x \geq 0} \max_{1 \leq i \leq n} \frac{(Ax)_i}{x_i}, \qquad (38)$$

coincides with the number r, and the vector $v \geq 0$ $(v \neq 0)$, on which this minimum is attained, is the characteristic vector of the matrix A for $\lambda = r$.

In fact,

$$\hat{r}v - Av \geq 0 \quad (v \geq 0,\ v \neq 0).$$

Let us assume that equality does not hold. Then, according to Lemma 1,

$$(E + A)^{n-1}(\hat{r}v - Av) > 0, \quad (E + A)^{n-1}v > 0. \qquad (39)$$

If we define u by

$$u = (E + A)^{n-1}v > 0,$$

we will have:

$$\hat{r}u > Au$$

and, consequently, for some sufficiently small $\varepsilon > 0$,

$$(\hat{r} - \varepsilon)u > Au \quad (u > 0),$$

which contradicts the definition of the number $\hat{r}$. Thus,

$$Av = \hat{r}v.$$

But then

$$u = (E + A)^{n-1}v = (1 + \hat{r})v.$$

Therefore, from $u > 0$ it follows that $v > 0$.

Hence, on the basis of Remark 3,

$$\hat{r} = r.$$

Thus, we have established for the number r the two properties

$$r = \max_{x \geq 0} \min_{1 \leq i \leq n} \frac{(Ax)_i}{x_i} = \min_{x \geq 0} \max_{1 \leq i \leq n} \frac{(Ax)_i}{x_i}, \qquad (40)$$

and furthermore, the $\max_{(x \geq 0)}$ or $\min_{(x \geq 0)}$ is attained only on the positive characteristic vector which corresponds to $\lambda = r$.

From these properties of the number r, the inequalities [19]

$$\min_{1 \leq i \leq n} \frac{(Ax)_i}{x_i} \leq r \leq \max_{1 \leq i \leq n} \frac{(Ax)_i}{x_i} \quad (x \geq 0, \quad x \neq 0) \qquad (41)$$

follow.

REMARK 5. If $A \geq 0$ is an irreducible matrix, then since in (40) $\max_{(x \geq 0)}$ and $\min_{(x \geq 0)}$ are attained only on a positive characteristic vector, then either of the inequalities

$$rz \leq Az, \quad z \geq 0, \quad z \neq 0$$

or

$$rz \geq Az, \quad z \geq 0, \quad z \neq 0$$

implies equality:

$$Az = rz, \quad z > 0.$$

§ 3. Reducible matrices

1. The spectral properties of irreducible nonnegative matrices established in the preceding section are not valid for reducible

[19] See [10, 24].

matrices. However, since an arbitrary nonnegative matrix $A \geq 0$ may always be represented as the limit of a sequence of irreducible, positive matrices A_m

$$A = \lim_{m \to \infty} A_m \quad (A_m > 0, \ m = 1, 2, \ldots), \tag{42}$$

then certain of the spectral properties of irreducible matrices also hold (in weak form) for reducible matrices.

For an arbitrary nonnegative matrix $A = (a_{ik})_1^n$ we will prove the following theorem:

THEOREM 3. *A nonnegative matrix* $A = (a_{ik})_1^n$ *always has a nonnegative characteristic number* r *such that no characteristic number of the matrix* A *has modulus exceeding* r. *To this "dominant" characteristic number* r *there corresponds a nonnegative characteristic vector* y:

$$Ay = ry \quad (y \geq 0, \ y \neq 0).$$

For the adjoint matrix $B(\lambda) = B_{ik}(\lambda)_1^n = (\lambda E - A)^{-1} \Delta(\lambda)$, *the following inequalities hold*:

$$B(\lambda) \geq 0, \quad \frac{d}{d\lambda} B(\lambda) \geq 0 \text{ for } \lambda \geq r. \tag{43}$$

Proof. Let the matrix A be expressed as (42). Let us denote the dominant characteristic number of the positive matrix A_m by $r^{(m)}$ and the unit [20] positive characteristic vector corresponding to it by $y^{(m)}$:

$$A_m y^{(m)} = r^{(m)} y^{(m)} \quad [(y^{(m)} y^{(m)}) = 1, \ y^{(m)} > 0; \ m = 1, 2, \ldots]. \tag{44}$$

Then from (42) it follows that the limit

$$\lim r^{(m)} = r,$$

exists, where r is a characteristic number of the matrix A. Since $r^{(m)} > 0$ and $r^{(m)} > |\lambda_0^{(m)}|$, where $\lambda_0^{(m)}$ is any characteristic number of the matrix A_m ($m = 1, 2, \ldots$), then in the limit we have:

$$r \geq 0, \ r \geq |\lambda_0|,$$

---

[20] By a unit vector we mean a column $(y_1, \ldots, y_n)$, normalized so that $(y, y) = \Sigma y^2_i = 1$.

where λ_0 is any characteristic number of the matrix A. Also, in the limit, (35) gives

$$B(r) \geqq 0. \qquad (45)$$

Further, in the sequence of unit characteristic vectors $y^{(m)}$ ($m = 1, 2, \ldots$) it is possible to select a convergent subsequence $y^{(m_p)}$ ($p = 1, 2, \ldots$), which converges to a certain unit vector y, which is obviously different from 0. By giving m the sequence of values m_p ($p = 1, 2, \ldots$) in (44), we obtain, in the limit,

$$Ay = ry \quad (y \geqq 0, \, y \neq 0).$$

We will establish inequalities (43) by using induction with respect to the order n. For $n = 1$, the inequalities are obvious.[21] Let us assume that they are true for matrices of order $< n$, and let us establish (43) for the matrix $A = (a_{ik})_1^n$ of order n.

If we expand the characteristic determinant $\Delta(\lambda) = \det(\lambda E - A)$ according to the elements of the last row and the last column, we obtain:

$$\Delta(\lambda) = (\lambda - a_{nn}) B_{nn}(\lambda) - \sum_{i,k=1}^{n-1} B_{ki}^{(n)}(\lambda) a_{in} a_{nk}. \qquad (46)$$

Here $B_{nn}(\lambda) = \det(\lambda \delta_{ik} - a_{ik})_1^{n-1}$ is the characteristic determinant of the "curtailed" nonnegative matrix of $(n-1)$th order, and $B_{ki}^{(n)}(\lambda)$ is the algebraic cofactor of the element $\lambda \delta_{ik} - a_{ik}$ in the determinant $B_{nn}(\lambda)$ ($i, k = 1, 2, \ldots, n-1$). Let r_n be the dominant nonnegative root of $B_{nn}(\lambda)$. If we set λ equal to r_n in (46), and use the induction assumption in the form

$$B_{ki}^{(n)}(r_n) \geqq 0 \quad (i, k = 1, 2, \ldots, n - 1),$$

we obtain from (46):

$$\Delta(r_n) \leqq 0.$$

On the other hand, $\Delta(\lambda) = \lambda^n + \ldots$ and therefore $\Delta(+\infty) = +\infty$. Therefore, r_n is either a root of $\Delta(\lambda)$, or is less than a certain real root of $\Delta(\lambda)$. In either case,

$$r_n \leqq r.$$

---

[21] In fact, since $B(\lambda) \equiv (\lambda E - A)^{-1}\Delta(\lambda)$, then for $n = 1$, $B(\lambda) \equiv E$, and $dB(\lambda)/d\lambda \equiv 0$.

If we permute (renumber) the indices, we see that any principal $(n-1)^2$ matrix $B_{jj}(\lambda)$ $(j = 1, 2, \ldots, n)$ can replace $B_{nn}(\lambda)$ in the above argument. Thus it is generally true that, if r_j is a dominant root of $B_{jj}(\lambda)$ then

$$r_j \leqq r \qquad (j = 1, 2, \ldots, n). \tag{47}$$

Further, $B_{ik}(\lambda)$ is the product of $(-1)^{i+k}$ by the determinant of a minor of $(n-1)$th order of the characteristic matrix $\lambda E - A$. If we differentiate this determinant with respect to λ, we easily obtain:

$$\frac{d}{d\lambda} B_{ik}(\lambda) = \sum B_{ik}^{(j)}(\lambda) \quad (i, k = 1, 2, \ldots, n-1), \tag{48}$$

where $B^{(j)}(\lambda) = \left(B_{ik}^{(j)}(\lambda)\right)$ $(i \neq j, k \neq j; j = 1, 2, \ldots, n)$ is the adjoint matrix of the $(n-1)$th order matrix (a_{ik}) $(i, k = 1, 2, \ldots, j-1, j+2, \ldots, n)$. But according to the induction hypothesis,

$$B^{(j)}(\lambda) \geqq 0 \text{ for } \lambda \geqq r_j \qquad (j = 1, 2, \ldots, n),$$

therefore, by (47) and (48),

$$\frac{d}{d\lambda} B(\lambda) \geqq 0 \quad \text{for} \quad \lambda \geqq r. \tag{49}$$

It follows from (45) and (49) that:

$$B(\lambda) \geqq 0 \quad \text{for} \quad \lambda \geqq r.$$

The theorem is completely proved.

REMARK. Inequalities (37) remain valid in the limit (42). Therefore, these inequalities hold for an arbitrary nonnegative matrix. However, the conditions under which the sign of equality holds in (37) are no longer valid for a reducible matrix.

2. A number of important proposition follow from Theorem 3:
    1. *If $A = (a_{ik})_1^n$ is a nonnegative matrix with dominant characteristic number r, and $C(\lambda)$ is its reduced adjoint matrix, then*

$$C(\lambda) \geqq 0 \quad \text{for} \quad \lambda \geqq r. \tag{50}$$

Indeed,

$$C(\lambda) = \frac{B(\lambda)}{D_{n-1}(\lambda)} \tag{51}$$

where $D_{n-1}(\lambda)$ is the greatest common divisor of the elements of the matrix $B(\lambda)$. Since $D_{n-1}(\lambda)$ is a divisor of the characteristic polynomial $\varDelta(\lambda)$ and $D_{n-1}(\lambda) = \lambda^{n-1} + \ldots$, then

$$D_{n-1}(\lambda) > 0 \quad \text{for} \quad \lambda > r, \tag{52}$$

(50) follows from (43), (51), and (52).

2. *If* $A \geq 0$ *is an irreducible matrix with dominant characteristic number* r, *then*

$$B(\lambda) > 0, \; C(\lambda) > 0 \quad \text{for} \quad \lambda > r. \tag{53}$$

Indeed, according to (35), $B(r) > 0$. But we have already seen that

$$\frac{d}{d\lambda} B(\lambda) \geq 0 \quad \text{for} \quad \lambda \geq r.$$

Therefore,

$$B(\lambda) > 0 \quad \text{for} \quad \lambda \geq r. \tag{54}$$

The second of inequalities (53) follows from (51), (52), and (54).

3. *If* $A \geq 0$ *is an irreducible matrix with dominant characteristic number* r, *then*

$$(\lambda E - A)^{-1} > 0 \quad \text{for} \quad \lambda < r. \tag{55}$$

This inequality follows from the formula

$$(\lambda E - A)^{-1} = \frac{B(\lambda)}{\varDelta(\lambda)},$$

since $B(\lambda) > 0$ and $\varDelta(\lambda) > 0$ for $\lambda > r$.

4. *The dominant characteristic number* r' *of any principal minor* [22] *(of order* $< n$*) of the nonnegative matrix* $A = (a_{ik})_1^n$

---

[22] A principal minor of A is any matrix (a_{ij}) $(i, j = t_1, t_2, \ldots, t_s)$, where $\{t_k, \; k = 1, \ldots, s\}$ is a proper subset of $\{1, \ldots, n\}$. Thus a principal minor is obtained by erasing all rows of A which have certain indices, and then erasing all columns of A which have these same indices.

does not exceed the maximum characteristic number r of matrix A:

$$r' \leqq r. \tag{56}$$

If A is an irreducible matrix, then the inequality in (56) is a strict inequality.

If A is a reducible matrix, then the sign of equality holds in (56) for at least one principal minor.

Indeed, inequality (56) is true at least for any principal minor of $(n-1)$th order (see equation (47)]. If A is an irreducible matrix, then according to (35') $B_{jj}(r) > 0$ $(j = 1, 2, \ldots, n)$, and, consequently, $r' \neq r$.

By descent from $n - 1$ to $n - 2$, from $n - 2$ to $n - 3$, etc., we can convince ourselves of the validity of inequality (56) for a principal minor of any order.

If A is a reducible matrix, then by a permutation of the indices it can be brought into the form

$$A = \begin{bmatrix} B & 0 \\ C & D \end{bmatrix}.$$

Then the number r must be a characteristic number of one of the two principal minors B and D. Proposition *4* is proved.

The following is a consequence of *4*.

5.   If $A \geqq 0$ and if any of the principal minors in the characteristic determinant

$$\varDelta(r) = \det \begin{bmatrix} r - a_{11}, & -a_{12}, & \ldots, & -a_{1n} \\ -a_{21}, & r - a_{22}, & \ldots, & -a_{2n} \\ \multicolumn{4}{c}{\cdots\cdots\cdots\cdots\cdots\cdots\cdots\cdots} \\ -a_{n1}, & -a_{n2}, & \ldots, & r - a_{nn} \end{bmatrix}$$

has the value zero (the matrix A is reducible!), then any "enveloping" principal minor is also zero, in particular, one of the principal minors of order $n - 1$

$$B_{11}(r), \ B_{22}(r), \ \ldots, \ B_{nn}(r)$$

is zero.

From *4* and *5* there follows:

6. *The matrix* $A \geqq 0$ *is reducible if and only if at least one of the relations*

$$B_{ii}(r) \geqq 0 \quad (i = 1, 2, \ldots, n)$$

degenerates to an equality.

From *4*, there follows also

7. *If* r *is the dominant characteristic number of the matrix* $A \geqq 0,$ *then for any* $\lambda > r$ *all the principal minors of the characteristic matrix* $A_\lambda \equiv \lambda E - A$ *are positive*:

$$A_\lambda \begin{bmatrix} i_1, i_2, \ldots, i_p \\ i_1, i_2, \ldots, i_p \end{bmatrix} > 0 \ (\lambda > r; \ 1 \leqq i_1 < i_2 < \ldots < i_p \leqq n; \ p = 1, 2, \ldots, n).$$

$$(57)$$

It is easily seen that conversely, (57) implies $\lambda > r$. For we have

$$\varDelta(\lambda + \mu) = \det\left((\lambda + \mu)E - A\right) = \det\left(A_\lambda + \mu E\right) = \sum_{k=0}^{n} S_k \mu^{n-k}$$

where S_k is the sum of all the principal $k \times k$ minors of the characteristic matrix $A_\lambda \equiv \lambda E - A \ (k = 1, 2, \ldots, n)$. Therefore, if all the principal minors of the characteristic matrix A are positive for some real λ, then for any $\mu \geqq 0$ we have

$$\varDelta(\lambda + \mu) \neq 0,$$

i.e., no number $\geqq \lambda$ is a characteristic number of the matrix A. Consequently,

$$r < \lambda.$$

Thus, inequalities (57) are necessary and sufficient conditions for the number λ to be an upper bound for the moduli of the characteristic numbers of the matrix A.[23] However, the set of inequalities (57) is not independent.

The matrix $\lambda E - A$ is a matrix with nonpositive nondiagonal elements.[24] D. M. Kotelyanskiĭ showed [25] that if the nondiagonal

---

[23] This method of proof appears in papers of B. A. Sevast'nov and D. M. Kotelyanskiĭ.

[24] It is easily seen that conversely, any matrix with negative or zero nondiagonal elements can always be represented in the form $\lambda E - A$, where A is a nonnegative matrix, and λ is a real number.

[25] [35]. This work contains a number of results which deal with matrices, all the nondiagonal elements of which are of the same sign.

elements g_{ik} $(i \neq k)$ of a matrix are nonpositive, and if the (nested sequence of) leading principal minors are all positive, then every principal minor is positive. The corresponding theorem, in which the hypothesis $g_{ik} > 0$ is replaced by $g_{ik} = g_{ki}$, is well known. In a later paper, Kotelyanskii was able to give a general theorem which included both the above theorems as spec a cases.

LEMMA 3 (Kotelyanskii). *If all the nondiagonal elements of the real matrix* $G = (g_{ik})_1^n$ *are negative or zero*

$$g_{ik} \leqq 0 \quad (i \neq k;\ i,\ k = 1,\ 2,\ \ldots,\ n), \tag{58}$$

and the leading principal minors are positive then all the principal minors of the matrix G *are positive:*

$$G \begin{bmatrix} i_1, i_2, \ldots, i_p \\ i_1, i_2, \ldots, i_p \end{bmatrix} > 0\,(1 \leqq i_1 < i_2 < \ldots < i_p \leqq n;\ p = 1,\ 2,\ \ldots,\ n).$$

Proof. We will prove the lemma by induction on the order n of the matrix. For $n = 2$, the lemma holds, since the hypotheses

$$g_{12} \leqq 0,\ g_{21} \leqq 0,\ g_{11} > 0,\ g_{11}g_{22} - g_{12}g_{21} > 0$$

imply $g_{22} > 0$. Suppose the lemma to be true for matrices of order $< n$; we will prove it for the matrix $G = (g_{ik})_1^n$. We consider the bordered determinants

$$t_{ik} = G \begin{bmatrix} 1 & i \\ 1 & k \end{bmatrix} = g_{11}g_{ik} - g_{1k}g_{i1} \quad (i,\ k = 2,\ \ldots,\ n).$$

From (58) and $g_{11} > 0$, we have the relation

$$t_{ik} \leqq 0 \quad (i \neq k;\ i,\ k = 2,\ \ldots,\ n).$$

On the other hand, if we apply Sylvester's determinental identity ([47]; Appendix IV) to the matrix $T = (t_{ik})_2^n$, we obtain:

$$T \begin{bmatrix} i_1, i_2, \ldots, i_p \\ i_1, i_2, \ldots, i_p \end{bmatrix} = (g_{11})^{p-1} G \begin{bmatrix} 1, i_1, i_2, \ldots, i_p \\ 1, i_1, i_2, \ldots, i_p \end{bmatrix}$$

$$(2 \leqq i_1 < i_2 < \ldots < i_p \leqq n,\ p = 1,\ 2,\ \ldots,\ n-1). \tag{60}$$

Since the leading principal minors of G are positive, it follows that the leading principal minors of the matrix $T = (t_{ik})_2^n$ are positive:

$$t_{22} = T\begin{bmatrix} 2 \\ 2 \end{bmatrix} > 0, \quad T\begin{bmatrix} 2 & 3 \\ 2 & 3 \end{bmatrix} > 0, \ldots, \quad T\begin{bmatrix} 2, 3, \ldots, n \\ 2, 3, \ldots, n \end{bmatrix} > 0.$$

Thus, the matrix $T = (t_{ik})_2^n$ of order $(n-1)$ satisfies the conditions of the lemma. Therefore, all the principal minors of the matrix T are positive by the induction hypothesis:

$$T\begin{bmatrix} i_1, i_2, \ldots, i_p \\ i_1, i_2, \ldots, i_p \end{bmatrix} > 0 \ (2 \leq i_1 < i_2 < \ldots < i_p \leq n; p = 1, 2, \ldots, n-1).$$

But then, it follows from (60) that all those principal minors of the matrix G which include the first row are positive:

$$G\begin{bmatrix} 1, i_1, i_2, \ldots, i_p \\ 1, i_1, i_2, \ldots, i_p \end{bmatrix} > 0 \ (2 \leq i_1 < i_2 < \ldots < i_p \leq n; p = 1, 2, \ldots, n-1).$$
$$(61)$$

Now let us take any fixed indices $(1 <)i_1 < i_2 < \ldots < i_{n-2}$ $(\leq n)$ and consider the $(n-1)$th order matrix:

$$(g_{\alpha\beta}) \quad (\alpha, \beta = 1, i_1, i_2, \ldots, i_{n-1}).$$

On the basis of (61), the leading principal minors of this matrix are positive:

$$G\begin{bmatrix} 1, i_1, i_2, \ldots, i_{n-2} \\ 1, i_1, i_2, \ldots, i_{n-2} \end{bmatrix} > 0, \ldots \quad G\begin{bmatrix} 1 & i_1 \\ 1 & i_1 \end{bmatrix} > 0, \ g_{11} > 0,$$

and the nondiagonal elements are nonpositive:

$$g_{\alpha\beta} \leq 0 \quad (\alpha \neq \beta; \alpha, \beta = 1, i_1, i_2, \ldots, i_{n-2}).$$

But the order of matrix (62) is equal to $n-1$. Again by the induction hypothesis, all the principal minors of this matrix are positive; in particular,

$$G\begin{bmatrix} i_1, i_2, \ldots, i_p \\ i_1, i_2, \ldots, i_p \end{bmatrix} > 0$$
$$(63)$$
$$(2 \leq i_1 < i_2 < \ldots < i_p \leq n; p = 1, 2, \ldots, n-2).$$

Thus, *all* the minors of order $\leq n-2$ of the matrix G are positive.

From (63) we can conclude that $g_{22} > 0$, so that we may now consider the 2×2 determinants obtained by bordering element g_{22} (instead of g_{11}, as before):

$$t_{ik}^* = G \begin{bmatrix} 2 & i \\ 2 & k \end{bmatrix} \quad (i,\ k = 1,\ 3,\ \ldots,\ n).$$

Operating with the matrix $T^* = (t_{ik}^*)$ as we did with the matrix T, we obtain, in a similar manner, inequalities which are analogous to inequalities (61):

$$G \begin{bmatrix} 2, & i_1, & \ldots, & i_p \\ 2, & i_1, & \ldots, & i_p \end{bmatrix} > 0 \tag{64}$$

$$(i_1 < i_2 < \ldots < i_p;\ i_1, \ldots, i_p = 1,\ 3,\ \ldots,\ n;$$
$$p = 1,\ 2,\ \ldots,\ n - 1).$$

Since any principal minor of the matrix $G = (g_{ik})_1^n$ either contains the first or second row, or has order $\leqq n - 2$, it follows from inequalities (61), (63), and (64) that all the principal minors of the matrix A are positive. The lemma is proved.

In view of this theorem, some of the conditions in (57) are seen to be redundant; we need assume only that the leading principal minors are positive. Thus we have

THEOREM 4. *A necessary and sufficient condition that the real number λ be greater than the dominant characteristic number r of the matrix $A = (a_{ik})_1^n \geqq 0$,*

$$r < \lambda,$$

is that, for this value of λ, all the leading principal minors of the characteristic matrix $A_\lambda \equiv \lambda E - A$ be positive:

$$\lambda - a_{11} > 0,$$

$$\det \begin{bmatrix} \lambda - a_{11}, & -a_{12} \\ -a_{21}, & \lambda - a_{22} \end{bmatrix} > 0, \ldots, \det \begin{bmatrix} \lambda - a_{11}, & -a_{12}, & \ldots, & -a_{1n} \\ -a_{21}, & \lambda - a_{22}, & \ldots, & -a_{2n} \\ \ldots & \ldots & \ldots & \ldots \\ -a_{n1}, & -a_{n2}, & \ldots, & \lambda - a_{nn} \end{bmatrix} > 0.$$

$$\tag{65}$$

Let us consider an application of this theorem. Let all the nondiagonal elements of the matrix $C = (c_{ik})_1^n$ be nonnegative. Then for a certain $\lambda > 0$ the matrix $A = C + \lambda E$ is ≥ 0. Let us index the characteristic numbers λ_i $(i = 1, 2, \ldots, n)$ of the matrix C according to the values of their real parts:

$$\text{Re } \lambda_1 \leq \text{Re } \lambda_2 \leq \ldots \leq \text{Re } \lambda_n.$$

Let r be the dominant characteristic number of the matrix A. Since the characteristic numbers of A are the sums $\lambda_i + \lambda$ $(i = 1, 2, \ldots, n)$, then the relation $\lambda_n + \lambda = r$ must hold.

In the present case, the inequality $r < \lambda$ holds only when $\lambda_n < 0$, that is, only when all the characteristic numbers of the matrix C have negative real parts. If we write down inequalities (65) for the matrix $-C = \lambda E - A$, we obtain the following theorem.[26]

THEOREM 5. *A necessary and sufficient condition that all the characteristic numbers of the real matrix* $C = (c_{ik})_1^n$ *having nonnegative nondiagonal elements*

$$c_{ik} \geq 0 \quad (i \neq k; \ i, \ k = 1, 2, \ldots, n)$$

should have negative real parts, is that the following inequalities be satisfied:

$$c_{11} < 0, \ \det \begin{bmatrix} c_{11} & c_{12} \\ c_{21} & c_{22} \end{bmatrix} > 0, \ \ldots, \ (-1)^n \det C > 0.$$

§ 4. Normal form for a reducible matrix

Let us consider an arbitrary reducible matrix $A = (a_{ik})_1^n$. After a permutation of the indices it can be represented in the form

$$A = \begin{bmatrix} B & 0 \\ C & B \end{bmatrix} \tag{67}$$

where B, D are square matrices.

---

[26] Since $C = A - \lambda E$, $A \geq 0$, then λ_n is real (this follows from the equality $\lambda_n + \lambda = r$), and the characteristic vector of the matrix C which corresponds to this characteristic number is nonnegative:

$$Cy = \lambda_n y \ (y \geq 0, \ y \neq 0).$$

If either of the matrices B and D is reducible, then it can also be brought into a form similar to (67), after which the matrix A assumes the form

$$A = \begin{bmatrix} K & 0 & 0 \\ H & L & 0 \\ F & G & M \end{bmatrix}.$$

If any one of the matrices K, L, M is reducible, then this process can be continued. Thus, after a suitable permutation of indices, the matrix A takes the triangular block form:

$$A = \begin{bmatrix} A_{11} & 0 & \ldots & 0 \\ A_{21} & A_{22} & \ldots & 0 \\ \multicolumn{4}{c}{\ldots\ldots\ldots\ldots} \\ A_{s1} & A_{s2} & \ldots & A_{ss} \end{bmatrix}, \tag{68}$$

where the diagonal blocks are square irreducible matrices.

We will call the diagonal block A_{ii} $(1 \leq i \leq s)$ *isolated*, if

$$A_{ik} = 0 \quad (k = 1, 2, \ldots, i - 1, i + 1, \ldots, s).$$

By further permuting the indices in the matrix (68), if necessary, all the isolated blocks may be put first along the principal diagonal, after which the matrix A assumes the form

$$A = \begin{bmatrix} A & 0 & \ldots 0 & 0 & \ldots 0 \\ 0 & A_2 & \ldots 0 & 0 & \ldots 0 \\ \multicolumn{5}{c}{\ldots\ldots\ldots\ldots\ldots\ldots} \\ 0 & 0 & \ldots A_g & 0 & \ldots 0 \\ A_{g+1,1} & A_{g+1,2} & \ldots A_{g+1,g} & A_{g+1} & \ldots 0 \\ \multicolumn{5}{c}{\ldots\ldots\ldots\ldots\ldots\ldots} \\ A_{s1} & A_{s2} & \ldots A_{sg} & A_{s,g+1} & \ldots A_s \end{bmatrix} \tag{69}$$

Here A_1, A_2, $\ldots$, A_s are irreducible matrices, and in each row

$$A_{f1}, A_{f2}, \ldots, A_{f,f-1} \quad (f = g + 1, \ldots, s)$$

at least one of the matrices is not equal to zero.

We will call matrix (69) the *normal form* of the reducible matrix A.

We will show that *the normal form of the matrix A is uniquely determined up to a permutation of the blocks of indices.*[27] To do this, let us consider the linear operator A, which corresponds to the matrix A in the n-dimensional vector space R. In view of the fact that A has the form (69), R decomposes into a sum

$$R = R_1 + R_2 + \ldots + R_g + R_{g+1} + \ldots + R_s; \qquad (70)$$

of coordinate subspaces, where R_s, $R_{s-1} + R_s$, $R_{s-2} + R_{s-1} + R_s$, $\ldots$ are invariant coordinate subspaces for the operator A, and where no intermediate invariant coordinate subspace can be interposed between two adjacent subspaces in this set.

Let us assume that the given matrix has not only the normal form (69), but also another normal form, to which there corresponds another decomposition of R into coordinate subspaces:

$$R = R_1' + R_2' + \ldots + R_g' + R_{g+1}' + \ldots + R_t'.$$

To establish uniqueness of the normal form, it is enough to prove that decompositions (70) and (71) coincide except for the order of the summands.

Let the invariant subspace R_t' have coordinate vectors in common with R_k, but none in common with $R_{k+1}, \ldots, R_s$. Then R_t' must be entirely contained in R_k, since otherwise R_t' would contain a "smaller" invariant subspace—the intersection of R_t' with $R_k + R_{k+1} + \ldots + R_s$. Further, R_t' must coincide with R_k, since otherwise the invariant subspace $R_t + R_{k+1} + \ldots + R_s$ would be intermediate between the invariant subspaces $R_k + R_{k+1} + \ldots + R_s$ and $R_{k+1} + \ldots + R_s$. Since R_k coincides with R_t', R_k is an invariant subspace. Therefore, the normal form of the matrix is maintained if we write R_k in place of R_s. Thus, we suppose that, in decompositions (70) and (71), $R_s \equiv R_t'$.

Let us now consider the coordinate subspace R_{t-1}'. Let it have coordinate vectors in common with R_l ($l < s$), but none in common with $R_{l+1} + \ldots + R_s$. Then the invariant subspace

[27] After reaching normal form, we are still free to interchange the position of the first g blocks of rows arbitrarily. In addition, certain permutations among the last $s - g$ blocks of rows are sometimes possible without disturbing the normal form.

$R'_{t-1} + R'_t$ must be entirely contained in $R_l + R_{l+1} + \ldots + R_s$ since otherwise there would exist an intermediate invariant coordinate subspace between R'_t and $R'_{t-1} + R'_t$. Therefore $R'_{t-1} \subset R_l$. Further, $R'_{t-1} \equiv R_l$, since otherwise $R'_{t-1} + R_{l+1} + \ldots + R_s$ would be an intermediate invariant subspace between $R_l + R_{l+1} + \ldots + R_s$ and $R_{l+1} + \ldots + R_s$. From $R'_{t-1} \equiv R_l$, it follows that $R_l + R_s$ is an invariant subspace. Therefore R_l can be put in place of R_{s-1}; and then we have:

$$R'_{t-1} \equiv R_{s-1}, \quad R'_t \equiv R_s.$$

By continuing this process, we can show eventually that $s = t$ and that decompositions (70) and (71) coincide except for the order of the summands. This amounts to the statement that the corresponding normal forms also coincide except for a possible permutation of the blocks of indices.[28]

From the uniqueness of the normal form, it follows that the numbers g and s are numerical invariants for a reducible matrix A.[29] In particular, these invariants apply of course to nonnegative matrices.

Using the normal form of the matrix, we will prove the following theorem:

THEOREM 6. *There is a positive characteristic vector corresponding to the dominant characteristic number r of the matrix $A \geq 0$ if and only if* (i) *each of the matrices $A_1, A_2, \ldots, A_g$ in the normal form* (69) *of the matrix A has r as its characteristic number; and (when $g < s$)* (ii) *none of the matrices $A_{g+1}, \ldots, A_s$ possesses this property.*

Proof. (i) Let the positive characteristic vector $z > 0$ correspond to the dominant characteristic number r. We partition the column z into the parts z^k $(k = 1, 2, \ldots, s)$ conformal with the partitioning in (69). Then the equality

$$Az = rz \quad (z > 0) \tag{72}$$

---

[28] The last two paragraphs are purely expository. A suitable inductive argument could replace them.

[29] For an irreducible matrix, $g = s = 1$.

can be written as the two systems of equalities:

$$A_i z^i = rz \quad (i = 1, 2, \ldots, g) \tag{72'}$$

$$\sum_{h=1}^{j-1} A_{jh} z^h + A_j z^j = rz^j \quad (j = g+1, \ldots, s) \tag{72''}$$

It follows from (72') that the number r is a characteristic number of each of the matrices $A_1, A_2, \ldots, A_g$. From (72'') we find that

$$A_j z^j \leqq rz^j, \quad A_j z^j \neq rz^j \quad (j = g+1, \ldots, s). \tag{73}$$

Let us denote the dominant characteristic number of the matrix A_j $(j = g+1, \ldots, s)$ by r_j. Then (see (41) on p. 79) we find from (73) that:

$$r_j \leqq \max_i \frac{(A_j z^j)_i}{z_i^j} \leqq r \quad (j = g+1, \ldots, s).$$

On the other hand, the equality $r_j = r$ would contradict the second relation of (73) (see Remark 5 on p. 79). Therefore

$$r_j < r \quad (j = g+1, \ldots, s). \tag{74}$$

(ii) Now let us suppose conversely, that the dominant characteristic number of the matrix A_i $(i = 1, 2, \ldots, g)$ is equal to r, and that inequalities (74) hold for the matrices A_j $(j = g+1, \ldots, s)$. We have to find a positive vector z satisfying (72). This amounts to satisfying (72') and (72'') separately. We first solve (72'), thus obtaining a positive characteristic column vector z^i for each of the matrices A_i $(i = 1, 2, \ldots, g)$. The columns z^j $(j = g+1, \ldots, s)$ are found from (72'') by means of the formulas

$$z^j = (rE_j - A_j)^{-1} \sum_{h=1}^{j-1} A_{jh} z^h \quad (j = g+1, \ldots, s), \tag{75}$$

where E_j is the identity matrix of the same order as the matrix A_j $(j = g+1, \ldots, s)$.

Since $r_j < r$ $(j = g+1, \ldots, s)$, then [see (55) on p. 83]

$$(rE_j - A_j)^{-1} > 0 \quad (j = g+1, \ldots, s). \tag{76}$$

Let us prove inductively that the columns $z^{y+1}, \ldots, z^s$ defined by means of formulas (75) are positive. We will show that the relation $z^j > 0$ for any j $(g + 1 \leq j \leq s)$ follows from the fact that the preceding column vectors $z^1, z^2, \ldots, z^{j-1}$ are positive. Indeed, we have by hypothesis

$$\sum_{h=1}^{j-1} A_{jh} z^h \geq 0, \quad \sum_{h=1}^{j-1} A_{jh} z^h \neq 0,$$

and if we combine this with (76) and (75), we have the desired conclusion $z^j > 0$.

This shows that the column

$$z = \begin{bmatrix} z^1 \\ \cdot \\ \cdot \\ z^s \end{bmatrix}$$

obtained by joining the columns z^i, is positive and is a characteristic vector for the matrix A, corresponding to the characteristic number r. The theorem is proved.

The following theorem characterizes a matrix $A \geq 0$ which is such that both A and A' possess a positive characteristic vector corresponding to a dominant characteristic root.

THEOREM 7. *A necessary and sufficient condition that there be positive vectors z, w satisfying the equations $Az = rz$; $A'w = rw$, where $A \geq 0$ and r is a dominant characteristic root of A, is that A can be reduced by a permutation of indices to the block diagonal form*

$$A = \operatorname{diag}(A_1, A_2, \ldots, A_s), \tag{77}$$

where each of the blocks $A_1, A_2, \ldots, A_s$ is an irreducible matrix, each of which has the number r as a dominant characteristic root.

Proof. Suppose that there are positive vectors such that the relations $Az = rz$; $A'w = rw$ hold. By Theorem 6, the matrix A' can be written (after a permutation of the indices) in the normal form (69), where r is a dominant characteristic root of each of the matrices $A_1, A_2, \ldots, A_g$, and (if $g < s$) each of the matrices $A_{g+1}, \ldots, A_s$ has dominant characteristic root less than r. By direct transposition, we obtain

$$A' = \begin{bmatrix} A'_1 & \ldots & 0 & A'_{g+1,1} & \ldots & A'_{s1} \\ & \cdot & \cdot & & & \\ & \cdot & & \cdot & & \\ & \cdot & & & & \\ 0 & \ldots & A'_g & A'_{g+1,g} & \ldots & A'_{sg} \\ 0 & \ldots & 0 & A'_{g+1} & & \\ & \cdot & & & \cdot & \\ & \cdot & & & & \cdot \\ & \cdot & & & & \cdot \\ 0 & \ldots & 0 & 0 & \ldots & A'_s \end{bmatrix}.$$

But we can permute the blocks of indices in this form, so as to obtain

$$\begin{bmatrix} A'_s & 0 & 0 \ldots & 0 \\ A'_{s,s-1} & A'_{s-1} & 0 \ldots & 0 \\ \cdot & \cdot & & \cdot \\ \cdot & & \cdot & \cdot \\ \cdot & & & \cdot \\ A'_{s1} & A'_{s-1,1} & \ldots & A'_1 \end{bmatrix}. \tag{78}$$

Since each of the matrices A'_s, A'_{s-1}, ..., A'_1 is irreducible, the normal form can be obtained from (78) by a permutation of the blocks of rows so as to bring the isolated blocks to the leading positions along the main diagonal. Now the block A'_s is an isolated block. Since the normal form of the matrix A' must satisfy the conditions of the preceding theorem, it follows that r must be a dominant characteristic number of the matrix A'_s. This can occur only for $g = s$. Thus the normal form (69) takes the form (77).

The converse is clear. For suppose A has the form (77). Then A' has the form

$$A' = \text{diag}(A'_1, A'_2, \ldots, A'_s). \tag{79}$$

The preceding theorem applies, and shows that in each of the cases (77), (79), the matrix A (resp. A') has a positive characteristic vector corresponding to the dominant characteristic root r. The theorem is proved.

COROLLARY. *Suppose that* $A \geq 0$ *is a nonnegative matrix for which a dominant characteristic root* r *is simple. Suppose further that both* A *and* A' *possess characteristic vectors corresponding to* r *which are positive. Then* A *is irreducible.*

The converse statement, that an irreducible matrix $A \geq 0$ has the properties spelled out in the corollary, is obvious. Thus, these properties form a set of necessary and sufficient conditions for a nonnegative matrix to be irreducible; note that these are spectral properties.

§ 5. Primitive and imprimitive matrices

The following definition gives a classification of irreducible matrices.

DEFINITION 3. *Let* $A \geq 0$ *be an irreducible matrix, and let the dominant characteristic root be* r. *Suppose there are exactly* h *characteristic numbers of modulus* r $(\lambda_1 = |\lambda_2| = \ldots = |\lambda_h| = r.)$ *If* h *is* 1, *the matrix is called* primitive; *if* $h > 1$, *the matrix is called* imprimitive, *and the number* h *is called the* index of imprimitivity.

The index of imprimitivity can be quickly calculated if all the nonzero coefficients of the characteristic equation

$$\Delta(\lambda) \equiv \lambda^n + a_1 \lambda^{n_1} + a_2 \lambda^{n_2} + \ldots + a_t \lambda^{n_t} = 0$$
$$(n > n_1 > \ldots > n_t; \quad a_1 \neq 0, \, a_2 \neq 0, \ldots, a_t \neq 0)$$

of the matrix are known; h *is the greatest common divisor of the differences*

$$n - n_1, \, n_1 - n_2, \ldots, n_{t-1} - n_t. \tag{80}$$

To see this, we recall that Frobenius' theorem asserts that the spectrum of the matrix A is carried into itself by a rotation through the angle $2\pi/h$ about the origin. Thus the polynomial $\Delta(\lambda)$ must be related to some polynomials $g(\mu)$ by means of the formula

$$\Delta(\lambda) = g(\lambda^h) \lambda^{n'}.$$

This does show that h is a common divisor of the differences (80). Also, h must be equal to the greatest common divisor d of these differences, since the spectrum is carried into itself by a rotation through $2\pi/d$, which would be impossible if $h < d$.

The following theorem gives an important property of primitive matrices.

THEOREM 8. *A nonnegative matrix A (≥ 0) is primitive if and only if there is a power of A which is positive*:

$$A^p > 0 \quad (for\ some\ p \geq 1). \tag{81}$$

Proof. If $A^p > 0$, the matrix A must be irreducible, since every power of a reducible matrix is reducible. Further, the index h for the matrix A must be 1, since otherwise, the positive matrix A^p would have h (> 1) characteristic roots $\lambda_1^p, \lambda_2^p, \ldots, \lambda_h^p$ (equal or unequal) of maximal modulus r^p, which would contradict the Perron theorem.

Suppose conversely that A is a primitive matrix. We use a special formula for A^p: [29a]

$$A^p = \sum_{k=1}^{s} \frac{1}{(m_k - 1)!} \left[\frac{C(\lambda)\lambda^p}{\psi^{[k]}(\lambda)} \right]^{(m_k-1)}_{\lambda=\lambda_k}, \tag{82}$$

where

$$\psi(\lambda) = (\lambda - \lambda_1)^{m_1}(\lambda - \lambda_2)^{m_2} \ldots (\lambda - \lambda_s)^{m_s}\ (\lambda_j \neq \lambda_f\ \text{for}\ j \neq f)$$

is the minimal polynomial of the matrix A,

$$\psi^{[k]}(\lambda) = \frac{\psi(\lambda)}{(\lambda - \lambda_k)^{m_k}}\ (k = 1, 2, \ldots, s),$$

and $C(\lambda)$ is the reduced adjoint matrix

$$C(\lambda) = (\lambda E - A)^{-1}\psi(\lambda).$$

In the present case, we can take

$$\lambda_1 = r > |\lambda_2| \geq \ldots \geq |\lambda_s|,\quad m_1 = 1. \tag{83}$$

The formula (82) takes the form

$$A^p = \frac{C(r)}{\psi'(r)}r^p + \sum_{k=2}^{s} \frac{1}{(m_k - 1)!} \left[\frac{C(\lambda)\lambda^p}{\psi^{[k]}(\lambda)} \right]^{(m_k-1)}_{\lambda=\lambda_k}.$$

[29a] See Note 9, p. 16.

Hence it follows easily from (83) that

$$\lim_{p\to\infty} \frac{A^p}{r^p} = \frac{C(r)}{\psi'(r)}. \tag{84}$$

On the other hand, $C(r)$ is positive by (53) and $\psi'(\lambda)$ is positive by (83). Thus

$$\lim_{p\to\infty} r^{-p}A^p > 0,$$

and therefore inequality (73) holds from some p onwards. (A lower bound for p in (81) is given in [72].)

The theorem is proved.

Now we turn to the following theorem.

THEOREM 9. *Let A ($\geqq 0$) be a nonnegative irreducible matrix, and let some power A^q of A be reducible. Then A^q is completely reducible, i.e., there is a permutation of indices such that A^q can be written in the form*

$$A^q = \{A_1, A_2, \ldots, A_d\}, \quad d > 1$$

after the permutation. Moreover, $A_1, A_2, \ldots, A_d$ are irreducible matrices. The dominant characteristic numbers of these matrices are equal. Here, d is the greatest common divisor of the numbers q, h, where h is the index of imprimitivity of the matrix A.

Proof. Since the matrix A is irreducible, Frobenius' theorem shows that both A and A' have positive characteristic vectors corresponding to the dominant characteristic number r: $Az = rz$, $A'w = rw$. These same vectors z, w are then characteristic vectors for A^q, $(A^q)'$ corresponding to the dominant characteristic number r^q: $A^q z = r^q z$, $(A^q)'x = r^q w$. Theorem 7 shows that, by a permutation of the indices, we can write A^q in the form (85), where A_1, A_2, ..., A_d are irreducible matrices, each of which has r^q as dominant characteristic root. Now the matrix A has exactly h characteristic roots of maximal modulus r:

$$r, \; r\varepsilon, \ldots, r\varepsilon^{h-1} \quad (\varepsilon = \exp\{2\pi i/h\}).$$

Thus, the matrix A^q has h characteristic numbers of maximal modulus r^q:

$$r^q, \; r^q \varepsilon^q, \ldots, r^q \varepsilon^{q(h-1)},$$

and d of these numbers are equal to r^q. From this, it follows that d is the greatest common divisor of the numbers q, h. The theorem is proved.

If $h = 1$ in the hypotheses, we get the corollary below.

COROLLARY 1. *Every power of a primitive matrix $A \geq 0$ is irreducible, and therefore primitive.*

Again, if $q = h$, the theorem yields

COROLLARY 2. *If $A \geq 0$ is an imprimitive matrix, the index of imprimitivity being h, then the matrix A^h is* (after a permutation of indices) *a diagonal block matrix* (85), *in which the number of blocks is h, each block is irreducible, and each block has the same dominant characteristic number.*

§ 6. *Stochastic matrices*

We consider a physical system capable of existing in n possible states

$$S_1, S_2, \ldots, S_n, \tag{86}$$

and an ordered sequence of instants of time

$$t_0, t_1, t_2, \ldots.$$

We suppose that at each instant of time, the system is in one and only one of the states (86). We denote by p_{ij} the *conditional probability that the system is in state S_j at the instant t_k, supposing that the system was in state S_i at the preceding instant t_{k-1}* ($i, j = 1, 2, \ldots, n$; $k = 1, 2, \ldots$). We assume further that the *transition probabilities p_{ij}* are all independent of the index k (of the number of the instant of time). That is, we assume that the transition probabilities do not vary with time.

We say that the matrix

$$P = (p_{ij})_1^n$$

defines a *homogeneous Markov chain with a finite number of states* [20]. Here we make the obvious restrictions

$$p_{ij} \geq 0, \quad \sum_{j=1}^{n} p_{ij} = 1 \quad (i, j = 1, 2, \ldots, n). \tag{87}$$

DEFINITION 4. *A square matrix* $P = (p_{ij})_1^n$ *is called* stochastic *if the matrix* P *is nonnegative, and if every row sum is equal to* 1, *i.e., if the relations* (87) *hold.*[30]

Thus, the matrix of transitional probabilities for a *homogeneous Markov chain is stochastic*; and, *conversely*, an arbitrary stochastic matrix may be taken to be the matrix of transition probabilities of some homogeneous Markov chain. This reduces the problem of investigating homogeneous Markov chains to a problem, or a set of problems in matrix theory, as we shall see.[31]

A stochastic matrix is a special case of a nonnegative matrix. We can therefore apply the definitions and theorems of the preceding section of a stochastic matrix.

Special additional properties of a stochastic matric are the following. It follows from the definition, that such a matrix has characteristic number 1, to which the positive characteristic vector $z = (1, 1, \ldots, 1)'$ corresponds. Conversely, it is clear that if a nonnegative matrix $P \geqq 0$ has $(1, 1, \ldots, 1)'$ for a characteristic vector, and if the corresponding characteristic number is 1, then the matrix P is stochastic. Further, the number 1 is the dominant characteristic number of every stochastic matrix, since the dominant characteristic number always lies between the largest and smallest row sums [see (37), and the remark at the end of Section 3, 1]; and each row sum is 1. These facts are restated as follows.

1. *A nonnegative matrix* P ($\geqq 0$) *is stochastic if and only if the vector* $(1, 1, \ldots, 1)'$ *is a characteristic vector of* P, *with corresponding characteristic number* 1. *For a stochastic matrix,* 1 *is the dominant characteristic root.*

---

[30] In the definition of a stochastic matrix, the additional requirement $\Sigma_{i=1}^n p_{ij} \neq 0$ is sometimes made.

[31] The theory of homogeneous Markov chains with a finite (or countable) number of states was developed by A. N. Kolmogorov. Further discussion and development of the matrix method as applied to homogeneous Markov chains is found in a memoir of Romanovskiĭ, the book of Feller, and papers of Doeblin and Doob, in addition to the authors mentioned in the text [13—16, 20, 33, 34, 58].

Now we establish a representation (2 following) for certain nonnegative matrices. Let $A = (a_{ij})_1^n$ be a nonnegative matrix; let the positive number r (> 0) be a characteristic root of A, and let the corresponding characteristic vector $z = (z_1, z_2, \ldots, z_n)$ (> 0) be positive:

$$\sum_{j=1}^{n} a_{ij} z_j = r z_i \quad (i = 1, 2, \ldots, n). \qquad (88)$$

We define the diagonal matrix Z by

$$Z = \text{diag} (z_1, z_2, \ldots, z_n),$$

and the matrix $P = (p_{ij})_1^n$ by

$$P = r^{-1} \cdot Z^{-1} A Z.$$

The elements p_{ij} of P are clearly nonnegative:

$$p_{ij} = r^{-1} z_i^{-1} p_{ij} z_j \geqq 0 \quad (i, j = 1, 2, \ldots, n),$$

and from (88) we have the further relation

$$\sum_{j=1}^{n} p_{ij} = 1 \quad (i = 1, 2, \ldots, n).$$

We have established

2. *If A ($\geqq 0$) is a nonnegative matrix which has a positive dominant characteristic root, to which there corresponds a positive characteristic vector $z = (z_1, z_2, \ldots, z_n) > 0$, it is similar to the product rP of r by some stochastic matrix P:*

$$A = Z r P Z^{-1} \quad (Z = \text{diag} (z_1, z_2, \ldots, z_n) > 0). \qquad (89)$$

(This assertion holds also (trivially) for $r = 0$, since $A \geqq 0$, $z > 0$ imply $A = 0$.)

In the preceding section we gave a necessary and sufficient condition (Theorem 6) that a nonnegative matrix has a positive characteristic vector corresponding to $\lambda = r$. Formula (89) gives another characterization of such matrices, and shows the intimate relation between a matrix of this type and a suitable stochastic matrix.

Now we turn to the following theorem.

THEOREM 10. *Every elementary divisor of a stochastic matrix which corresponds to the characteristic number 1 is of the first degree.*

Proof. By (69), Section 4, the stochastic matrix $P = (p_{ij})_1^n$ can be decomposed as follows

$$
P = \begin{bmatrix}
A_1 & 0 & & & \cdots & \cdots & , & \cdots & \cdots & 0 \\
0 & A_2 & & & \cdots & \cdots & \cdots & \cdots & & 0 \\
\vdots & & & & & & & & & \vdots \\
0 & & \cdots & \cdots & A_g & 0 & \cdots & \cdots & & 0 \\
A_{g+1,1} & \cdots & \cdots & , & A_{g+1,g} & A_{g+1} & \cdots & \cdots & & 0 \\
\vdots & & & & & & & & & \vdots \\
A_{s1} & & \cdots & \cdots & A_{sg} & & \cdots & \cdots & \cdots & A_s
\end{bmatrix}
$$

where $A_1, A_2, \ldots, A_s$ are irreducible matrices, and

$$
A_{f1} + A_{f2} + \ldots + A_{f,f-1} \neq 0 \quad (f = g + 1, \ldots, s).
$$

Now the isolated matrices $A_1, A_2, \ldots, A_g$ are irreducible *stochastic* matrices; therefore the number 1 is a simple characteristic root for each of them. On the other hand, the other diagonal blocks $A_{g+1}, \ldots, A_s$ are irreducible, and by Remark 2 on p. 76, the dominant characteristic number of each of them is less than 1 (< 1), since at least one row sum in each of these matrices is strictly less than unity.[32]

Thus the matrix P can be represented in the form

$$
P = \begin{bmatrix} Q_1 & 0 \\ S & Q_2 \end{bmatrix}.
$$

The submatrix Q_1 has characteristic root 1, the corresponding elementary divisor being of the first degree. The matrix Q_2 does not have 1 for a characteristic root. The theorem is now intuitively clear; we make the proof rigorous by establishing the following lemma, which will conclude the proof.

---

[32] These properties of the matrices $A_1, \ldots, A_s$ also follow from Theorem 6.

LEMMA 4. *Let a matrix A have the form*

$$A = \begin{bmatrix} Q_1 & 0 \\ S & Q_2 \end{bmatrix}, \tag{90}$$

and suppose that Q_1 is a (square) matrix which has characteristic number λ_0, while Q_2 is a (square) matrix for which λ_0 is not a characteristic root:

$$\det (Q_1 - \lambda_0 E) = 0, \quad \det (Q_2 - \lambda_0 E) \neq 0.$$

Then λ_0 is a characteristic root of A, and the elementary divisors of A and of Q_1 which correspond to the characteristic root λ_0 are the same.

The proof of this lemma depends essentially on the fact that the equation $Q_2 U - U Q_1 = S$ has a solution U whenever Q_1, Q_2 have no characteristic root in common; and this last fact can be proved by relying on the Jordan normal of the matrices Q_1, Q_2. Taking this fact for granted, the proof proceeds as follows.

(i). First suppose that Q_1, Q_2 have no common characteristic root. We begin by showing that, in this case, the elementary divisors of Q_1 and Q_2 form in their collection the elementary divisors of the matrix A; i.e., that there is a matrix T (det $T \neq 0$) such that

$$TAT^{-1} = \begin{bmatrix} Q_1 & 0 \\ 0 & Q_2 \end{bmatrix}. \tag{91}$$

Indeed, the matrix T can be taken to have the special form

$$T = \begin{bmatrix} E_1 & 0 \\ U & E_2 \end{bmatrix},$$

where the partitioning in T is conformal with that in A, and where E_1, E_2 are identity matrices. The computation for TAT^{-1} is

$$TAT^{-1} = \begin{bmatrix} E_1 & 0 \\ U & E_2 \end{bmatrix} \begin{bmatrix} Q_1 & 0 \\ S & Q_2 \end{bmatrix} \begin{bmatrix} E_1 & 0 \\ -U & E_2 \end{bmatrix} = \begin{bmatrix} Q_1 & 0 \\ UQ_1 - Q_2U + S & Q_2 \end{bmatrix}. \tag{91'}$$

Equation (91') will read the same as equation (91) if the

rectangular matrix U is chosen so as to satisfy the matrix equation

$$Q_2 U - U Q_1 = S.$$

(ii). We turn now to the remaining case, in which Q_1, Q_2 have characteristic roots in common. We employ a preliminary similarity transformation, with transforming matrix diag (T_1, E_2), in order to bring Q_1 in (90) to its Jordan normal form

$$J = \mathrm{diag}\,(J_1, J_2) = T_1 Q_1 T_1^{-1},$$

where J_1 is a submatrix consisting of all the Jordan blocks which have characteristic number λ_0. Then A takes the form

$$A = \begin{bmatrix} J_1 & 0 & 0 & 0 \\ 0 & J_2 & 0 & 0 \\ S_{11} & S_{12} & \multicolumn{2}{c}{Q_2} \\ S_{21} & S_{22} & & \end{bmatrix} = \begin{bmatrix} J_1 & 0 & 0 & 0 \\ 0 & & & \\ S_{11} & & \hat{Q}_2 & \\ S_{21} & & & \end{bmatrix}.$$

Since the matrices J_1, $\hat{Q}_2$ have no common characteristic numbers, this matrix comes under the preceding case. That is, the elementary divisors of the form $(\lambda - \lambda_0)^p$ for the matrices A and J_1 are the same, which is to say that the elementary divisors of the matrices A, Q_1 which correspond to λ_0 are the same. The lemma is proved.

By (31), if an irreducible stochastic matrix P has a nonreal characteristic number λ_0 with $|\lambda_0| = 1$, then the matrix $\lambda_0 P$ is similar to the matrix P. By Theorem 10, the elementary divisors of P which correspond to λ_0 must all be of the first degree. This conclusion is easily extended to the case of a reducible matrix P, by making use of the normal form of P, and Lemma 4. We have proved

COROLLARY 1. *Let P be a stochastic matrix, and let λ_0 be a characteristic number of P, $|\lambda_0| = 1$. Then the elementary divisors $(\lambda - \lambda_0)^p$ of P which correspond to λ_0 are all of the first degree $(p=1)$.*

We can obtain another corollary of Theorem 10 if we use assertion 2 on p. 101.

COROLLARY 2. *Let A (≥ 0) be a nonnegative matrix with dominant characteristic root r, and let a corresponding characteristic vector be positive. Then if λ_0 is any characteristic root of A with $|\lambda_0| = r$,* *then all the elementary divisors of A corresponding to λ_0 are of the first degree.*

We conclude this section with a résumé of certain papers dealing with the location of the characteristic roots of stochastic matrices and related nonnegative matrices. Every characteristic root of a stochastic matrix must lie in the circular disk $|\lambda| \leq 1$ of the λ-plane. We denote by M_n the collection of all points which are characteristic roots of some stochastic matrix of order n.

In connection with the investigation of Markov chains, A. N. Kolmogorov, in 1938 [34], called attention to the problem of describing the sets M_n. In 1945, N. A. Dmitriev and E. B. Dynkin gave a partial solution of this problem [12], and the solution was completed in 1951 by F. I. Karpelevich [32]. It turned out that the boundary of M_n is a simple curvilinear polygon with vertices on $|\lambda| = 1$.

If A is a nonnegative matrix, with dominant characteristic root r, to which there corresponds a positive characteristic vector, then the characteristic roots of A are respectively r times those of a certain stochastic matrix (see p. 101). Thus the set of characteristic roots of such matrices, for fixed r and fixed order n, fills out the set $r \cdot M_n$, where this last symbol denotes the collection of all points of the λ-plane of the form $r\mu$, $\mu \in M_n$. Now an arbitrary nonnegative $n \times n$ matrix A (≥ 0) is the limit of a sequence of nonnegative matrices of the above type. Moreover, the set $r \cdot M_n$ is closed. Thus for fixed r and fixed order n, the characteristic numbers of the nonnegative matrices A with dominant characteristic number r fill out [33] the set $r \cdot M_n$.

To this circle of problems belongs also [34] the work of H. R. Suleĭmanova [64], which establishes certain sufficient criteria for n preassigned real numbers $\lambda_1, \lambda_2, \ldots, \lambda_n$ to be characteristic numbers of some n-dimensional stochastic matrix P.

---

[33] This argument is due essentially to A. N. Kolmogorov ([12, Appendix]).

[34] See also [54].

§ 7. Limiting probabilities for homogeneous Markov chains with a finite number of states

1. Let there be given a homogeneous Markov chain, for which the matrix $P = (p_{ij})_1^n$ is the (stochastic) matrix of transition probabilities. Suppose the n possible states of the system to be (see p. 99)

$$S_1, S_2, \ldots, S_n.$$

Now we introduce the symbol $p_{ij}^{(q)}$ to represent the probability of finding the system in state S_j at the instant t_k, supposing that the system was in state S_i at the instant t_{k-q} ($i, j = 1, 2, \ldots, n$; $q = 1, 2, \ldots$). According to this definition, we have automatically $p_{ij}^{(1)} = p_{ij}$ ($i, j = 1, 2, \ldots, n$). The rules for multiplying and adding probabilities give the recursion relation

$$p_{ij}^{(q+1)} = \sum_{h=1}^{n} (p_{ih}^{(q)}) \, p_{hj} \qquad (i, j = 1, 2, \ldots, n),$$

which amounts in matrix notation to the equation

$$(p_{ij}^{(q+1)}) = (p_{ij}^{(q)})_1^n \, (p_{ij})_1^n.$$

This is all that is needed to complete an inductive proof of the formula [35]

$$(p_{ij}^{(q)}) = P^q \qquad (q = 1, 2, \ldots).$$

If the limits

$$\lim_{q \to \infty} p_{ij}^{(q)} = p_{ij}^{\infty} \qquad (i, j = 1, 2, \ldots, n)$$

exist, i.e., if the matrix limit

$$\lim_{q \to \infty} P^q = P^{\infty} = (p_{ij}^{\infty})_1^n,$$

exists, then the numbers p_{ij}^{∞} ($i, j = 1, 2, \ldots, n$) are called the *limiting* or *final transition probabilities*.[36]

---

[35] Thus it is seen that both the probabilities $p_{ij}^{(q)}$ and the probabilities p_{ij} ($i, j = 1, 2, \ldots, n$; $q = 1, 2, \ldots$) are independent of the index k of the initial time t_k.

[36] The matrix P^{∞} is stochastic, as it is the limit of stochastic matrices.

In order to find conditions for the existence of limiting transition probabilities, and to derive relevant formulas, we introduce the following terms.

We call a stochastic matrix P and the corresponding homogeneous Markov chain *proper* if the matrix P has no characteristic roots ($\neq 1$) of modulus 1, and call a matrix or chain *regular* if it is proper and if 1 is a simple characteristic root (simple root of the characteristic equation) of P.

A matrix P is proper if and only if the matrices $A_1, A_2, \ldots, A_g$ of the normal form (69), p. 90, are primitive. For a regular matrix, $g = 1$ as well.

A homogeneous Markov chain is called *irreducible, reducible, aperiodic, periodic* if the corresponding stochastic matrix P is respectively irreducible, reducible, primitive, imprimitive.

According to these definitions, every primitive stochastic matrix is proper, and similarly, every aperiodic Markov chain is proper.

We show that only proper homogeneous Markov chains have limiting transition probabilities.

To this end, let $P = (p_{ij})_1^n$ be a proper stochastic matrix, and let $\psi(\lambda)$ be its minimal polynomial:

$$\psi(\lambda) = (\lambda - \lambda_1)^{m_1} (\lambda - \lambda_2)^{m_2} \ldots (\lambda - \lambda_u)^{m_u} \quad (\lambda_i \neq \lambda_k; i, k = 1, 2, \ldots, u). \tag{92}$$

By Theorem 10, we may renumber the roots so that

$$\lambda_1 = 1, \quad m_1 = 1. \tag{93}$$

The special formula which was used to derive (82) yields in this case

$$P^q = \frac{C(1)}{\psi^{[1]}} + \sum_{k=\infty}^{u} \frac{1}{(m_k - 1)!} \left[\frac{C(\lambda)}{\psi^{[k]}(\lambda)} \lambda^q \right]^{(m_k - 1)}_{\lambda = \lambda_k}, \tag{94}$$

where $C(\lambda) = (\lambda E - P)^{-1} \psi(\lambda)$ is the reduced adjoint matrix;

$$\psi^{[k]}(\lambda) = \frac{\psi(\lambda)}{(\lambda - \lambda_k)^{m_k}} \quad (k = 1, 2, \ldots, u);$$

$$\psi^{[1]}(\lambda) = \frac{\psi(\lambda)}{\lambda - 1} \quad \text{and} \quad \psi^{[1]}(1) = \psi'(1).$$

For a proper matrix P, we have

$$|\lambda_k| < 1 \qquad (k = 2, 3, \ldots, u),$$

so that all but the first of the summands in the right member of (94) have limit 0 as $q \to \infty$. We have shown that when P is a proper matrix, the matrix P^∞ of limiting transition probabilities exists, and is given by the formula

$$P^\infty = \frac{C(1)}{\psi'(1)}. \tag{95}$$

The converse of this statement is obvious. For if the limit

$$P^\infty = \lim_{q \to \infty} P^q \tag{96}$$

exists, then the matrix P cannot have any characteristic number λ_k ($\neq 1$) of absolute value 1; indeed if $|\lambda_k| = 1$, $\lambda_k \neq 1$, then $\lim_{q \to \infty} \lambda_k^q$ could not exist. But this limit must exist if (96) holds.

To summarize: if P is the matrix of transition probabilities of a homogeneous Markov chain, then the matrix P^∞ of limiting transition probabilities exists if and only if the chain is proper. The matrix P^∞ is the matrix defined by (95).

We can also express the matrix P^∞ in terms of the characteristic polynomial

$$\Delta(\lambda) = (\lambda - \lambda_1)^{n_1}(\lambda - \lambda_2)^{n_2} \ldots (\lambda - \lambda_u)^{n_u} \tag{97}$$

and the adjoint matrix $B(\lambda) = (\lambda E - P)^{-1}\Delta(\lambda)$. The identity needed for this purpose is

$$\frac{B(\lambda)}{\Delta(\lambda)} = \frac{C(\lambda)}{\psi(\lambda)}.$$

From this identity, we obtain

$$\frac{(\lambda - 1)B(\lambda)}{\Delta(\lambda)} = \frac{(\lambda - 1)C(\lambda)}{\psi(\lambda)}, \tag{98}$$

and on the assumption $n_1 = 1$, which is certainly valid for a proper, and hence for the regular Markov chain we are considering, this leads to $B(1)/\Delta'(1) = C(1)/\psi'(1)$, and hence, by (95)

$$P^{\infty} = B(1)/\varDelta'(1). \tag{99}$$

2. Let P be a general (not necessarily regular) proper stochastic matrix. We consider the corresponding Markov chain. We write P in the normal form

$$P = \begin{bmatrix} Q_1 & \cdots & 0 & 0 & \cdots & 0 \\ & \ddots & & \vdots & & \vdots \\ 0 & & Q_g & 0 & & 0 \\ U_{g+1,1} & \cdots & U_{g+1,g} & Q_{g+1} & & \\ \vdots & & \vdots & & \ddots & \\ U_{s1} & \cdots & U_{sg} & \cdots & U_{s,s-1} & Q_s \end{bmatrix}, \tag{100}$$

where each of $Q_1, \ldots, Q_g$ is a primitive stochastic matrix, and where each of the irreducible matrices $Q_{g+1}, \ldots, Q_s$ has dominant characteristic root less than 1.

We make the abbreviations

$$U = \begin{bmatrix} U_{g+1,1} & \cdots & U_{g+1,g} \\ \cdots & \cdots & \cdots \\ U_{s1} & \cdots & U_{sg} \end{bmatrix}, \quad W = \begin{bmatrix} Q_{g+1} & \cdots & 0 \\ \cdots & \cdots & \cdots \\ U_{s,g+1} & \cdots & Q_s \end{bmatrix},$$

and write P in the form

$$P = \begin{bmatrix} Q_1 & \cdots & 0 & 0 \\ & \ddots & & \vdots \\ \vdots & & \ddots & \vdots \\ 0 & \cdots & Q_g & 0 \\ & U & & W \end{bmatrix}.$$

Because P can be written in the above form, it follows that P^q can be written as

$$
P^q = \begin{bmatrix} Q_1^q & \cdots & 0 & 0 \\ & \cdot & & \cdot \\ \cdot & & \cdot & \cdot \\ \cdot & & & \cdot \\ \cdot & & \cdot & \cdot \\ 0 & \cdots & Q_g^q & 0 \\ & U_q & & W_q \end{bmatrix}. \tag{101}
$$

Now (see below) the matrices Q_h^∞, W^∞ exist, so we may write

$$
P^\infty = \lim_{q \to \infty} P^q = \begin{bmatrix} Q_1^\infty & \cdots & 0 & 0 \\ & \cdot & & \cdot \\ \cdot & & \cdot & \cdot \\ \cdot & & & \cdot \\ \cdot & & \cdot & \cdot \\ 0 & \cdots & Q_g^\infty & 0 \\ & U_\infty & & W^\infty \end{bmatrix}.
$$

In the first place, $W^\infty = \lim_{q \to \infty} W^q = 0$, since the moduli of the characteristic roots of W are strictly less than 1. Thus

$$
P^\infty = \begin{bmatrix} Q_1^\infty & \cdots & 0 & 0 \\ & \cdot & & \cdot \\ \cdot & & \cdot & \cdot \\ \cdot & & & \cdot \\ \cdot & & \cdot & \cdot \\ 0 & \cdots & Q_g^\infty & 0 \\ & U_\infty & & 0 \end{bmatrix}. \tag{102}
$$

Next we show that the matrices $Q_1^\infty, \ldots, Q_g^\infty$ are positive:

$$
Q_1^\infty > 0, \ldots, Q_g^\infty > 0.
$$

To do this, we apply formula (99), and refer to formula (35), p. 75; note that formula (99) applies, since Q_h is primitive $(h = 1, 2, \ldots, g)$.

Finally, we note that if P is a stochastic matrix, each column in the adjoint matrix $E - P$ is constant since the row sums are all zero. Thus all the elements in a fixed column of a particular Q_h are equal:

$$
Q_h^\infty = (q_{*j}^{(h)})_{i,j=1}^{n_h} \qquad (h = 1, 2, \ldots, g).
$$

We can partition the states $S_1, S_2, \ldots, S_n$ of the system under consideration into groups

$$\Sigma_1, \Sigma_2, \ldots, \Sigma_g, \Sigma_{g+1}, \ldots, \Sigma_s, \qquad (103)$$

the number of states in the first group being equal to the number of rows in the block Q_1 in formula (100), etc.

The states of the various groups $\Sigma_1, \Sigma_2, \ldots, \Sigma_g$ are called *essential* by A. N. Kolmogorov; the states of the remaining groups are called inessential.

We observe from the forms (100), (101) of the matrix P^q that only the following q-step transitions (from instant t_{k-q} to instant t_k) are possible: (a) from an essential state to another essential state of the same group; (b) from an inessential state to an essential state; and (c) from an inessential state to another inessential state of the same group or of an earlier group.

From formula (102) for the matrix P^∞, it follows further that the *limiting probabilities are zero except for transition into an essential state*, i.e., that the probability of transition into an inessential state after q steps tends to zero as $q \to \infty$. For this reason, essential states are sometimes called *limiting states*.

3. By use of formula (95), or by the method of the footnote,[37] we obtain the relation

$$(E - P)P^\infty = 0.$$

This shows that *each of the columns of the matrix P^∞ is a characteristic vector of the stochastic matrix P, corresponding to the characteristic root $\lambda = 1$.*

If P is a regular matrix, the number 1 is a simple root of the characteristic equation. In such a case, there can be only one characteristic vector $(1, 1, \ldots, 1)'$ (to within a scalar factor). Thus, all the elements in a fixed column, say the jth, of the matrix P^∞ have the same value p_{*j}^∞:

$$p_{ij}^\infty = p_{*j}^\infty \geqq 0 \qquad (j = 1, 2, \ldots, n; \ \sum_{j=1}^{n} p_{*j}^\infty = 1). \qquad (104)$$

This can be translated into physical terms: for a regular chain,

---

[37] Allow q to increase without limit in the relation $P^q - P \cdot P^{q-1} = 0$.

the limiting transition probabilities do not depend on the initial state S_i.

Suppose conversely that the limiting transition probabilities for a certain proper homogeneous Markov chain are independent of the initial state, i.e., suppose formulas (104) hold. Then in formula (102) for the matrix P^∞, we must have $g = 1$. But then, $n_1 = 1$, and the chain is regular.

If we suppose that the chain is not only regular, but also acyclic, then P is a primitive matrix. If we refer to Theorem 8 (p. 97), we recall that, for some $q > 0$, $P^q > 0$. From this fact we can conclude that P^∞ is positive by using the equation [38] $P^\infty = P^\infty P^q > 0$. A second proof of the fact that P^∞ is positive can be constructed from formula (99) and inequality (35) (p. 75).

Conversely, suppose that $P^\infty > 0$. Then for some $q > 0$, we must have $P^q > 0$. By Theorem 8, the matrix P must be primitive, and the corresponding homogeneous Markov chain is therefore acyclic.

We formulate the results just obtained in

THEOREM 11. *A necessary and sufficient condition that a homogeneous Markov chain possess limiting (or final) transition probabilities between every pair of states is that the chain be proper. If this condition is fulfilled, the matrix P^∞ of limiting transition probabilities is given by formula (95).*

A necessary and sufficient condition that the limiting transition probabilities of a proper homogeneous Markov chain be independent of the initial state is that the chain be regular. If this condition is fulfilled, the matrix P^∞ is given by (99).

A necessary and sufficient condition that the limiting transition probabilities of a homogeneous Markov chain all be positive is that the chain be acyclic.[39]

[38] Allow m to increase without limit in the relation $P^m = P^{m-q} \cdot P^q$ ($m > q$). Note that P^∞ is a stochastic matrix; $P^\infty \geqq 0$. Moreover, every row of P^∞ contains nonzero elements. Hence $P^\infty P^q > 0$.

[39] If $P^\infty > 0$, the chain is acyclic and hence regular. Thus, the relation $P^\infty > 0$ implies that the limiting transitional probabilities are independent of the initial state, i.e., that formula (104) holds.

4. Now we turn to a discussion of the vector of *absolute probabilities*

$$p^{[k]} = (p_1^{[k]}, p_2^{[k]}, \ldots, p_n^{[k]}) \quad (k = 0, 1, 2, \ldots). \quad (105)$$

Here, $p_i^{[k]}$ is the probability that the system should be in the state S_i at instant t_k $(i = 1, 2, \ldots, n; \ k = 0, 1, 2, \ldots)$. The theorems on addition and multiplication of probabilities yield the relations

$$p_i^{[k]} = \sum_{k=1}^{n} p_h^{[0]} p_{hi}^{(k)} \quad (i = 1, 2, \ldots, n; \ k = 1, 2, \ldots),$$

which is the same as the matrix equation

$$p^{[k]} = P'^k p^{[0]} \quad (k = 1, 2, \ldots), \quad (106)$$

where P' is the transpose of the matrix P.

As soon as the initial probabilities $p_1^{[0]}, p_2^{[0]}, \ldots, p_n^{[0]}$ and the matrix of transition probabilities $P = (p_{ij})_1^n$ are given, all the absolute probabilities (105) are determined (by formula 106).

From the absolute probabilities (105) we can define the *limiting absolute probabilities*

$$p_i^{[\infty]} = \lim_{k \to \infty} p_i^{[k]} \quad (i = 1, 2, \ldots, n)$$

or

$$p^{[\infty]} = (p_1^{[\infty]}, p_2^{[\infty]}, \ldots, p_n^{[\infty]}) = \lim_{k \to \infty} p^{[k]}.$$

If we let $k \to \infty$ in (106), we find

$$p^{[\infty]} = P^{\infty\prime} p^{[0]}. \quad (107)$$

Thus if the matrix P^∞ of limiting transition probabilities exists, then the limiting absolute probabilities $p^{[\infty]} = (p_1^{[\infty]}, p_2^{[\infty]}, \ldots, p_n^{[\infty]})'$ must exist for an arbitrary assignment $p^{[0]} = (p_1^{[0]}, p_2^{[0]}, \ldots p_n^{[0]})'$ of initial probabilities, and conversely.

Since the matrix P^∞ has the form (102), it follows from formula (107) that *the limiting absolute probabilities which corrrespond to inessential states are zero.*

The equality $P' \cdot P^{\infty\prime} = P^{\infty\prime}$ obviously holds. If we multiply both members of this equality on the right by $p^{[0]}$, and use (107), we obtain

$$P' \cdot p^{[\infty]} = p^{[\infty]}, \qquad (108)$$

which says that *the column-vector $p^{[\infty]}$ of limiting absolute probabilities is a characteristic vector of the matrix P', corresponding to the characteristic number $\lambda = 1$.*

If the given Markov chain is regular, then $\lambda = 1$ is a simple root of the characteristic equation of the matrix P'. Thus, the vector of limiting absolute probabilities is uniquely determined from (108), since the components $p_j^{[\infty]}$ ($\geqq 0$) are nonnegative, and their sum is 1: $\sum_{j=1}^{n} p_j^{[\infty]} = 1$.

A further property of a regular Markov chain can be derived as follows, by combining (104) with (107):

$$p_j^{[\infty]} = \sum_{h=1}^{n} p_h^{[0]} p_{hj}^{\infty} = p_{*j}^{\infty} \sum_{h=1}^{n} p_h^{[0]} = p_{*j}^{\infty} \qquad (j = 1, 2, \ldots, n). \quad (109)$$

Thus the limiting absolute probabilities $p_1^{[\infty]}, p_2^{[\infty]}, \ldots, p_n^{[\infty]}$ are independent of the initial probabilities $p_1^{[0]}, p_2^{[0]}, \ldots, p_n^{[0]}$.

Conversely we see from (107) that if $p^{[\infty]}$ is independent of $p^{[0]}$, then the rows of P^{∞} are identical:

$$p_{hj}^{\infty} = p_{*j}^{\infty} \qquad (h, j = 1, 2, \ldots, n);$$

this means that P is a regular matrix, by Theorem 11.

If P is a primitive matrix, then $P^{\infty} > 0$; by (109), then,

$$p_j^{[\infty]} > 0 \quad (j = 1, 2, \ldots, n).$$

Conversely if these last relations hold, and if the limiting probabilities $p_j^{[\infty]}$ are independent of the initial probabilities in addition, then every column of the matrix P^{∞} is constant (by (109) with $p_1^{[0]} = 1$, etc.). Further, the matrix P^{∞} is positive: $P^{\infty} > 0$, so that P is a primitive matrix, by Theorem 11; and the given chain is acyclic.

We have proved that Theorem 11 can be reformulated as follows.

THEOREM 11′. *1. A necessary and sufficient condition that all the limiting absolute probabilities for a given homogeneous Markov chain should exist for each set of initial probabilities is that the chain be proper.*

2. *A necessary and sufficient condition that all the limiting absolute probabilities for a given homogeneous Markov chain should exist and be independent of the initial probabilities is that the chain be regular.*

3. *A necessary and sufficient condition that all the limiting absolute probabilities for a given homogeneous Markov chain should exist, be positive, and be independent of the initial probabilities is that the chain be acyclic.*

N.B. The second part of Theorem 11′ is sometimes called the *ergodic theorem*; the first part, the *general quasi-ergodic theorem* for homogeneous Markov chains.

5. Now let us consider a general homogeneous Markov chain, with matrix P of transition probabilities.

Let (69) be the normal form of the matrix P, and let the indices of imprimitivity of the submatrices $A_1, A_2, \ldots, A_g$ in (69) be $h_1, h_2, \ldots, h_g$. Let h be the least common multiple of the integers $h_1, h_2, \ldots, h_g$. Then no characteristic root ($\neq 1$) of P^h has absolute value 1, i.e., P^h is a proper matrix; moreover, $P, P^2, \ldots, P^{h-1}$ are not proper. Let us call the number h the period of the given homogeneous Markov chain.

Since P^h is a proper matrix, the limit

$$\lim_{q \to \infty} P^{hq} = (P^h)^\infty$$

exists, and thus the limits

$$\lim_{q \to \infty} P^{r+qh} = P_r = P^r (P^h)^\infty$$

exist for $r = 0, 1, \ldots, h - 1$.

In the general case, then, it is clear that the sequence $P, P^2, P^3, \ldots$ splits into h mutually disjoint subsequences, each of which has a limit $P_r = P^r (P^h)^\infty$ $(r = 0, 1, \ldots, h - 1)$.

Formula (106) enables us to compute the absolute probabilities from the transition probabilities. We find that the sequence

$$p^{[1]}, p^{[2]}, p^{[3]}, \ldots$$

splits into h subsequences, each of which has a limit:

$$\lim_{q\to\infty} p^{[r+qh]} = (P'^h)^\infty p^r \quad (r = 0, 1, 2, \ldots, h-1).$$

For an arbitrary homogeneous Markov chain with a finite number of states, the displayed limits (110), (110') always exist as limits of arithmetic means

$$\tilde{P} = \lim_{N\to\infty} \frac{1}{N} \sum_{k=1}^{N} P^k = \frac{1}{h}(E + P + \ldots + P^{h-1})(P^h)^\infty \quad (110)$$

$$\tilde{p} = \lim_{N\to\infty} \frac{1}{N} \sum_{k=1}^{N} p^{[k]} = \tilde{P}' p^{[0]}. \quad (110')$$

Here $\tilde{P} = (\tilde{p}_{ij})_1^n$ and $\tilde{p} = (\tilde{p}_1, \tilde{p}_2, \ldots, \tilde{p}_n)$. The quantities $\tilde{p}_{ij}$ $(i, j = 1, 2, \ldots, n)$ and $\tilde{p}_j$ $(j = 1, 2, \ldots, n)$ are called the *mean limiting transition probabilities* and *mean limiting absolute probabilities* respectively.

Because of the equality

$$\lim_{N\to\infty} \frac{1}{N} \sum_{k=2}^{N+1} P^k = \lim_{N\to\infty} \frac{1}{N} \sum_{k=1}^{N} P^k,$$

the relation

$$\tilde{P}P = \tilde{P}$$

must hold, from which we can conclude by using (110') that

$$P'\tilde{p} = \tilde{p}, \quad (111)$$

i.e., $\tilde{p}$ is a characteristic vector of the matrix P' for $\lambda = 1$.

Further, we note that, because of formulas (69) and (110), we can represent the matrix $\tilde{P}$ in the form

$$\tilde{P} = \begin{bmatrix} \tilde{A}_1 & 0 & \ldots & 0 & \\ 0 & \tilde{A}_2 & \ldots & 0 & 0 \\ \multicolumn{5}{c}{\ldots\ldots\ldots\ldots\ldots} \\ 0 & 0 & \ldots & \tilde{A}_g & \\ & & \tilde{U} & & \tilde{W} \end{bmatrix},$$

$$\tilde{A}_i = \lim_{N\to\infty} \frac{1}{N} \sum_{k=1}^{N} A_i^k \ (i = 1, 2, \ldots, g), \quad \tilde{W} = \lim_{N\to\infty} \frac{1}{N} \sum_{k=1}^{N} W^k,$$

where

$$W = \begin{bmatrix} A_{g+1} & 0 & . & . & . & 0 \\ * & A_{g+2} & & . & & 0 \\ . & . & . & . & . & . & . & . \\ * & * & & . & . & A_s \end{bmatrix}.$$

But the absolute value of every characteristic number of the matrix W is less than 1. From this, the conclusions

$$\lim_{k \to \infty} W^k = 0, \qquad \tilde{W} = 0$$

follow.

Thus

$$\tilde{P} = \begin{bmatrix} \tilde{A}_1 & 0 & . & . & . & 0 \\ 0 & \tilde{A}_2 & . & . & . & 0 & & 0 \\ . & . & . & . & . & . & . & . & . \\ 0 & 0 & . & . & . & \tilde{A}_g \\ & & \tilde{U} & & & & 0 \end{bmatrix}. \tag{112}$$

Since $\tilde{P}$ is a stochastic matrix, the matrices $\tilde{A}_1, \tilde{A}_2, \ldots, \tilde{A}_g$ are also stochastic.

From this representation of $\tilde{P}$, and from (107), it follows that *those mean limiting absolute probabilities which correspond to inessential states are all equal to zero.*

If the number g in the normal form of the matrix P is equal to 1 ($g = 1$), then the number $\lambda = 1$ is a simple characteristic number for the matrix P'.

In this case $\tilde{p}$ is determined uniquely from (111), and the mean limiting probabilities $\tilde{p}_1, \tilde{p}_2, \ldots, \tilde{p}_n$ do not depend on the initial probabilities $p_1^{[0]}, p_2^{[0]}, \ldots, p_n^{[0]}$. Conversely, if $\tilde{p}$ does not depend upon $p^{[0]}$, then, by (110') the matrix $\tilde{P}$ has rank 1. But the matrix (112) has rank exceeding 1 unless $g = 1$.

We formulate the above results in the following theorem.

THEOREM 12. (Sometimes called *the asymptotic theorem for homogeneous Markov chains.*) *Let an arbitrary homogeneous Markov chain have period h. Then the matrices P^k and $p^{[k]}$ of probabilities tend towards periodic repetition $(k \to \infty)$; the mean* *limiting transition probabilities* $\tilde{P} = (\tilde{p}_{ij})_1^n$ *and mean limiting absolute probabilities* $\tilde{p} = (\tilde{p}_1, \tilde{p}_2, \ldots, \tilde{p}_n)$ *defined by formulas* (110), (110)′ *always exist.*

All the mean limiting absolute probabilities which correspond to inessential states are zero.

If the number g in the normal form of the matrix P is 1 $(g = 1)$, *and only if* $g = 1$, *the mean limiting absolute probabilities are independent of the initial probabilities* $p_1^{[0]}$, $p_2^{[0]}$, \ldots, $p_n^{[0]}$ *and are uniquely determined from equation* (111).

§ 8. Totally nonnegative matrices

In this section and the following one, we shall consider matrices of real elements, in which the minor determinants of all orders, in particular the elements themselves, are nonnegative. Such matrices have important applications in the theory of small oscillations of elastic systems. The reader will find a detailed study of these matrices and their applications in [24]. In the present treatment we give only basic properties of these matrices.

1. We begin with the definition

DEFINITION 5. *A rectangular matrix*

$$A = (a_{ik}) \quad (i = 1, 2, \ldots, m; \ k = 1, 2, \ldots, n)$$

is called totally nonnegative (totally positive) *if every square minor of this matrix has nonnegative (positive) determinant:*

$$A \begin{bmatrix} i_1, i_2, \ldots, i_p \\ k_1, k_2, \ldots, k_p \end{bmatrix} \geqq 0 \quad (respectively > 0)$$

$$\left(1 \leqq \frac{i_1 < i_2 < \ldots < i_p}{k_1 < k_2 < \ldots < k_p} \leqq n; \ p = 1, 2, \ldots, \min(m, n) \right).$$

In the sequel, we consider only square matrices which are totally nonnegative (positive).

Examples. 1. The generalized matrix of Vandermonde

$$V = (a_i^{\alpha_k})_1^n \quad (0 < a_1 < a_2 < \ldots < a_n; \ \alpha_1 < \alpha_2 < \ldots < \alpha_n)$$

is totally positive. First we prove that V has nonzero determinant $(\det V \neq 0)$. In the contrary case, there would exist real numbers $c_1, c_2, \ldots, c_h$, not all zero, such that the polynomial

$$f(x) = \sum_{k=1}^{n} c_k x^{\alpha_k}$$

has n zeros, $x_i = a_i$ $(i = 1, 2, \ldots, n)$, where n is the number of powers being added. This is impossible for $n = 1$. We assume, as an induction hypothesis, that this has been proved impossible for any number of summands fewer than n, and on the basis of this assumption prove it impossible for n summands. By Rolle's theorem, the function $[x^{-\alpha_1} f(x)]'$ has a zero between every two zeros of $f(x)$; since this last function has only $n - 1$ summands, it cannot have $n - 1$ positive zeros, so $f(x)$ cannot have n positive zeros.

Thus $\det V$ is not 0. If we allow the exponents α_k to vary continuously by replacing α_k by $t\alpha_k + (1 - t)(k - 1)$, where t varies from 1 to 0, we see that the various exponents are unequal for each value of t; and for $t = 0$, the matrix becomes the ordinary Vandermonde matrix, which is known to have positive determinant. Since the determinant of V would vary continuously with t, and since it is never 0, it must be positive.

Since any square minor of a generalized Vandermonde matrix is again a generalized Vandermonde matrix, all minors of V have positive determinant.

2. As a second example we consider the *matrix of Jacobi*

$$J = \begin{bmatrix} a_1, & b_1, & 0, & \ldots, & 0, & 0 \\ c_1, & a_2, & b_2, & \ldots, & 0, & 0 \\ 0, & c_2, & a_3, & \ldots, & 0, & 0 \\ \multicolumn{6}{c}{\cdot \quad \cdot \quad \cdot \quad \cdot \quad \cdot \quad \cdot \quad \cdot \quad \cdot \quad \cdot \quad \cdot} \\ \multicolumn{6}{c}{\cdot \quad \cdot \quad \cdot \quad \cdot \quad \cdot \quad \cdot \quad \cdot \quad \cdot \quad \cdot \quad \cdot} \\ 0, & 0, & 0, & \ldots, & c_{n-1}, & a_n \end{bmatrix}, \qquad (113)$$

that is, a matrix in which all the elements are zero except those on the principal diagonal, and those on the diagonals just above and just below the principal diagonal. We derive a formula which expresses the value of the determinant of an arbitrary minor of this matrix in terms of the determinants of the prinicpal minors, and the elements b_i, c_i. Suppose

$$1 \leqq \begin{matrix} i_1 < i_2 < \ldots < i_p \\ k_1 < k_2 < \ldots < k_p \end{matrix} \leqq n$$

and

$$i_1 = k_1, \; i_2 = k_2, \ldots, i_{\nu_1} = k_{\nu_1}; \; i_{\nu_1+1} \neq k_{\nu_1+1}, \ldots, i_{\nu_2} \neq k_{\nu_2};$$
$$i_{\nu_2+1} = k_{\nu_2+1}, \ldots, i_{\nu_3} = k_{\nu_3}; \ldots$$

Then

$$J \binom{i_1, \, i_2, \ldots, \, i_p}{k_1, \, k_2, \ldots, \, k_p} = J \binom{i_1, \ldots, \, i_{\nu_1}}{k_1, \ldots, \, k_{\nu_1}} J \binom{i_{\nu_1+1}}{k_{\nu_1+1}} \cdots J \binom{i_{\nu_2}}{k_{\nu_2}} J \binom{i_{\nu_2+1}, \ldots, \, i_{\nu_3}}{k_{\nu_2+1}, \ldots, \, k_{\nu_3}} \cdots$$

$$(114)$$

The truth of this formula follows from the equality

$$J \binom{i_1, \ldots, \, i_p}{k_1, \ldots, \, k_p} = J \binom{i_1, \ldots, \, i_{\nu-1}}{k_1, \ldots, \, k_{\nu-1}} J \binom{i_\nu}{k_\nu} J \binom{i_{\nu+1}, \ldots, \, i_p}{k_{\nu+1}, \ldots, \, k_p} \; (\text{for } i_\nu \neq k_\nu), \; (115)$$

which is easily verified.

Formula (114) says in effect that any minor determinant is equal to the product of certain principal minors by certain elements of the matrix J. Thus, *the matrix J is totally nonnegative if and only if all its elements and all its principal minors are nonnegative.*

2. The following important determinantal inequality[40] always

---

[40] See [24]. There it is shown that the sign of equality in (116) can hold only in the following obvious cases:

1. if one of the factors of the right member is zero; *2.* if all the elements a_{ik} ($i = 1, 2, \ldots, p; \, k = p+1, \ldots, n$), or all the elements a_{ik} ($i = p+1, \ldots, n; \, k = 1, 2, \ldots, p$) are zero.

Inequality (116) has the same character as a generalization of an inequality of Hadamard concerning positive definite Hermitian or quadratic forms.

holds for a totally nonnegative matrix

$$A\begin{bmatrix}1, 2, \ldots, n\\ 1, 2, \ldots, n\end{bmatrix} \leqq A\begin{bmatrix}1, 2, \ldots, p\\ 1, 2, \ldots, p\end{bmatrix} A\begin{bmatrix}p+1, \ldots, n\\ p+1, \ldots, n\end{bmatrix} \quad (p < n). \quad (116)$$

The following preliminary lemma is needed.

LEMMA 5. *Let* $A = (a_{ij})_1^n$ *be a totally nonnegative matrix, and let some principal minor be singular (have zero determinant). Then every principal minor containing it (as a submatrix) is also zero.*

Proof. The lemma will be proved, if we show that whenever $A = (a_{ij})_1^n$ is a totally nonnegative matrix, the equality

$$A\begin{bmatrix}1, 2, \ldots, q\\ 1, 2, \ldots, q\end{bmatrix} = 0 \quad (q < n) \quad (117)$$

implies

$$A\begin{bmatrix}1, 2, \ldots, n\\ 1, 2, \ldots, n\end{bmatrix} = 0. \quad (118)$$

We consider two cases.

(i) $a_{11} = 0$. Since $\det\begin{pmatrix}a_{11} a_{1k}\\ a_{i1} a_{ik}\end{pmatrix} = -a_{i1}a_{1k} \geqq 0$,

$a_{i1} \geqq 0$, $a_{1k} \geqq 0$ $(i, k = 2, \ldots, n)$, then either all $a_{i1} = 0$ $(i = 2, \ldots, n)$ or else all $a_{1k} = 0$ $(k = 2, \ldots, n)$. Relation (118) follows from these equalities and from $a_{11} = 0$.

(ii). $a_{11} \neq 0$. Then for some p $(1 \leqq p \leqq q)$

$$A\begin{bmatrix}1, 2, \ldots, p-1\\ 1, 2, \ldots, p-1\end{bmatrix} \neq 0, \quad A\begin{bmatrix}1, 2, \ldots, p-1, p\\ 1, 2, \ldots, p-1, p\end{bmatrix} = 0. \quad (119)$$

We define the bordered determinants

$$d_{ik} = A\begin{bmatrix}1, 2, \ldots, p-1, i\\ 1, 2, \ldots, p-1, k\end{bmatrix} (i, k = p, p+1, \ldots, n) \quad (120)$$

and form the matrix $D = (d_{ik})_p^n$ which has them for elements. By the determinantal identity of Sylvester [47], we have

$$D \begin{bmatrix} i_1, & i_2, & \ldots, & i_g \\ k_1, & k_2, & \ldots, & k_g \end{bmatrix}$$

$$= \left\{ A \begin{bmatrix} 1, 2, \ldots, p-1 \\ 1, 2, \ldots, p-1 \end{bmatrix} \right\}^{g-1} A \begin{bmatrix} 1, 2, \ldots, p-1, i_1, i_2, \ldots, i_g \\ 1, 2, \ldots, p-1, k_1, k_2, \ldots, k_g \end{bmatrix} \geqq 0$$

$$\left(p \leqq \begin{matrix} i_1 < i_2 < \ldots < i_g \\ k_1 < k_2 < \ldots < k_g \end{matrix} \leqq n; g = 1, 2, \ldots, n-p+1 \right) \tag{121}$$

so that D is a totally nonnegative matrix.

Now by (119) we see that d_{pp} is zero:

$$d_{pp} = A \begin{bmatrix} 1, 2, \ldots, p \\ 1, 2, \ldots, p \end{bmatrix} = 0,$$

so that the matrix $D = (d_{ik})$ falls under case (i) above, and the relation

$$0 = D \begin{bmatrix} p, p+1, \ldots, n \\ p, p+1, \ldots, n \end{bmatrix} = \left\{ A \begin{bmatrix} 1, 2, \ldots, p-1 \\ 1, 2, \ldots, p-1 \end{bmatrix} \right\}^{n-p} A \begin{bmatrix} 1, 2, \ldots, n \\ 1, 2, \ldots, n \end{bmatrix}$$

holds. Moreover, since the first factor of the right member is not 0, relation (118) follows, and the lemma is proved.

3. It is now clear that in proving (116), we can assume that each of the principal minors of A has nonzero determinant, for by Lemma 5, if one of the principal minors has zero determinant, then so has A, and then inequality (116) is obvious.

In case $n = 2$, we can check inequality (116) directly. We know that $a_{12} \geqq 0$, $a_{21} \geqq 0$, so that

$$A \begin{bmatrix} 1 & 2 \\ 1 & 2 \end{bmatrix} = a_{11} a_{22} - a_{12} a_{21} \leqq a_{11} a_{22}.$$

Now we give an inductive proof of (116), assuming it is true for totally nonnegative matrices of dimension less than n ($n > 2$). By numbering the indices of the rows and columns backwards if necessary, we can further assume that p exceeds 1 ($p > 1$), since such a renumbering merely interchanges the roles of p and $n - p$.

If we refer to the matrix $D = (d_{ik})_p^n$, where d_{ik} (i, $k = p$, $p + 1, \ldots, n$) is defined by (120), and if we apply the Sylvester determinantal inequality (116) for matrices of order $< n$ twice, we arrive at the following proof:

$$A\begin{bmatrix} 1, 2, \ldots, n \\ 1, 2, \ldots, n \end{bmatrix} = \frac{D\begin{bmatrix} p, p+1, \ldots, n \\ p, p+1, \ldots, n \end{bmatrix}}{\left\{ A\begin{bmatrix} 1, 2, \ldots, p-1 \\ 1, 2, \ldots, p-1 \end{bmatrix} \right\}^{n-p}} \leq \frac{d_{pp} D\begin{bmatrix} p+1, \ldots, n \\ p+1, \ldots, n \end{bmatrix}}{\left\{ A\begin{bmatrix} 1, 2, \ldots, p-1 \\ 1, 2, \ldots, p-1 \end{bmatrix} \right\}^{n-p}}$$

$$= \frac{A\begin{bmatrix} 1, 2, \ldots, p \\ 1, 2, \ldots, p \end{bmatrix} A\begin{bmatrix} 1, 2, \ldots, p-1, p+1, \ldots, n \\ 1, 2, \ldots, p-1, p+1, \ldots, n \end{bmatrix}}{A\begin{bmatrix} 1, 2, \ldots, p-1 \\ 1, 2, \ldots, p-1 \end{bmatrix}}$$

$$\leq A\begin{bmatrix} 1, 2, \ldots, p \\ 1, 2, \ldots, p \end{bmatrix} A\begin{bmatrix} p+1, \ldots, n \\ p+1, \ldots, n \end{bmatrix}. \tag{122}$$

Thus inequality (116) is proved in all cases.
We make the following definition.

DEFINITION 6. *A minor*

$$A\begin{bmatrix} i_1, i_2, \ldots, i_p \\ k_1, k_2, \ldots, k_p \end{bmatrix} \left(1 \leq \begin{matrix} i_1 < i_2 < \ldots < i_p \\ k_1 < k_2 < \ldots < k_p \end{matrix} \leq n \right) \tag{123}$$

of the matrix $A = (a_{ij})_1^n$ *is called* almost principal, *if exactly one of the differences* $i_1 - k_1, i_2 - k_2, \ldots, i_p - k_p$ *is different from* 0.

We call attention to the fact that both inequality (116) and the auxiliary lemma maintain their validity if the condition "A is a totally nonnegative matrix" is replaced by the weaker condition "all the principal and almost principal minors of A are nonnegative."

§ 9. Oscillating matrices

1. A good many remarkable theorems can be stated for the characteristic roots and characteristic vectors of totally positive matrices. This class is, however, too restricted from the point of view of applications to small oscillations of elastic systems. For these applications, the class of totally nonnegative matrices would be sufficiently wide; but the necessary spectral properties are not

valid for such a wide class of matrices. There is an intermediate class of matrices which is sufficiently wide for the applications, and sufficiently restricted to maintain the spectral properties desired. This is the class of *oscillating matrices*. This name is used because the matrices of this class give a useful mathematical apparatus for investigating the properties of small oscillations of linear elastic systems.[41]

DEFINITION 7. *A matrix* $A = (a_{ik})_1^n$ *is called an* oscillating *matrix if A is a totally nonnegative matrix, and if there is a positive integer q $(q > 0)$ such that A^q is a totally positive matrix.*

Example. The matrix J of Jacobi (113) is an oscillating matrix if and only if (i) all the numbers b, c are positive, and (ii) the leading principal minors are positive:

$$a_1 > 0, \det \begin{bmatrix} a_1 & b_1 \\ c_1 & c_2 \end{bmatrix} > 0.$$

$$\det \begin{bmatrix} a_1 & b_1 & 0 \\ c_1 & a_2 & b_2 \\ 0 & c_2 & a_3 \end{bmatrix} > 0, \ldots, \det \begin{bmatrix} a_1, b_1, 0, \ldots, 0, 0 \\ c_1, a_2, b_2, \ldots, 0, 0 \\ 0, c_2, a_3, \ldots, 0, 0 \\ \cdots\cdots\cdots\cdots \\ 0, 0, 0, \ldots c_{n-1}, a_n \end{bmatrix} > 0. \quad (124)$$

Necessity of conditions (i), (ii). The numbers b, c are nonnegative in any case, if J is an oscillating matrix. Further, none of the b_i or c_i can be zero, since the matrix J would then be reducible, and no power of a reducible matrix is totally positive. Thus the b_i and c_i are all positive. As for the principal minors (124), they must all have positive determinant, for $\det J$ is nonnegative, and even positive (since $\det J^q > 0$); so we can apply Lemma 5.

Sufficiency of conditions (i), (ii). We give first a detailed proof of the fact that J is nonnegative. If we expand a leading (and hence positive) principal minor by Laplace's expansion on the first i rows, we obtain

[41] See [24].

$$A\begin{bmatrix}1, \ldots, p \\ 1, \ldots, p\end{bmatrix} = A\begin{bmatrix}1, \ldots, i \\ 1, \ldots, i\end{bmatrix} A\begin{bmatrix}i+1, \ldots, p \\ i+1, \ldots, p\end{bmatrix}$$

$$- b_i c_i \, A\begin{bmatrix}1, \ldots, i-1 \\ 1, \ldots, i-1\end{bmatrix} A\begin{bmatrix}i+2, \ldots, p \\ i+2, \ldots, p\end{bmatrix},$$

$(1 \leqq i < p)$, where empty determinants mean 1. If we take as an induction hypothesis $\det (a_{kj})_{i+2}^p > 0$, then it follows that $\det (a_{kj})_{i+1}^p$ is positive, that is, all principal minors on consecutive rows are positive. Any principal minor determinant is a product of principal minor determinants of this special type; for non-principal minors, (114) gives the desired conclusion. In passing we note that the principal minor determinants of J remain unchanged if we change b_i, c_i so as to keep their product $b_i c_i$ constant.

To show that J is an oscillating matrix, it is only necessary to show that all minors of a certain power J^q of J have positive determinant. In order to motivate the argument, we first point out that this is certainly true for the 1×1 minors of J; indeed in J^q $(q > 0)$ all elements a_{ij} no more than q steps from the main diagonal $(|i - j| \leqq q)$ are positive. This statement is to be thought of as being established for $q = 1, 2, \ldots$ by induction, since it is true for $q = 1$ by assumption.

The corresponding fact for $r \times r$ minors $(r > 1)$ depends for its proof on the lemma that every $r \times r$ special almost-principal minor

$$J\begin{bmatrix}i_1, \ldots, i_r \\ j_1, \ldots, j_r\end{bmatrix}, \quad q = \sum |i_k - j_k| = 1,$$

of J has positive determinant. Once this fact is established, the argument given above for the 1×1 minors a_{ij} of J^q can be applied to the 1×1 minors of successive powers $(J^{(r)})^q$ of the compound matrix $J^{(r)}$, where q is now $\sum |i_k - j_k|$ instead of $|i - j|$.

All hinges, then, on showing that a special almost-principal $r \times r$ minor of J has positive determinant. This is true by hypothesis for $r = 1$, and in any case is seen immediately on expanding such a minor in a manner corresponding to that used above in the case of principal minors (see also p. 120).

We state without proof the following necessary and sufficient conditions that a totally nonnegative matrix should be an oscillating matrix [24, II, § 7].

1. det A must be positive (and not 0).

2. No element on the main diagonal, no element just above the main diagonal, no element just below the main diagonal of A be 0 $(a_{ik} > 0$ for $|i - k| \leqq 1.)$

2. The spectral properties of an oscillating matrix are conveniently formulated in terms of certain concepts and notations which we now introduce.

For a column vector $u = (u_1, u_2, \ldots, u_n)$ we count the number of changes of sign in the sequence $u_1, u_2, \ldots, u_n$ of coordinates, giving arbitrary signs to the zero coordinates (if any). Depending on the particular signs ascribed to the zero coordinates, the number of changes of sign can vary between well-determined bounds. We denote the *maximum* and *minimum* numbers of changes of sign by S_u^+ and S_u^- respectively. In case these numbers are equal, $S_u^+ = S_u^-$, we speak of the *exact* number of changes of sign, and denote this by S_u. It is clear that the relation $S_u^+ = S_u^-$ holds if and only if *1* the first and last coordinates u_1, u_n of the vector u are nonzero, and *2*, whenever the equality $u_i = 0$ holds $(1 < i < n)$, the inequality $u_{i-1} u_{i+1} < 0$ also holds.

We now prove the following fundamental theorem.

THEOREM 13. *1. An oscillating matrix $A = (a_{ik})_1^n$ always has n distinct positive characteristic numbers*

$$\lambda_1 > \lambda_2 > \ldots > \lambda_n > 0. \tag{126}$$

2. If $u^{(1)}$ is any nonnull vector $(u_{11}, u_{21}, \ldots, u_{n1})$ such that $A u^{(1)} = u^{(1)}\lambda_1$, the coordinates u_{i1} are all different from zero and of the same sign. If $u^{(2)}$ is a characteristic vector $(u_{12}, u_{22}, \ldots, u_{n2})$ corresponding to $\lambda_2 : A u^{(2)} = u^{(2)}\lambda_2$, the sequence of coordinates u_{i2} has exactly one change of sign; and in general, if $u^{(k)}$ is a characteristic vector corresponding to $\lambda_k : A u^{(k)} = u^{(k)}\lambda_k$, $u^{(k)} =

$(u_{1k}, u_{2k}, \ldots, u_{nk})$, the sequence u_{ik}, k fixed, has exactly $k-1$ changes of sign $(k = 1, 2, \ldots, n)$.

3. If $c_g, c_{g+1}, \ldots, c_h$ $(1 \leq g \leq h \leq n)$ are any real numbers, not all zero, then the number of changes of sign in the sequence of coordinates of the vector

$$u = \sum_{k=g}^{h} c_k u^{(k)} \tag{127}$$

is between $g-1$ and $h-1$ inclusive:

$$g - 1 \leq S_u^- \leq S_u^+ \leq h - 1. \tag{128}$$

Proof. (i). We order the characteristic numbers of the matrix A in such a way that

$$|\lambda_1| \geq |\lambda_2| \geq \ldots \geq |\lambda_n|,$$

and consider the pth compound $A_{(p)}$ of the matrix A $(p = 1, 2, \ldots, n)$, i.e., the matrix whose elements are the $p \times p$ minor determinants of A, indexed in some order. The characteristic numbers of $A_{(p)}$ are the various products of the characteristic numbers of A, taken p at a time:

$$\lambda_1 \lambda_2 \ldots \lambda_p, \; \lambda_1 \lambda_2 \ldots \lambda_{p-1} \lambda_{p+1}, \; \ldots.$$

By hypothesis, there is an integer q so that A^q is totally positive. From $A_{(p)} A_{(p)} = (A^2)_{(p)}$, we see that $A_{(p)}^q$ is the pth compound of A^q, and is therefore totally positive. On the other hand, $A_{(p)}$ is nonnegative $(A_{(p)} \geq 0)$. Thus $A_{(p)}$ is actually an irreducible nonnegative matrix, and so is a primitive matrix. By the theorem of Frobenius (Section 2, Theorem 2, p. 65), applied to $A_{(p)}$, we conclude

$$\lambda_1 \lambda_2 \ldots \lambda_p > 0 \quad (p = 1, 2, \ldots, n),$$
$$\lambda_1 \lambda_2 \ldots \lambda_p > \lambda_1 \lambda_2 \ldots \lambda_{p-1} \lambda_{p+1} \quad (p = 1, 2, \ldots, n-1).$$

These inequalities imply (126).

(ii). Having established inequalities (126), we see that $A = (a_{ik})_1^n$ is diagonalizable. It follows that every compound matrix $A_{(p)}$ is also diagonalizable.

Let $U = (u_{ik})_1^n$ be the matrix of characteristic vectors of A, so that the kth column of U is the characteristic vector $u^{(k)}$ of A corresponding to the characteristic number λ_k. The characteristic vector of $A_{(p)}$ which corresponds to the characteristic number $\lambda_1 \lambda_2 \ldots \lambda_p$ has coordinates

$$U\begin{bmatrix} i_1, i_2, \ldots, i_p \\ 1, 2, \ldots, p \end{bmatrix} \quad (1 \leqq i_1 < i_2 < \ldots < i_p \leqq n). \tag{129}$$

By Frobenius' theorem, each of the numbers (129) is nonzero, and they are all of the same sign. By multiplying $u^{(1)}, u^{(2)}, \ldots, u^{(n)}$ by ± 1, we can arrange that these signs are all positive:

$$U\begin{bmatrix} i_1, i_2, \ldots, i_p \\ 1, 2, \ldots, p \end{bmatrix} > 0 \quad \left(\begin{array}{c} (1 \leqq i_1 < i_2 < \ldots < i_p \leqq n) \\ p = 1, 2, \ldots, n \end{array} \right). \tag{130}$$

The following relation holds for the matrix U of characteristic vectors of A:

$$A = U \operatorname{diag}(\lambda_1, \lambda_2, \ldots, \lambda_n) U^{-1}. \tag{131}$$

Thus

$$A' = U'^{-1} \operatorname{diag}(\lambda_1, \lambda_2, \ldots, \lambda_n) U'. \tag{132}$$

From (131) and (132), we see that the matrix

$$V = U'^{-1} \tag{133}$$

is the matrix of characteristic vectors of A', and that moreover the kth column of V is the characteristic vector corresponding to λ_k. Now since A is an oscillating matrix, A' is also an oscillating matrix. Thus, each of the minors

$$V\begin{bmatrix} i_1, i_2, \ldots, i_p \\ 1, 2, \ldots, p \end{bmatrix} \quad (1 \leqq i_1 < i_2 < \ldots < i_p \leqq n) \tag{134}$$

is nonzero and they all have the same sign (p fixed, $p = 1, 2, \ldots, n$).

On the other hand, (133) shows that the matrices U, V satisfy the relation $U'V = E$. Forming the pth compound matrices, we obtain

$$U'_{(p)} V_{(p)} = E_{(p)}.$$

In particular, since the diagonal element of $E_{(p)}$ is unity, we have

$$\sum_{1 \le i_1 < i_2 < \ldots < i_p \le n} U\begin{bmatrix} i_1, & i_2, & \ldots, & i_p \\ 1, & 2, & \ldots, & p \end{bmatrix} V\begin{bmatrix} i_1, & i_2, & \ldots, & i_p \\ 1, & 2, & \ldots, & p \end{bmatrix} = 1. \quad (135)$$

The left member is a sum of terms, each of which is the product of two factors. In each term, the first factor is positive, and the second factors are known all to have the same sign. Thus they are all positive:

$$V\begin{bmatrix} i_1, & i_2, & \ldots, & i_p \\ 1, & 2, & \ldots, & p \end{bmatrix} > 0 \quad \begin{pmatrix} 1 \le i_1 < i_2 < \ldots < i_p \le n; \\ p = 1, 2, \ldots, n \end{pmatrix}. \quad (136)$$

We have shown that the inequalities (130), (136) hold for $V = U'^{-1}$ whenever they hold for U.

Since the minor determinants of the matrix V can be expressed in terms of the minors of the inverse matrix V^{-1}, we obtain

$$V\begin{bmatrix} j_1, & j_2, & \ldots, & j_{n-p} \\ 1, & 2, & \ldots, & n-p \end{bmatrix} = \frac{(-1)^{np + \sum\limits_{v=1}^{p} i_v}}{\det U} U\begin{bmatrix} i_1, & i_2 & , \ldots, & i_p \\ n, & n-1, & \ldots, & n-p+1 \end{bmatrix}, \quad (137)$$

where $i_1 < i_2 < \ldots < i_p$ and $j_1 < j_2 < \ldots < j_{n-p}$ are complementary sets of indices; i.e. in their collection they are a permutation of $1, 2, \ldots, n$. The exponent of (-1) is correct since $\sum_{n-p+1}^{n} i$ plus the number of transpositions required to invert the arrangement $(n - p + 1, \ldots, n - 1, n)$ is congruent to np mod 2. From this we can derive the further conclusion

$$(-1)^{np + \sum\limits_{v=1}^{p} i_v} U\begin{bmatrix} i_1, & i_2, & \ldots, & i_p \\ n, & n-1, & \ldots, & n-p+1 \end{bmatrix} > 0 \begin{pmatrix} 1 \le i_1 < i_2 < \ldots < i_p \le n; \\ p = 1, 2, \ldots, n \end{pmatrix} \quad (138)$$

since $\det U$ is positive by (130), and the left member of (137) is positive by (136).

Now we take any linear combination

$$u = \sum_{k=g}^{h} c_k u^{(k)}$$

of the characteristic vectors $u^{(k)}$, with coefficients not all zero.

From (130) we shall derive the second part of (128):

$$S_u^+ \leqq h - 1; \qquad (139)$$

and from (138) we shall derive

$$S_u^- \geqq g - 1, \qquad (140)$$

to complete the proof of (128).

To this end, let us suppose that $S_u^+ > h - 1$. Then there must be $h + 1$ coordinates u_{i_α} of the vector u

$$u_{i_1}, u_{i_2}, \ldots, u_{i_{h+1}} \quad (1 \leqq i_1 \leqq i_2 \leqq \ldots \leqq i_{h+1} \leqq n) \quad (141)$$

such that

$$u_{i_\alpha} u_{i_{\alpha+1}} \leqq 0 \qquad (\alpha = 1, 2, \ldots, h). \qquad (141a)$$

Moreover, not all the coordinates (141) can be zero, for if they were, we should be able to say of the vector

$$u = \sum_{k=1}^h c_k u^{(k)} \quad (c_1 = \ldots = c_{g-1} = 0)$$

that the corresponding coordinates are all zero. This would mean in turn that the system

$$\sum_{k=1}^h c_k u_{i_\alpha k} = 0 \quad (\alpha = 1, 2, \ldots, h)$$

of homogeneous equations has a nonzero solution $(c_1, c_2, \ldots, c_h)$. But the determinant

$$U \begin{bmatrix} i_1, i_2, \ldots, i_h \\ 1, 2, \ldots, h \end{bmatrix}$$

of this system is not zero, according to (130).

Next, we use the relation

$$u = \sum_{k=1}^h c_k u^{(k)}$$

and the facts established above to conclude that the determinant

$$\det \begin{bmatrix} u_{i_1 1} & \cdots & u_{i_1 h} & u_{i_1} \\ u_{i_2 1} & \cdots & u_{i_2 h} & u_{i_2} \\ \cdot\cdot\cdot\cdot\cdot\cdot\cdot\cdot\cdot\cdot\cdot \\ \cdot\cdot\cdot\cdot\cdot\cdot\cdot\cdot\cdot\cdot\cdot \\ u_{i_{h+1} 1} & \cdots & u_{i_{h+1} h} & u_{i_{h+1}} \end{bmatrix}$$

is zero. We get a contradiction by expanding this determinant by minors of the last column:

$$\sum_{\alpha=1}^{h+1} (-1)^{h+\alpha+1} u_{i\alpha} U \begin{bmatrix} i_1, \ldots, i_{\alpha-1}, i_{\alpha+1}, \ldots, i_{h+1} \\ 1, \ldots\ldots\ldots h \end{bmatrix} = 0.$$

By (141a) all the terms of the left member have the same sign; and we have seen that at least one term is not zero. Thus the assumption $S^+ > h - 1$ has led to a contradiction, and inequality (139) must be correct.

To establish (140), we introduce the vectors

$$u^{*(k)} = (u_{1k}^*, u_{2k}^*, \ldots, u_{nk}^*) \quad (k = 1, 2, \ldots, n),$$

where

$$u_{ik}^* = (-1)^{n+i+k} u_{ik} \quad (i, k = 1, 2, \ldots, n).$$

If we apply (138), we see that the matrix $U^* = (u_{ik}^*)_1^n$ must be such that the relations

$$U^* \begin{bmatrix} i_1, & i_2, & \ldots, & i_p \\ n, & n-1, & \ldots, & n-p+1 \end{bmatrix} > 0 \quad \begin{pmatrix} 1 \leq i_1 < i_2 < \ldots < i_p \leq n; \\ p = 1, 2, \ldots, n \end{pmatrix} \quad (142)$$

hold. But these last inequalities (142) are similar to the set (130). To carry the analogy further, we set

$$u^* = \sum_{k=g}^{h} (-1)^k c_k u^{*(k)}. \quad (143)$$

Then the assertion corresponding to (139) which we can make is [42]

$$S_{u^*}^+ \leq n - g. \quad (144)$$

We denote the components of u by $(u_1, u_2, \ldots, u_n)$, and those of u^* by $(u_1^*, u_2^*, \ldots, u_n^*)$. It is easily seen that

$$u_i^* = (-1)^i u_i \quad (i = 1, 2, \ldots, n).$$

Thus we have the relation

---

[42] As they appear in inequalities (142), the vectors $u^{(k)}$ are in inverse order $u^{(n)}, u^{(n-1)}, \ldots$ The vector $u^{(g)}$ is preceded by $n - g$ vectors of the set.

$$S^+_{u*} + S^-_u = n - 1,$$

from which (140) is an immediate consequence, in view of (144).

Having established inequality (128), we can verify assertion 2 of Theorem 13 as the corollary of (128) with $g = h = k$. This completes the proof of the theorem.

3. In this section we apply the theorem just proved to study small oscillations of a system of n masses $m_1, m_2, \ldots, m_n$ which are situated at the n points $x_1 < x_2 < \ldots < x_n$ of a continuous elastic segment (string or rod of finite length). The equilibrium position of the rod is the segment $0 \leq x \leq l$ of the x-axis.

We denote by $K(x, s)$ $(0 \leq x, s \leq l)$ the strain function of the segment (i.e. $K(x, s)$ is the strain at the point x induced by the action of a force of one unit at the point s.) Further we denote by k_{ij} the strain coefficient pertaining to the n mass-coordinates:

$$k_{ij} = K(x_i, x_j) \quad (i, j = 1, 2, \ldots, n).$$

If n forces $F_1, F_2, \ldots, F_n$ are applied at the n points $x_1, x_2, \ldots, x_n$, the corresponding static strain $y(x)$ $(0 \leq x \leq l)$ can be found by making the following linear combination of strains:

$$y(x) = \sum_{j=1}^{n} K(x, x_j) F_j.$$

The equation for the free oscillations is obtained by substituting for F_j the inertial forces $m_j (\partial^2/\partial t^2) y(x_j; t)$ $(j = 1, 2, \ldots, n)$:

$$y(x) = - \sum_{j=1}^{n} m_j K(x, x_j) \frac{\partial^2}{\partial t^2} y(x_j; t). \tag{145}$$

We attempt to find harmonic oscillations of the segment, of the form

$$y(x) = u(x) \sin (pt + \alpha) \quad (0 \leq x \leq l). \tag{146}$$

Here $u(x)$ is the amplitude function, p is the frequency, and α is the phase angle for $t = 0$. We substitute (146) into (145) and obtain, after cancelling $\sin (pt + \alpha)$,

$$u(x) = p^2 \sum_{j=1}^{n} m_j K(x, x_j) u(x_j). \tag{147}$$

It is convenient to introduce the following abbreviations for the amplitudes and the variable strains at points x_i at which the masses are located

$$y_i = y(x_i, t), \quad u_i = u(x_i) \quad (i = 1, 2, \ldots, n).$$

Then

$$y_i = u_i \sin(pt + \alpha) \quad (i = 1, 2, \ldots, n).$$

It is also convenient to define the following *reduced amplitudes of strain* and *reduced coefficients of strain*

$$\tilde{u}_i = \sqrt{m_i}\, u_i, \quad a_{ij} = \sqrt{m_i m_j}\, k_{ij} \quad (i, j = 1, 2, \ldots, n). \quad (148)$$

Now we return to (147), and replace x in turn by each x_i, and obtain the following system of equations for the strain amplitudes

$$\sum_{j=1}^{n} a_{ij} \tilde{u}_j = \lambda \tilde{u}_i \quad \left(\lambda = \frac{1}{p^2}; \; i = 1, 2, \ldots, n\right). \quad (149)$$

It is obvious from (149) that the amplitude vector $\tilde{u} = (\tilde{u}_1, \tilde{u}_2, \ldots, \tilde{u}_n)$ is a characteristic vector of the matrix

$$A = (a_{ij})_1^n = (\sqrt{m_i m_j}\, k_{ij})_1^n$$

corresponding to the characteristic root $\lambda = 1/p^2$.

It is possible to establish the fact that *the matrix* $(k_{ij})_1^n$ *of train coefficients of a continuous segment is always an oscillating natrix*. As a consequence, the matrix A is also an oscillating natrix! By Theorem 13 it follows that A has n positive characteristic numbers

$$\lambda_1 > \lambda_2 > \ldots > \lambda_n = 0,$$

o that there are n simple harmonic oscillations of the continuous egment with the discrete frequencies p_i,

$$(0 <)p_1 < p_2 < \ldots < p_n \quad (\lambda_i = 1/p_i^2; i = 1, 2, \ldots, n).$$

according to the same theorem, the strain amplitudes which orrespond to the fundamental oscillation of frequency p_1 are ither all 0 or all of the same sign. The sequence of strain amplitudes which correspond to the first overtone (frequency p_2) have similarly exactly one change of sign; and in general, the sequence of strain amplitudes for the overtone of frequency p_j, there are exactly $j - 1$ changes of sign $(j = 1, 2, \ldots, n)$.

From the fact that the matrix (k_{ij}) of strain coefficients is an oscillating matrix, the following properties of the oscillating continuous segment can also be derived. *1*. For $p = p_1$, the amplitude function $u(x)$ which defines the strain amplitudes in (147) has no nodes; and in general, for $p = p_j$, the function $u(x)$ has exactly $j - 1$ nodes $(j = 1, 2, \ldots, n)$. *2*. The nodes for two adjacent overtones separate one another; etc.

We do not pause here to establish these properties.

CHAPTER IV

Applications of the Theory of Matrices to the Study of Systems of Linear Differential Equations

§ 1. Systems of linear differential equations with variable coefficients: general remarks

Let us consider the following system of linear homogeneous differential equations of the first order:

$$\frac{dx_i}{dt} = \sum_{k=1}^{n} p_{ik}(t) x_k \quad (i = 1, 2, \ldots, n), \tag{1}$$

where $p_{ik}(t)$ $(i, k = 1, 2, \ldots, n)$ are complex functions of the real argument t, continuous in a certain (finite or infinite) interval.[1]

If we write $P(t) = (p_{ik}(t))_1^n$ and $x = (x_1, x_2, \ldots, x_n)$, we can write system (1) as follows:

$$dx/dt = P(t)x. \tag{2}$$

A matrix integral of system (1) is a square matrix $X(t) = (x_{ik}(t))_1^n$, the columns of which are n linearly independent solutions of the system.

Since each column of the matrix X satisfies equation (2), then the integral matrix X also satisfies the equation

$$dX/dt = P(t)X. \tag{3}$$

In what follows, we will study the matrix equation (3) instead of system (1).

From the theorem on the existence and uniqueness of solutions

---

[1] All the relations of this section which involve functions of t are to hold on the given interval.

of a system of linear differential equations,[2] it follows that the matrix integral $X(t)$ is determined uniquely if the value of this matrix is prescribed for a certain ("initial") value [3] $t = t_0$, $X(t_0) = X_0$. For the matrix X_0, one may take any nonsingular square matrix of nth order. For the special case $X(t_0) = E$, we say that the integral matrix $X(t)$ is *normalized*.

We differentiate the determinant of the matrix X, by differentiating according to rows of the matrix $X(t)$. If we use the differential relations

$$\frac{dx_{ij}}{dt} = \sum_{k=1}^{n} p_{ik} x_{kj} \quad (i, j = 1, \ldots, n),$$

we obtain:

$$(d/dt) \det X = (p_{11} + p_{22} + \ldots + p_{nn}) \det X.$$

This gives the well-known *Jacobi identity*

$$\det X = c \exp \int_{t_0}^{t} \text{Sp } P \, dt \tag{4}$$

where c is a constant, and

$$\text{Sp } P = p_{11} + p_{22} + \ldots + p_{nn}$$

is the trace of the matrix $P(t)$.

Since the determinant $\det X$ cannot be identically equal to zero, then $c \neq 0$. But then from the Jacobi identity it follows that the determinant $\det X$ is different from zero for any value of the argument,

$$\det X \neq 0,$$

i.e., *a matrix integral is nonsingular for any value of the argument.*

If $\tilde{X}(t)$ is a particular nonsingular ($\det \tilde{X} \neq 0$) solution of equation (3), then the general solution of this equation is determined by the formula

$$X = \tilde{X} C \tag{5}$$

where C is an arbitrary constant matrix.

---

[2] The proof of this theorem is given below in Section 5. Cf. also any standard text on ordinary linear differential equations.

[3] It is assumed that t_0 belongs to the given interval.

Indeed, multiplying both sides of the equality

$$d\tilde{X}/dt = P\tilde{X} \tag{6}$$

by C on the right, we see that the matrix $\tilde{X}C$ also satisfies equation (3). On the other hand, if X is an arbitrary solution of equation (3), then from (6) it follows that:

$$\frac{dX}{dt} = \frac{d(\tilde{X} \cdot \tilde{X}^{-1}X)}{dt} = \frac{d\tilde{X}}{dt}\tilde{X}^{-1}X + \tilde{X}\frac{d(\tilde{X}^{-1}X)}{dt}$$

$$= PX + \tilde{X}\frac{d(\tilde{X}^{-1}X)}{dt},$$

hence from (3)

$$\frac{d(\tilde{X}^{-1}X)}{dt} = 0$$

and

$$\tilde{X}^{-1}X = \text{const} = C,$$

i.e., (5) holds.

All the integral matrices X of system (1) can be written in the form (5) for some C, $\det C \neq 0$.

We consider the special case:

$$dX/dt = AX \tag{7}$$

where A is a constant matrix. Here, $\tilde{X} = \exp(At)$ is a particular nonsingular solution[4] of equation (7) and therefore the general solution of this equation has the form

$$X = (\exp At)C, \tag{8}$$

where C is an arbitrary constant matrix.

If we set t equal to t_0 in (8), we find that: $X_0 = \exp At_0 \cdot C$. Hence $C = \exp(-At_0) \cdot X_0$ and therefore formula (8) may be rewritten in the form

$$X = [\exp A(t - t_0)]X_0, \tag{9}$$

[4] The exponential of the matrix M is defined by the series $E + M + M^2/2! + M^3/3! + \ldots$, which always converges. Differentiating the series $\exp At$ term by term, we find: $d(\exp At)/dt = A\exp(At)$.

the familiar formula for a system with constant coefficients. As a second example, let us consider the so-called *system of Cauchy*:

$$\frac{dX}{dt} = \frac{A}{t-a} X \quad (A \text{ a matrix of constants}). \tag{10}$$

This case can be reduced to the previous case by making the change of independent variable

$$u = \ln (t - a).$$

Therefore, the general solution of system (10) has the following form:

$$X = e^{A \ln (t-a)} C = (t-a)^A C. \tag{11}$$

The functions e^{At} and $(t-a)^A$, which occur in formulas (8) and (11), may be represented in the form

$$e^{At} = \sum_{k=1}^{s} (Z_{kl} + Z_{k2} t + \ldots + Z_{km_k} t^{m_k-1}) e^{\lambda_k t}, \tag{12}$$

$$(t-a)^A = \sum_{k=1}^{s} (Z_{k1} + Z_{k2} \ln (t-a) + \ldots + Z_{km_k} [\ln (t-a)]^{m_k-1}) (t-a)^{\lambda_k}. \tag{13}$$

Here,

$$\psi(\lambda) = (\lambda - \lambda_1)^{m_1} (\lambda - \lambda_2)^{m_2} \ldots (\lambda - \lambda_s)^{m_s}$$

$$(\lambda_i \neq \lambda_k \text{ for } i \neq k; \; i, \; k = 1, 2, \ldots, s)$$

is the minimal polynomial of the matrix A, and $Z_{kj}(j=1, 2, \ldots, m_k; k = 1, 2, \ldots, s)$ are linearly independent constant matrices, which are polynomials [5] in A.

---

[5] In the right member of formula (12), each summand
$$X_k = (Z_{k1} + Z_{k2} t + \ldots + Z_{km_k} t^{m_k-1}) e^{\lambda_k t} \quad (k = 1, 2, \ldots, s)$$
is a solution of equation (7). For, this equation is satisfied by the product $g(A)e^{At}$, for arbitrary $g(\lambda)$. But $X_k = f(A) = g(A)e^{At}$, if $f(\lambda) = g(\lambda)e^{\lambda t}$ and $g(\lambda_k) = 1$, and all the remaining $m - 1$ values of the function $g(\lambda)$ on the spectrum of matrix A are equal to zero.

REMARK. Sometimes the matrix integral of the system of differential equations (1) is taken as a matrix W, in which the *rows* are linearly independent solutions of the system. It is obvious that the matrix W will be the transpose of the matrix X:

$$W = X'.$$

Taking the transpose of both sides of equality (3), we obtain instead of (3) the following equation for W:

$$dW/dt = WQ(t) \quad (Q = (q_{ij}), \ q_{ij} = p_{ji}). \tag{3'}$$

In the right member of this equation the matrix W is the first factor, and not the second, whereas in equation (3), X is the second factor.

§ 2. *Lyapunov's transformation*

Let us assume that the matrix of coefficients $P(t) = (p_{ik}(t))_1^n$ in system (1) and in equation (3) is a continuous bounded function [6] of t in the interval (t_0, ∞).

Let us introduce new unknown functions $y_1, y_2, \ldots, y_n$ in place of the unknown functions $x_1, x_2, \ldots, x_n$ by means of the transformation

$$x_i = \sum_{k=1}^{n} l_{ik}(t) y_k \quad (i = 1, 2, \ldots, n). \tag{14}$$

We put the following restrictions on the matrix $L(t) = (l_{ik}(t))_1^n$ of the transformation:

(i) $L(t)$ has a continuous derivative dL/dt in the interval $[t_0, \infty)$;

(ii) $L(t)$ and dL/dt are bounded in the interval $[t_0, \infty)$;

(iii) there exists a constant m such that

$$0 < m < |\det L(t)|, \ t \geqq t_0,$$

i.e., the determinant $\det L(t)$ is bounded below in modulus by the positive constant m.

---

[6] That is to say, each of the functions $p_{ik}(t)$ $(i, k = 1, 2, \ldots, n)$ is continuous and bounded in the interval (t_0, ∞), i.e., for $t \geqq t_0$.

If the matrix of coefficients $L(t) = (l_{ik}(t))_1^n$, in transformation (14), satisfies conditions (i)—(iii), we will call it a *Lyapunov transformation*, and the corresponding matrix $L(t)$, a *Lyapunov matrix*.

Such transformations were considered by A. M. Lyapunov in his famous memoir "General Problem of the Stability of Motion" [42].

Examples. *1.* If $L = $ const and det $L \neq 0$, then the matrix L satisfies conditions (i)—(iii). Consequently, a nonsingular transformation with constant coefficients is always a Lyapunov transformation.

2. If $D = (d_{ik})_1^n$ is a diagonable matrix the characteristic numbers of which are pure imaginaries, then the matrix

$$L(t) = e^{Dt}$$

satisfies conditions (i)—(iii), and thus is a Lyapunov matrix.[7]

It is easily verified that properties (i)—(iii) imply the existence of an inverse matrix $L^{-1}(t)$, and that L^{-1} satisfies the same conditions (i)—(iii), i.e., the inverse of a Lyapunov transformation is again a Lyapunov transformation. Also it can be seen that the resultant of two Lyapunov transformations is again a Lyapunov transformation. Thus, the Lyapunov transformations form a group. Lyapunov transformations possess the following important property:

If transformation (14) *carries the system of equations* (1) *into the system*

$$\frac{dy_i}{dt} = \sum_{k=1}^n q_{ik}(t)\, y_k\,, \qquad (15)$$

the null solution of which is stable, asymptotically stable or unstable in the sense of Lyapunov, then the null solution $x_i \equiv 0$ *of the initial system* (1) *possesses the same property.*

In other words, Lyapunov transformations do not change the stability property of the null solution. For this reason, these

---

[7] In this connection, in formula (12) all $m_k = 1$, and $\lambda_k = i\varphi_k$ (φ_k are real, $k = 1, 2, \ldots, s$).

transformations may be utilized to simplify the original system of equations when stability is being investigated.

A Lyapunov transformation establishes a one-to-one correspondence between the solutions of systems (1) and (15), and linearly independent solutions remain such after the transformation. Therefore a Lyapunov transformation carries a matrix integral X of system (1) into a certain matrix integral Y of system (15), where

$$X = L(t)Y. \tag{16}$$

In matrix form, system (15) has the form

$$dY/dt = Q(t)Y, \tag{17}$$

where $Q(t) = (q_{ik}(t))_1^n$ is the matrix of coefficients of system (15).

Substituting the product LY in (3) for X and comparing the resulting equation with (17), we easily find the following formula, which expresses the matrix Q in terms of the matrices P and L:

$$Q = L^{-1}PL - L^{-1}\,dL/dt. \tag{18}$$

We call two systems (1) and (15), or, what is the same thing, (3) and (17), *equivalent systems* (in the sense of Lyapunov), if one is carried into the other by a Lyapunov transformation. The matrices of coefficients P and Q of equivalent systems are always connected by formula (18), where the matrix L satisfies conditions (i)—(iii).

§ 3. Reduced systems

The most simple and the most studied systems of linear differential equations of the first order, are systems with constant coefficients. For this reason, systems which can be reduced to systems with constant coefficients by means of a Lyapunov transformation are of interest. A. M. Lyapunov named such systems *reducible systems*.

Given the reducible system

$$dX/dt = PX. \tag{19}$$

Then a certain Lyapunov transformation

$$X = L(t)Y \tag{20}$$

carries it into the system

$$dY/dt = AY, \tag{21}$$

where A is a constant matrix. Therefore system (19) has the particular solution

$$\tilde{X} = L(t) e^{At}. \tag{22}$$

It is easily seen that, conversely, if the system (19) has a particular solution of the form (22), where $L(t)$ is a Lyapunov matrix, and A a constant matrix, then (19) is reducible, and further that it is reduced to form (21) by means of the Lyapunov transformation (20).

Following A. M. Lyapunov, we will show that *every system* (19) *with periodic coefficients is reducible.*[8]

In the given system (19), let $P(t)$ be a continuous function in the interval $(-\infty, +\infty)$ with period τ:

$$P(t + \tau) = P(t). \tag{23}$$

In (19), substituting $t + \tau$ for t and applying (23), we obtain:

$$\frac{dX(t + \tau)}{dt} = P(t)X(t + \tau).$$

Thus, $X(t + \tau)$, is a matrix integral of the system (19) whenever $X(t)$ is. Thus,

$$X(t + \tau) = X(t)V$$

where V is some constant nonsingular matrix. Since $\det V \neq 0$ it is possible to define [9]

$$V^{t/\tau} = \exp(t \ln V / \tau).$$

---

[8] See [42], Section 47.

[9] Here $\ln V = f(V)$, where $f(\lambda)$ is any single-valued branch of the function $\ln \lambda$ in a simply-connected region G, which contains all the characteristic numbers of matrix V and does not contain the number 0.

If the argument of this matrix function of t is increased by τ, this function is also multiplied by V. Therefore the "quotient"

$$L(t) = X(t)V^{-t/\tau} = X(t) \exp(-t \ln V/\tau)$$

is a continuous periodic function with period τ:

$$L(t + \tau) = L(t)$$

and with nonzero determinant: $\det L(t) \neq 0$. The matrix $L(t)$ satisfies conditions (i)—(iii) of the preceding section, and is thus a Lyapunov matrix.

On the other hand, since the solution X of system (19) can be represented in the form

$$X = L(t) \exp(t \ln V/\tau)$$

then system (19) is reducible.

In the present case the Lyapunov transformation

$$X = L(t)Y$$

which reduces system (19) to the form

$$\frac{dY}{dt} = \frac{1}{\tau} \ln V \cdot Y,$$

has coefficients which are periodic with period τ.

A. M. Lyapunov established [10] an extremely important criterion for stability and instability of the first degree (linear) approximation for nonlinear systems of differential equations

$$\frac{dx_i}{dt} = \sum_{k=1}^{n} a_{ik} x_k + (**)(i = 1, 2, \ldots, n) \tag{24}$$

where the right members are convergent power series in $x_1, x_2, \ldots, x_n$, and (**) denotes terms of these series of degrees two and greater in $x_1, x_2, \ldots, x_n$; the coefficients a_{ik} $(i, k = 1, 2, \ldots, n)$, in the linear members are constant.[11]

---

[10] See [42], Section 24. We call $x_i \equiv 0$ the *null* solution.

[11] The coefficients of the linear members could depend on t. The classical restrictions which are imposed on these functional coefficients are well known (see [42], Section 11).

CRITERION OF LYAPUNOV. *The null solution of system* (24) *will be stable (and also asymptotically stable), if all the characteristic numbers of the matrix of coefficients $A = (a_{ik})_1^n$ of the first linear approximation have negative real parts, and unstable, if at least one of these characteristic numbers has a positive real part.*

We can apply the above discussion and criterion to a system with periodic coefficients in the linear members:

$$\frac{dx_i}{dt} = \sum_{k=1}^{n} p_{ik}(t) x_k + (**). \qquad (25)$$

In fact, as the preceding discussion shows, system (25) can be reduced to form (24) by a Lyapunov transformation, where

$$A = (a_{ik})_1^n = \frac{1}{\tau} \ln V,$$

and V is the constant matrix by which a matrix integral of the corresponding linear system (19) is multiplied when the argument is increased by τ. Without loss of generality, we may assume that $\tau > 0$. It is a property of Lyapunov's transformation, that the null solution of the initial system and the null solution of the transformed system are at the same time stable, asymptotically stable or unstable. But the characteristic numbers λ_i and ν_i $(i = 1, 2, \ldots, n)$ of the matrices A and V are connected by the formula

$$\lambda_i = \frac{1}{\tau} \ln \nu_i \quad (i = 1, 2, \ldots, n).$$

Therefore, by applying the Lyapunov criterion to the reduced system, we obtain the following result:[12]

The null solution of system (25) *will be asymptotically stable, if all the characteristic numbers $\nu_1, \nu_2, \ldots, \nu_n$ of the matrix V have modulus less than 1, and unstable, if at least one of these numbers has modulus exceeding 1.*

A. M. Lyapunov established his criterion of stability of the linear approximation for a considerably larger class of systems,

---

[12] See [42], Section 55.

namely for systems of form (24), in which the linear approximation is not necessarily a system with constant coefficients, but belongs to a class of systems which Lyapunov called proper.[13]

The class of proper linear systems contains as a subset all reducible systems.

A criterion of instability for the case when the first linear approximation is a proper system was established by N. G. Chetaev.[14]

§ 4. Canonical form of reduced systems.
Erugin's theorem

We consider the reducible system (19) and the corresponding equivalent system (equivalent under a Lyapunov transformation)

$$dY/dt = AY,$$

where A is a constant matrix.

We are interested in the extent to which the matrix A is determined by the given system (19). This problem may also be formulated as follows:

When are the two systems

$$dY/dt = AY, \qquad dZ/dt = BZ$$

where A and B are constant matrices, equivalent in the sense of Lyapunov, i.e., when can these systems be transformed into one another by a Lyapunov transformation?

To answer this question, we make the following definition.

We say that two matrices A and B of nth order *have spectra with the same real part* if and only if the elementary divisors of the matrices A and B have the respective forms

$$(\lambda - \lambda_1)^{m_1}, \ (\lambda - \lambda_2)^{m_2} \ldots, \ (\lambda - \lambda_s)^{m_s}$$

$$(\lambda - \mu_1)^{m_1}, \ (\lambda - \mu_2)^{m_2}, \ldots, \ (\lambda - \mu_s)^{m_s}$$

13 See [42], Section 9.
14 See [9, p. 181]; also [1, Chap. V].

where

$$\operatorname{Re} \lambda_k = \operatorname{Re} \mu_k \quad (k = 1, 2, \ldots, s).$$

The following theorem is due to N. P. Erugin.[15]

THEOREM 1 (Erugin). *The two systems*

$$dY/dt = AY, \quad dZ/dt = BZ \qquad (26)$$

(where A and B are constant matrices of nth order) are equivalent in the sense of Liapounov if and only if the spectra of the matrices A and B have the same real part.

Proof. Consider the systems (26). We reduce the matrix A to the normal Jordan form [16] (see Appendix II)

$$A = T\{\xi_1 E_1 + H_1, \ \xi_2 E_2 + H_2, \ldots, \ \xi_s E_s + H_s\} T^{-1}, \quad (27)$$

where

$$\xi_k = \alpha_k + i\beta_k \quad (\alpha_k, \ \beta_k \text{ real}; \ k = 1, 2, \ldots, s). \qquad (28)$$

Formulas (27) and (28) suggest the definitions

$$\begin{aligned} A_1 &= T\{\alpha_1 E_1 + H_1, \ \alpha_2 E_2 + H_2, \ldots, \ \alpha_s E_s + H_s\} T^{-1}, \\ A_2 &= T\{i\beta_1 E_1, \ i\beta_2 E_2, \ldots, \ i\beta_s E_s\} T^{-1}. \end{aligned} \qquad (29)$$

Then

$$A = A_1 + A_2, \quad A_1 A_2 = A_2 A_1. \qquad (30)$$

We define the matrix $L(t)$ by the equality

$$L(t) = e^{A_2 t}.$$

Then $L(t)$ is a Lyapunov matrix (see Example 2 on p. 140).

But by (30), a particular solution of the first of the systems (26) is:

$$e^{At} = e^{A_2 t} e^{A_1 t} = L(t) e^{A_1(t)}.$$

[15] See [17], pp. 9—15. The proof of the theorem given here differs from N. P. Erugin's original proof.

[16] E_k is the identity matrix; H_k has the elements in the superdiagonal equal to unity, and the remaining elements are equal to zero; the order of E_k, H_k is equal to the degree of the kth elementary divisor of the matrix A, i.e., m_k $(k = 1, 2, \ldots, s)$.

Hence it follows that the first of systems (26) is equivalent to the system

$$dU/dt = A_1 U, \tag{31}$$

where, by (29), the matrix A_1 has real characteristic numbers and its spectrum coincides with the real part of the spectrum of matrix A.

In the same manner, we can replace the second of systems (26) by the equivalent system

$$dV/dt = B_1 V \tag{32}$$

where the matrix B_1 has real characteristic numbers and its spectrum coincides with the real part of the spectrum of the matrix B.

Our theorem will be proven if we show that *the two systems* (31) *and* (32), *in which the matrices A_1 and B_1 are constant matrices with real characteristic numbers, are equivalent if and only if the matrices A_1 and B_1 are similar.*[17]

Let the Lyapunov transformation

$$U = L_1 V$$

transform (31) into (32). Then the matrix L_1 satisfies the equation

$$dL_1/dt = A_1 L_1 - L_1 B_1. \tag{33}$$

This matrix equation in L_1 is equivalent to a system of n^2 differential equations in the n^2 elements of the matrix L_1. The right member of (33) is a linear operation on the "vector" L_1 in a space of n^2 dimensions

$$dL_1/dt = F(L_1), \quad [F(L_1) = A_1 L_1 - L_1 B_1]. \tag{33'}$$

Any characteristic number of the linear operator F (and the corresponding matrix of order n^2) can be expressed as a difference

---

[17] From this assertion Theorem 1 follows since the equivalence of systems (31) and (32) implies equivalence of systems (26), and similarity of the matrices A_1 and B_1 implies that these matrices have identical elementary divisors, hence the spectra of the matrices A and B have the same real part.

$\gamma - \delta$, where γ is a characteristic number of the matrix A_1, and δ, a characteristic number of the matrix B_1.[18] Hence it follows that all characteristic numbers of the operator F are real.

Let $\psi(\lambda) = (\lambda - \lambda_1)^{m_1}(\lambda - \lambda_2)^{m_2} \ldots (\lambda - \lambda_u)^{m_u}$ (λ_i real; $\lambda_i \neq \lambda_j$ for $i \neq j$; $i, j = 1, 2, \ldots, u$) be the minimal polynomial for F. Then, by formula (12) (p. 138), the solution $L_1(t) = (\exp Ft)L^{(0)}$ of system (33') can be written as follows:

$$L_1(t) = \sum_{k=1}^{u} \sum_{j=0}^{m_k-1} L_{kj} t^j e^{\lambda_k t}, \tag{34}$$

where L_{kj} are constant matrices of order n. Since the matrix $L_1(t)$ is bounded in the interval (t_0, ∞), the term L_{kj} is 0 if either the corresponding λ_k is positive $(\lambda_k > 0)$, or if λ_k is 0 and j is positive $(\lambda_k = 0, j > 0)$. Let us denote by $L_-(t)$ the sum of all the summands in (34), for which $\lambda_k < 0$. Then

$$L_1(t) = L_-(t) + L_0, \tag{35}$$

where

$$\lim_{t \to +\infty} L_-(t) = 0, \quad \lim_{t \to +\infty} \frac{dL_-(t)}{dt} = 0, \quad L_0 = \text{const.} \tag{35'}$$

Then, by (35) and (35')

$$\lim_{t \to +\infty} L_1(t) = L_0$$

whence it follows that

$$\det L_0 \neq 0,$$

[18] In fact, let Λ_0 be any characteristic number of the operator F. Then there exists a matrix $L \neq 0$, such that $F(L) = \Lambda_0 L$ or

$$(A_1 - \Lambda_0 E) L = L B_1. \tag{*}$$

The matrices $A_1 - \Lambda_0 E$ and B_1 have at least one common characteristic number, since otherwise there would exist a polynomial $g(\lambda)$ such that

$$g(A_1 - \Lambda_0 E) = 0, \quad g(B_1) = E,$$

but this is impossible, since from (*) it follows that: $g(A_1 - \Lambda_0 E) \cdot L = L \cdot g(B_1)$ and $L \neq 0$. But if the matrices $A_1 - \Lambda_0 E$ and B_1 have a common characteristic number, then $\Lambda_0 = \gamma - \delta$, where γ and δ are characteristic numbers, respectively, of the matrices A_1 and B_1. A detailed investigation of the operator F can be found in the work of F. Golubchikov [26].

since the determinant $\det L_1(t)$ is bounded below in modulus.
Substituting the sum $L_-(t) + L_0$ in (33) in place of $L_1(t)$, we obtain:

$$dL_-/dt - A_1 L_-(t) + B_1 L_-(t) = A_1 L_0 - B_1 L_0$$

whence, by (35′)

$$A_1 L_0 - L_0 B_1 = 0$$

and, therefore

$$B_1 = L_0^{-1} A_1 L_0. \qquad (36)$$

Conversely, if (36) holds, then the Lyapunov transformation

$$U = L_0 V$$

transforms system (31) into system (32). The theorem is proved.

From the above theorem, it follows that *any reducible system* (19) *can be reduced by means of a Lyapunov transformation* $X = LY$ *to the form*

$$dY/dt = JY$$

where J is a Jordan matrix with real characteristic numbers. If the matrix $P(t)$ is given, this canonical form is uniquely determined to within the arrangement of the diagonal blocks in J.

§ 5. The matrizer [19]

Let us consider the system of differential equations

$$dX/dt = P(t)X \qquad (37)$$

where $P(t) = (p_{ik}(t))_1^n$ is a continuous matrix function in a certain interval (a, b) of the t-axis.[20]

---

[19] Also called "matrizant."

[20] (a, b) is an arbitrary interval (finite or infinite). All the elements $p_{ik}(t)$ $(i, k = 1, 2, \ldots, n)$ of the matrix $P(t)$ are complex functions of the real argument t, which are continuous in the interval (a, b). All the following remain valid if instead of continuity, we require only boundedness and Riemann integrability in any finite subinterval of the interval (a, b) of all the functions $p_{ik}(t)$ $(i, k = 1, 2, \ldots, n)$.

We use the method of successive approximations to obtain a normalized solution of system (37), i.e., a solution which is the identity matrix for $t = t_0$ (t_0 being a fixed number in the interval (a, b)). We find the successive approximations X_k ($k = 0, 1, 2,\ldots$) from the recursion relations

$$dX_k/dt = P(t)X_{k-1} \quad (k = 1, 2, \ldots),$$

and taking the identity E as the initial approximation X_0.

If we take $X_k(t_0)$ equal to E ($k = 0, 1, 2, \ldots$), we can write X_k in the form

$$X_k = E + \int_{t_0}^t P(t)X_{k-1}\,dt \quad (k = 1, 2, \ldots).$$

Thus,

$$X_0 = E, \; X_1 = E + \int_{t_0}^t P(t)\,dt, \; X_2 = E + \int_{t_0}^t P(t)\,dt$$
$$+ \int_{t_0}^t P(t_2)\,dt_2 \int_{t_0}^{t_2} P(t_1)\,dt_1, \ldots,$$

i.e., X_k ($k = 0, 1, 2, \ldots$) is the sum of the first $k + 1$ members of the infinite series of matrices

$$E + \int_{t_0}^t P(t)\,dt + \int_{t_0}^t P(t_2)\,dt_2 \int_{t_0}^{t_2} P(t_1)\,dt_1 + \ldots \qquad (38)$$

To prove that this series is absolutely and uniformly convergent in any closed portion of the interval (a, b) and defines a solution of equation (37), we construct a dominating series.

We define two nonnegative functions $g(t)$ and $h(t)$ in the interval (a, b) by the equalities [21]

$$g(t) = \max \left[\,|\,p_{11}(t)\,|, \;|\,p_{12}(t)\,|, \ldots, |\,p_{nn}(t)|\right], \; h(t) = \left|\int_{t_0}^t g(t)\,dt\right|.$$

It is easily checked that the function $g(t)$ is continuous in the interval (a, b). Thus $h(t)$ is automatically continuous.[22]

---

[21] By definition, the value of the function $g(t)$ for any value of t is equal to the maximum of the n^2 moduli of the values $p_{ik}(t)$ ($i, k = 1, 2, \ldots, n$) for that value of t.

[22] The continuity of the function $g(t)$ at any point t_1 of the interval (a, b) follows from the fact that for t sufficiently close to t_1, the difference $g(t) - g(t_1)$ is always equal to one of the n^2 differences

$$p_{ik}(t) - p_{ik}(t_1) \quad (i, k = 1, 2, \ldots, n).$$

Each of the n^2 scalar infinite series into which matrix series (38) splits is dominated by the series

$$1 + h(t) + \frac{nh^2(t)}{2!} + \frac{n^2 h^3(t)}{3!} + \cdots \qquad (39)$$

This follows from the inequalities

$$\left| \left\{ \int_{t_0}^t P(t)\, dt \right\}_{i,k} \right| = \left| \int_{t_0}^t p_{ik}(t)\, dt \right| \leqq \left| \int_{t_0}^t g(t)\, dt \right| = h(t),$$

$$\left| \left\{ \int_{t_0}^t P(t)\, dt \int_{t_0}^t P(t)\, dt \right\}_{i,k} \right| = \left| \sum_{j=1}^n \int_{t_0}^t p_{ij}\, dt \int_{t_0}^t p_{jk}(t)\, dt \right|$$

$$\leqq n \left| \int_{t_0}^t g(t)\, dt \int_{t_0}^t g(t)\, dt \right| = \frac{nh^2(t)}{2}$$

etc.

Series (39) converges in the interval $(a,\, b)$, and it converges uniformly in any closed subinterval of the interval $(a,\, b)$. Hence it follows that the matrix series (38) also converges absolutely in $(a,\, b)$ and uniformly in any closed subinterval of $(a,\, b)$.

Differentiating term by term, we check that the sum of series (38) is a solution of equation (37); this solution reduces to E for $t = t_0$. It is permissible to differentiate series (38) term by term, since the resulting series differs from series (38) by the factor P, and thus converges uniformly in any closed portion of the interval $(a,\, b)$, as does (38).

Thus, we have proved the theorem on the existence of a normalized solution of equation (37). Let us denote this solution by $\Omega_{t_0}^t(P)$ or simply $\Omega_{t_0}^t$. As proved in section 1, any other solution has the form

$$X = \Omega_{t_0}^t C$$

where C is an arbitrary constant matrix. It follows from this formula that any solution, in particular the normalized one, is uniquely determined by its value for $t = t_0$.

The normalized solution $\Omega_{t_0}^t$ of equation (37) is often called the matrizer of the system (37).

We showed that the matrizer can be written as an infinite series [23]

$$\Omega^t_{t_0} = E + \int_{t_0}^t P(t)\,dt + \int_{t_0}^t P(t)\,dt \int_{t_0}^t P(t)\,dt + \dots \quad (40)$$

which converges absolutely and uniformly in any closed interval in which the function $P(t)$ is continuous.

Let us note certain formulas for the matrizer.

1. $\Omega^t_{t_0} = \Omega^t_{t_1}\Omega^{t_1}_{t_0} \quad (t_0,\ t_1,\ t \in (a,\ b))$.

In fact, since $\Omega^t_{t_0}$ and $\Omega^t_{t_1}$ are both solutions of equation (37), then

$$\Omega^t_{t_0} = \Omega^t_{t_1} C,$$

where C is a constant matrix.

Setting t equal to t_1, we obtain $C = \Omega^{t_1}_{t_0}$.

2. $\Omega^t_{t_0}(P + Q) = \Omega^t_{t_0}(P)\,\Omega^t_{t_0}(S)$,

where

$$S = [\Omega^t_{t_0}(P)]^{-1} Q\Omega^t_{t_0}(P).$$

To derive this formula, let us set X equal to $\Omega^t_{t_0}(P)$, and Y equal to $\Omega^t_{t_0}(P + Q)$, and

$$Y = XZ. \quad (41)$$

By differentiating both members of (41), we find

$$(P + Q)XZ = PXZ + X\,dZ/dt.$$

Hence

$$dZ/dt = X^{-1}QXZ$$

and thus, since (41) shows that $Z(t_0) = E$,

$$Z = \Omega^t_{t_0}(X^{-1}QX).$$

Substituting in (41) for X, Y, Z the corresponding matrizers, we obtain formula 2.

3. $\ln | \Omega^t_{t_0}(P)| = \int_{t_0}^t \mathrm{Sp}\, P\,dt.$

[23] The representation of the resolvent matrix in the form of such a series was first obtained by Peano [53].

This formula follows from the Jacobi identity (4) (p. 136), if $\Omega_{t_0}^t(P)$ is substituted for $X(t)$ there.

4.   If $A = (a_{ik})_1^n = \text{const}$, then

$$\Omega_{t_0}^t(A) = e^{A(t-t_0)}.$$

Let us introduce the following notation. If $P = (p_{ik})_1^n$, then we will denote by $\text{mod } P$ the matrix

$$\text{mod } P = (|\, p_{ik}\,|)_1^n$$

In addition, if $A = (a_{ik})_1^n$ and $B = (b_{ik})_1^n$ are two real matrices and

$$a_{ik} \leqq b_{ik} \quad (i,\ k = 1, 2, \ldots, n),$$

then we write:

$$A \leqq B.$$

Then from the representation (40) it follows that:

5.   If $\text{mod } P(t) \leqq Q(t)$, then

$$\text{mod } \Omega_{t_0}^t(P) \leqq \Omega_{t_0}^t(Q) \quad (t > t_0).$$

In the following we let I denote the nth order matrix in which every element is 1:

$$I = (1).$$

Let us consider the function $g(t)$, which was defined on p. 150. Then

$$\text{mod } P(t) \leqq g(t)I.$$

Hence, in view of 5

$$\text{mod } \Omega_{t_0}^t(P) \leqq \Omega_{t_0}^t(g(t)I) \quad (t > t_0). \tag{42}$$

But $\Omega_{t_0}^t(g(t)I)$ is the normalized solution of the equation

$$dX/dt = g(t)IX.$$

Consequently, from 4 above [24]

---

[24] Here we use the variable $h = \int_{t_0}^t g(t)dt$ in place of the independent variable t.

$$\Omega_{t_0}^t(g(t)I) = e^{h(t)I} = \left(1 + h(t) + \frac{nh^2(t)}{2!} + \frac{n^2 h^3(t)}{3!} + \ldots\right) I$$

where

$$h(t) = \int_{t_0}^t g(t) dt.$$

Therefore from (42) it follows that:

6. $\mathrm{mod}\,\Omega_{t_0}^t(P) \leqq \left(\dfrac{1}{n} e^{nh(t)} + \dfrac{n-1}{n}\right) I \leqq e^{nh(t)}\,I \quad (t > t_0),$

where

$$h(t) = \int_{t_0}^t g(t) dt, \qquad g(t) = \max_{1 \leqq i,\,k \leqq n} \{|\,p_{ik}(t)\,|\}.$$

Now let us show that the matrizer can be used to obtain the general solution of an arbitrary system of linear differential equations:

$$\frac{dx_i}{dt} = \sum_{k=1}^n P_{ik}(t)\,x_k + f_i(t) \quad (i = 1, 2, \ldots, n); \qquad (43)$$

where $p_{ik}(t)$, $f_i(t)$ $(i,\ k = 1, 2, \ldots, n)$ are continuous functions in the interval of the argument t being considered.

We let x denote the column matrix ("vector") $x = (x_1, x_2, \ldots, x_n)$, and f denote the column $f = (f_1, f_2, \ldots, f_n)$. We let P represent the square matrix $P = (p_{ik})_1^n$. Thus we can rewrite this system as follows:

$$dx/dt = P(t)x + f(t). \qquad (43')$$

We seek a solution of this equation of the form

$$x = \Omega_{t_0}^t(P)\,z, \qquad (44)$$

where z is an unknown column depending on t. Substituting this expression for x in (43'), we obtain:

$$P\Omega_{t_0}^t(P)z + \Omega_{t_0}^t(P)\,dz/dt = P\Omega_{t_0}^t(P)z + f(t)$$

whence

$$dz/dt = [\Omega_{0t}^t(P)]^{-1} f(t).$$

Integrating, we obtain:

$$z = \int_{t_0}^{t} [\Omega_{t_0}^{\tau}(P)]^{-1} f(\tau)\, d\tau + c$$

where c is an arbitrary constant vector. Substituting this expression in (44), we obtain:

$$x = \Omega_{t_0}^{t}(P) \int_{t_0}^{t} [\Omega_{t_0}^{\tau}(P)]^{-1} f(\tau) d\tau + \Omega_{t_0}^{t}(P)c. \qquad (45)$$

When t has the value t_0, we see that $x(t_0) = c$. Therefore formula (45) assumes the form

$$x = \Omega_{t_0}^{t}(P) x(t_0) + \int_{t_0}^{t} K(t,\ \tau) f(\tau)\, d\tau, \qquad (45')$$

where

$$K(t,\ \tau) = \Omega_{t_0}^{t}(P) [\Omega_{t_0}^{\tau}(P)]^{-1}$$

is the so-called Cauchy matrix.

§ 6. Multiplicative integration (product integration). The infinitesimal calculus of Volterra

Let us consider the matrizer $\Omega_{t_0}^{t}(P)$. We subdivide the original interval $(t_0,\ t)$ into n parts by means of the intermediate points $t_1, t_2, \ldots, t_{n-1}$, and we set Δt_k equal to $t_k - t_{k-1}$ $(k = 1, 2, \ldots, n;$ $t_n = t)$. Then from property 1 of the matrizer (see the preceding section), we have

$$\Omega_{t_0}^{t} = \Omega_{t_{n-1}}^{t} \ldots \Omega_{t_1}^{t_2} \Omega_{t_0}^{t_1} \qquad (46)$$

In each interval $(t_{k-1},\ t_k)$ we choose an intermediate point τ_k $(k = 1, 2, \ldots, n)$. Then if the Δt_k are taken as infinitesimals of the first order, we can calculate $\Omega_{t_{k-1}}^{t_k}$ to within infinitesimals of the second order, by taking $P(t) \approx \text{const} = P(\tau_k)$. Then

$$\Omega_{t_{k-1}}^{t_k} = \exp [P(\tau_k) \Delta t_k] + (**) = E + P(\tau_k) \Delta t_k + (**); \qquad (47)$$

where the symbol $(**)$ is used to denote a sum of terms, each of which is an infinitesimal of order two or greater.

From (46) and (47) we find:

$$\Omega_{t_0}^{t} = [\exp P(\tau_n) \Delta t_n] \ldots [\exp P(\tau_2) \Delta t_2][\exp P(\tau_1) \Delta t_1] + (*) \qquad (48)$$

and

$$\Omega^t_{t_0} = [E + P(\tau_n)\Delta t_n] \dots [E + P(\tau_2)\Delta t_2][E + P(\tau_1)\Delta t_1] + (*). \quad (49)$$

If we allow the number of intervals to become infinite in such a way that the length of the widest subinterval approaches zero, the terms (*) can be neglected [25] and in the limit, we have the formulas

$$\Omega^t_{t_0}(P) = \lim_{\Delta t_k \to 0} [\exp P(\tau_n)\Delta t_n] \dots [\exp P(\tau_2)\Delta t_2][\exp P(\tau_1)\Delta t_1] \quad (48')$$

and

$$\Omega^t_{t_0}(P) = \lim_{\Delta t_k \to 0} [E + P(\tau_n)\Delta t_n] \dots [E + P(\tau_2)\Delta t_2][E + P(\tau_1)\Delta t_1]. \quad (49')$$

The expression under the limit sign in the right side of the latter equality is a *product integral*.[26] We will call its limit a multiplicative integral and indicate it by the symbol

$$\overline{\int}^t_{t_0} [E + P(t)dt] = \lim_{\Delta t_k \to 0} [E + P(\tau_n)\Delta t_n] \dots [E + P(\tau_1)\Delta t_1]. \quad (50)$$

Formula (49') gives a representation of the matrizer as a multiplicative integral

$$\Omega^t_{t_0}(P) = \overline{\int}^t_{t_0} (E + P\,dt), \quad (51)$$

and equalities (48) and (49) may be used to calculate the matrizer approximately.

The multiplicative integral was first introduced by Volterra in 1887. By using this concept, Volterra constructed an original infinitesimal calculus for matrix functions (see [67]).[27]

[25] These considerations can be refined by estimation of the terms which we are indicating by (*).

[26] Analogous to the approximating sum defining an ordinary integral.

[27] The multiplicative integral ("Produkt-Integral" in German) was used by Schlesinger to investigate systems of linear differential equations with analytic coefficients; see also [57, 60, 61].

The multiplicative integral (50) exists not only for a function $P(t)$ which is continuous in the interval of integration, but also under considerably more general hypotheses (see [4]).

All the special properties of a multiplicative integral arise from the fact that the various values of the matrix function $P(t)$ under the integral are not permutable. In the very special case when all these values are permutable

$$P(t')P(t'') = P(t'')P(t') \quad (t', t'' \in (t_0, t))$$

the multiplicative integral, as seen from (48′) and (51), reduces to the matrix

$$\exp \int_{t_0}^{t} P(t)\, dt.$$

Now let us introduce the *multiplicative derivative*

$$D_t X = \frac{dX}{dt} X^{-1}. \tag{52}$$

The operations D_t and $\overline{\int}_{t_0}^{t}$ are inverse operations:
  If

$$D_t X = P,$$

then [28]

$$X = \overline{\int}_{t_2}^{t} (E + P\, dt) \cdot C \quad (C = X(t_0))$$

and vice versa. The latter formula can also be written as follows:[29]

$$\overline{\int}_{t_0}^{t} (E + P\, dt) = X(t)\, X(t_0)^{-1}. \tag{53}$$

We leave it to the reader to check the validity of the following differential and integral formulas:[30]

---

[28] Here the arbitrary constant matrix C corresponds to the additive arbitrary constant in the ordinary indefinite integral.

[29] Analogous to the formula $\int_{t_0}^{t} P\, dt = X(t) - X(t_0)$ in the case where $dX/dt = P$.

[30] These formulas can be derived directly from the definition of the multiplicative derivative and integral (see [67]). However, the integral formulas are obtained more quickly and simply if the multiplicative integral is considered as a matrizer, and use is made of the properties of the matrizer expounded in the preceding section (see [60, 61]).

Differential formulas

I. $D_t(XY) = D_t(X) + XD_t(Y)X^{-1},$
$D_t(XC) = D_t(X),$
$D_t(CY) = CD_t(Y)C^{-1}$ (C is a constant matrix).

II.[31] $D_t(X') = X'(D_t X)' X'^{-1}.$

III. $D_t(X^{-1}) = -X^{-1}D_t(X)X = -(D_t(X'))',$
$D_t(X'^{-1}) = -(D_t(X))'.$

Integral formulas

IV. $\displaystyle \overline{\int}_{t_0}^t (E + P\,dt) = \overline{\int}_{t_1}^t (E + P\,dt)\,\overline{\int}_{t_0}^{t_1} (E + P\,dt).$

V. $\displaystyle \overline{\int}_{t_0}^t (E + P\,dt) = \left[\,\overline{\int}_t^{t_0}(E+P\,dt)\right]^{-1}.$

VI. $\displaystyle \overline{\int}_{t_0}^t (E + CPC^{-1}\,dt) = C\,\overline{\int}_{t_0}^t (E + P\,dt)C^{-1}$

$\qquad\qquad\qquad\qquad\qquad$ (C is a constant matrix).

VII.[32] $\displaystyle \overline{\int}_{t_0}^t [E + (Q + D_t X)\,dt] = X(t)\overline{\int}_{t_0}^t (E + X^{-1}QX\,dt)X(t_0)^{-1}.$

Let us derive another important formula which gives an estimate of the modulus [33] of the difference between two multiplicative integrals:

VIII. $\displaystyle \operatorname{mod}\left[\,\overline{\int}_{t_0}^t (E + P\,dt) - \overline{\int}_{t_0}^t (E + Q\,dt)\right]$

$\qquad\qquad \leqq n^{-1}\exp\{nq(t - t_0)\}\,[\exp\{nd(t - t_0)\} - 1]I \qquad (t > t_0),$

if

$\qquad\qquad \operatorname{mod} Q \leqq qI,\ \operatorname{mod}(P - Q) \leqq d \cdot I,\ I = (1)$

(where q, d are nonnegative numbers, and n is the order of the matrices P and Q).

[31] The symbol $'$ indicates forming of the transposed matrix.

[32] Formula VII can be considered as the analog of the formula for integration by parts in ordinary (nonmultiplicative) integration. Formula VII follows from formula 2, Section 5.

[33] See p. 153 for definition of the modulus of a matrix and also the relation $\leqq$ between matrices.

Let us denote by D the difference $P - Q$. Then

$$P = Q + D, \ \text{mod} \ D \leqq d \cdot I.$$

If we consider the multiplicative integral as a matrizer and apply the expansion (40) of the matrizer in a series, we find:

$$\overline{\int}_{t_0}^{t} [E + (Q + D) \, dt] - \overline{\int}_{t_0}^{t} (E + Q \, dt)$$

$$= \int_{t_0}^{t} D \, dt + \int_{t_0}^{t} D \, dt \int_{t_0}^{t} Q \, dt + \int_{t_0}^{t} Q \, dt \int_{t_0}^{t} D \, dt + \int_{t_0}^{t} D \, dt \int_{0}^{t} D \, dt + \ldots$$

From this expansion, it is seen that

$$\text{mod} \left\{ \overline{\int}_{t_0}^{t} [E + (Q + D) \, dt] - \overline{\int}_{t_0}^{t} (E + Q \, dt) \right\}$$

$$\leqq \overline{\int}_{t_0}^{t} [E + (\text{mod} \, Q + \text{mod} \, D) \, dt] - \overline{\int}_{t_0}^{t} (E + \text{mod} \, Q) \, dt$$

$$\leqq \overline{\int}_{t_0}^{t} [E + (q + d) I \, dt] - \overline{\int}_{t_0}^{t} [E + qI] \, dt$$

$$= \exp \{ (q + d) I (t - t_0) \} - \exp \{ qI (t - t_0) \}$$

$$= \exp \{ qI (t - t_0) \} [\exp \{ d \cdot I (t - t_0 \} - E]$$

$$\leqq \frac{1}{n} \exp \{ nq(t - t_0) \} [\exp \{ nd(t - t_0) \} - 1] I.$$

Now let the matrices P and Q depend on a certain parameter α

$$P = P(t, \, \alpha), \quad Q = Q(t, \, \alpha)$$

and let

$$\lim_{\alpha \to \alpha_0} P(t, \, \alpha) = \lim_{\alpha \to \alpha_0} Q(t, \, \alpha) = P_0(t)$$

where the limits are uniform with respect to t in the interval $(t_0, \, t)$ under consideration. In addition, let us assume that for $\alpha \to \alpha_0$ the matrix $Q(t, \, \alpha)$ is dominated in modulus by the matrix qI, where q is a positive constant. Then, if we set

$$d(\alpha) = \max_{1 \leqq i, \, k \leqq n, \, t_0 \leqq \tau \leqq t} |p_{ik}(\tau, \, \alpha) - q_{ik}(\tau, \, \alpha)|,$$

we will have:

$$\lim_{\alpha \to \alpha_0} d(\alpha) = 0.$$

Therefore Formula VIII yields

$$\lim_{\alpha \to \alpha_0} \left[\overline{\int}_{t_0!}^{t} (E + P \, dt) - \overline{\int}_{t_0}^{t} (E + Q \, dt) \right] = 0.$$

In particular, if Q does not depend upon α $[Q(t, \alpha) = P_0(t)]$, we obtain:

$$\lim_{\alpha \to \alpha_0} \overline{\int}_{t_0}^{t} [E + P(t, \alpha) \, dt] = \overline{\int}_{t_0}^{t} [E + P_0(t) \, dt],$$

where

$$P_0(t) = \lim_{\alpha \to \alpha_0} P(t, \alpha).$$

§ 7. Differential systems in the complex domain: general properties

We consider the system of differential equations

$$\frac{dx_i}{dz} = \sum_{k=1}^{n} p_{ik}(z) \, x_k. \tag{54}$$

Here the given functions $p_{ik}(z)$, and the unknown functions $x_i(z)$ $(i, k = 1, 2, \ldots, n)$ are assumed to be single-valued analytic functions of the complex argument z, which are regular in a certain domain G of the complex z-plane.

As in Section 1 for real arguments, we introduce the square matrix $P(z) = (p_{ik}(z))_1^n$ and the column matrix $x = (x_1, x_2, \ldots, x_n)$. Then we can write system (54) in the form

$$dx/dz = P(z)x. \tag{54'}$$

We let X be an integral matrix, i.e., a matrix, the columns of which are n linearly independent solutions of system (54). Then in place of (54') we can write

$$dX/dz = P(z) X. \tag{55}$$

The Jacobi formula holds also for a complex argument z:

$$\det X = c \exp \int_{z_0}^{z} \operatorname{Sp} P \, dz. \tag{56}$$

Here, it is assumed that z_0 and all the points of the path along which the line integral [34] is taken are regular points for the single-valued analytical function

$$\mathrm{Sp}\, P(z) = p_{11}(z) + p_{22}(z) + \ldots + p_{nn}(z).$$

The special feature when z is a complex argument consists in the fact that when $P(z)$ is a single-valued function, the integral matrix $X(z)$ can be a multiple-valued function of z.

As an example, let us consider the Cauchy system

$$\frac{dX}{dz} = \frac{U}{z-a}X \qquad (U \text{ is a constant matrix}). \qquad (57)$$

As in the case of a real argument, one of the solutions of this system is the integral matrix (see p. 138)

$$X = \exp\{U \ln (z - a)\} = (z - a)^U. \qquad (58)$$

For the domain G we take the entire z-plane with the exception of the point $z = a$. All points of this domain are regular points of the matrix of coefficients

$$P(z) = \frac{U}{z-a}.$$

If $U \neq 0$, then the point $z = a$ is a singular point (simple pole) for the matrix function

$$P(z) = \frac{U}{z-a}.$$

If we make a single circuit in the positive direction around the point $z = a$, the elements of the matrix (58) return to a new value, which is found by multiplying on the right by the matrix

$$V = \exp (2\pi i U).$$

Using arguments similar to those used for real arguments, we see that two solutions X, $\tilde{X}$ of (58) which are single-valued in a certain portion of the domain G are always connected by means

---

[34] Here and subsequently, the paths of integration are piece-wise smooth curves.

of the formula

$$X = \tilde{X}C$$

where C is a certain constant matrix. This formula will remain valid under analytic continuation of the functions $X(z)$ and $\tilde{X}(z)$ in the domain G.

The theorem on the existence and uniqueness (for given initial conditions) of solutions of system (54) can be proved as in the real case.

We consider a *simply-connected* domain G_1 which is *star-shaped with respect to the point* z_0,[35] which is contained in the domain G, and let the matrix function $P(z)$ be regular [36] in the domain G_1. Let us construct the series

$$E + \int_{z_0}^z P \, dz + \int_{z_0}^z P \, dz \int_{z_0}^z P \, dz + \ldots \quad (59)$$

Since the domain G_1 is simply connected, it follows that each integral occurring in (59) does not depend on the path of integration and is a regular function in the domain G_1. Since the domain G_1 is star-shaped with respect to z_0, then in estimating the moduli of these integrals we can assume that all the integrals are taken along a rectilinear segment connecting the points z_0 and z.

Series (59) converges absolutely and uniformly in any closed portion of the domain G_1, which contains the point z_0, as follows from the convergence of the dominating series

$$1 + lM + \frac{n}{2!} l^2 M^2 + \frac{n^2}{3!} l^3 M^3 + \ldots$$

Here M is the upper bound of the modulus of matrix $P(z)$, and l is the upper bound of the distances of point z from point z_0, and both bounds refer to the closed portion of domain G_1 under consideration.

[35] A domain is called *star-shaped with respect to the point* z_0, if any segment connecting an arbitrary point z of the domain with the point z_0 lies entirely in the given domain.

[36] That is, all the elements $p_{ik}(z)$ ($i, k = 1, 2, \ldots, n$) of the matrix $P(z)$ are regular functions in the domain G_1.

By differentiating term by term, it can be checked that the sum of series (59) is a solution of equation (55). This solution is normalized, since for $z = z_0$ it becomes the identity matrix E. As in the real case, the single-valued normalized solution of system (55) is called the matrizer and denoted by $\Omega_{z_0}^z (P)$. Thus, we have a representation of the matrizer in the domain G_1 in the form of the series [37]

$$\Omega_{z_0}^z (P) = E + \int_{z_0}^z P \, dz + \int_{z_0}^z P \, dz \int_{z_0}^z P \, dz + \ldots \qquad (60)$$

Properties 1—4 of the matrizer which were established in Section 5, carry over automatically to the case of a complex argument.

An arbitrary solution of equation (55), which is regular in domain G and which becomes the matrix X_0 for $z = z_0$, can be represented in the form

$$X = \Omega_{z_0}^z (P) \cdot C \quad (C = X_0). \qquad (61)$$

Formula (61) applies to every single-valued solution which is regular in the neighborhood of the point z_0, if z_0 is a regular point for the matrix of coefficients $P(z)$. By analytic continuation, these solutions give all solutions of equation (55), i.e., equation (55) cannot have solutions for which z_0 would be a singular point.

To study analytic continuation of the matrizer in the domain G, it is convenient to employ the multiplicative integral.

§ 8. Multiplicative integrals in the complex domain

A multiplicative integral along a certain curve in the complex plane is defined in the following manner.

Let a certain path L and a matrix function $P(z)$, which is continuous on the curve L be given. Let us subdivide the path

---

[37] The proof presented for the existence of a normalized solution and its representation in domain G_1 by means of series (60) remains valid if, instead of a star-shaped domain, a more general assumption is made: for every closed portion of the domain G_1 there exists a positive number l, such that any point z of this closed portion can be connected with z_0 by a path of length at most l.

L into n parts $(z_0, z_1) (z_1, z_2) \ldots (z_{n-1}, z)$; here z_0 is the initial point, $z_n = z$ is the end of the path, and $z_1, z_2, \ldots, z_{n-1}$ are intermediate partition points. On the segment $z_{k-1} \, z_k$ of the path, we select an arbitrary point ζ_k and set $\Delta z_k = z_k - z_{k-1}$; $k = 1, 2, \ldots, n$. Then, by definition,

$$\overline{\int}_L [E + P(z) dz] = \lim_{\Delta z_k \to 0} [E + P(\zeta_n) \Delta z_n] \ldots [E + P(\zeta_1) \Delta z_1].$$

Comparing this definition with the definition on p. 156, we see that the new definition coincides with the previous one in the special case where the path L is a segment of the real axis. However, even in the general case, when the path L is an arbitrary path in the complex plane, the new definition can be reduced to the old one by changing the variable of integration. If

$$z = z(t)$$

is the parametric equation of the path, where $z(t)$ is contin ous in the interval (t_0, t) and has a piece-wise continuous derivative dz/dt in this interval, then, as is easily seen,

$$\overline{\int}_L [E + P(z) dz] = \overline{\int}_{t_0}^{t} \left\{ E + P[z(t)] \frac{dz}{dt} dt \right\}.$$

This formula shows that a multiplicative integral exists along an arbitrary path, if the matrix $P(z)$ under the integral is continuous along this path.[38] The multiplicative derivative is defined by the previous formula

$$D_z X = \frac{dX}{dz} X^{-1}.$$

Here, it is assumed that $X(z)$ is an analytic function.

---

[38] See footnote 26 (p. 156). Even in case $P(z)$ is a continuous function along L, the function $P[z(t)] \, dz/dt$ may be piece-wise continuous. In this case, we can split the interval (t_0, t) into partial intervals, in each of which the derivative dz/dt, is continuous, and understand the integral from t_0 to t as being the sum of the integrals along these subintervals.

All the differential formulas (I—III) of the preceding section carry over without change to the case of a complex argument. As for integral formulas (IV—VI), their form is somewhat modified:

IV'. $\displaystyle\overline{\int}_{(L'+L'')} (E + P\,dz) = \overline{\int}_{L''} (E + P\,dz)\,\overline{\int}_{L'} (E + P\,dz).$

V'. $\displaystyle\overline{\int}_{-L} (E + P\,dz) = \left[\overline{\int}_{L} (E + P\,dz)\right]^{-1}.$

VI'. $\displaystyle\overline{\int}_{L} (E + CPC^{-1}\,dz) = C\,\overline{\int}_{L} (E + P\,dz)\,C^{-1}.$ (C is a constant matrix)

In formula IV' the symbol $L' + L''$ denotes the composite path obtained by connecting paths L' and L'', assuming L'' has as initial point the end of path L'. In formula V', $-L$ denotes the path which differs from path L only in direction of traverse.

Formula VII now assumes the form

VII'. $\displaystyle\overline{\int}_{L} [E + (Q + D_z X)\,dz] = X(z)\,\overline{\int}_{L} (E + X^{-1}QX\,dz)\,X(z_0)^{-1}.$

Here $X(z_0)$ and $X(z)$ in the right side denote respectively the values of $X(z)$ in the initial and final points of path L.

Formula VIII is now replaced by the formula

VIII'. $\displaystyle\mathrm{mod}\left[\int_{L} (E + P\,dz) - \int_{L} (E + Q\,dz)\right]$

$$\leq \frac{1}{n}\exp{(nql)}\,[\exp{(nd\cdot l)} - 1]I,$$

where $\mathrm{mod}\,Q \leq qI$, $\mathrm{mod}\,(P - Q) \leq d\cdot I$, $I = (1)$, and l is the length of the path L.

Formula VIII' can be obtained directly from formula VIII if we make a change of variable in VIII, taking as new variable of integration the length of the arc s along the path L (so that $|\,dz/ds\,| = 1$).

As for a real argument, there is a close relation between the multiplicative integral and the matrizer when the argument is complex.

Let $P(z)$ be a single-valued analytic matrix function, regular in the domain G, and let G_0 be a simply-connected domain containing point z_0 and contained in G. Then the matrizer $\Omega_{z_0}^z(P)$ will be a regular function of z in the domain G_0.

We connect the points z_0 and z by an arbitrary path L, which lies entirely within G_0, and we select the intermediate points $z_1, z_2, \ldots, z_{n-1}$ on L. Then, by applying the equality

$$\Omega_{z_0}^z = \Omega_{z_{n-1}}^z \ldots \Omega_{z_1}^{z_2} \Omega_{z_0}^{z_1},$$

in exactly the same manner as in Section 6 (p. 155), we obtain in the limit:

$$\Omega_{z_0}^z(P) = \overline{\int}_L (E + P\,dz) = \overline{\int}_{z_0}^z (E + P\,dz). \tag{62}$$

It is seen from this formula that the multiplicative integral does not depend on the shape of the path, but depends only on the initial and end points of the path, provided the entire path of integration lies in a simply-connected domain G_0, in which the function $P(z)$ under the integral is regular. In particular, for a closed contour L, lying in the simply-connected domain G_0, we have:

$$\overline{\oint} (E + P\,dz) = E. \tag{63}$$

This formula is an analog of the well-known Cauchy theorem, according to which an ordinary (nonmultiplicative) integral along a closed contour is equal to zero, if this contour lies in a simply-connected domain in which the function under the integral is regular.

The representation of the matrizer in the form of the multiplicative integral (62) can be used to continue the matrizer analytically along an arbitrary path L in the domain G. In this case, the formula

$$X = \overline{\int}_{z_0}^z (E + P\,dz)X_0 \tag{64}$$

gives all these branches of the many-valued integral matrix X of the differential equation $dX/dz = PX$, which reduce to X_0 on some branch for $z = z_0$. The various branches are obtained by choosing various paths connecting z_0 and z.

According to the Jacobi formula (56)

$$\det X = (\det X_0) \exp \int_{z_0}^{z} \text{Sp } P \, dz$$

and, in particular, for $X_0 = E$

$$\det \overline{\int}_{z_0}^{z} (E + P \, dz) = \exp \int_{z_0}^{z} \text{Sp } P \, dz. \tag{65}$$

From this formula it follows that the multiplicative integral is always a nonsingular matrix, whenever the path of integration lies entirely in a domain in which the function $P(z)$ is regular.

If L is an arbitrary closed path in G, and G is not a simply-connected domain, then equality (63) may not hold. Also, in this case the value of the integral

$$\overline{\oint} (E + P \, dz)$$

is not determined by the function being integrated and the closed path of integration L, but depends also on the choice of the initial point of integration z_0 on the curve L. In fact, let us select two points z_0 and z_1 on the closed curve L and the portions of the path from z_0 to z_1 and from z_1 to z_0 (in the direction of integration) respectively, by L_1 and L_2. Then, by formula IV′ [39]

$$\overline{\oint}_{z_0} = \overline{\int}_{L_2} \cdot \overline{\int}_{L_1}, \quad \overline{\oint}_{z_1} = \overline{\int}_{L_1} \cdot \overline{\int}_{L_2}$$

and, consequently,

$$\overline{\oint}_{z_1} = \overline{\int}_{L_1} \cdot \overline{\oint}_{z_0} \cdot \overline{\int}_{L_1}^{-1}. \tag{66}$$

Formula (66) indicates that the symbol $\overline{\oint} (E + P \, dz)$ determines a certain matrix to within a similarity transformation, i.e., determines only the elementary divisors of a certain matrix.

We consider the element $X(z)$ of solution (64) in the neighborhood of the point z_0. Let L be an arbitrary closed path in G, beginning and terminating at the point z_0. By analytic continuation along L, the element $X(z)$ is carried into a certain element

[39] Here, in order to simplify the notation, we are omitting the expression $E + P \, dz$, which is the same in all integrals.

$\tilde{X}(z)$. Note that the new element $\tilde{X}(z)$ will satisfy the same differential equation (55), since $P(z)$ is a single-valued function in G. Therefore,

$$\tilde{X} = XV,$$

where V is a certain nonsingular constant matrix. From formula (64), the relation

$$X(z_0) = \oint_{z_0} \overleftarrow{(E + P\,dz)}X_0$$

is obtained.

Comparing this equality with the previous one, we find:

$$V = X_0^{-1} \oint_{z_0} \overleftarrow{(E + P\,dz)}\,X_0. \qquad (67)$$

In particular, for the matrizer, $X = \Omega_{z_0}^z$, we have $X_0 = E$, and then

$$V = \oint_{z_0} \overleftarrow{(E + P\,dz)}. \qquad (68)$$

§ 9. Isolated singular points

Let us consider the behavior of a solution (i.e., of a matrix integral) in the neighborhood of the isolated singular point a.

Let the matrix function $P(z)$ be regular for values of z which satisfy the inequalities

$$0 < |z - a| < R.$$

These values of z fill out a doubly-connected domain G. The matrix function $P(z)$ can be expanded in a Laurent series

$$P(z) = \sum_{n=-\infty}^{+\infty} P_n(z - a)^n \qquad (69)$$

in the domain G.

After a single circuit in the positive direction about a, along path L, the element $X(z)$ of the integral matrix is carried into the element

$$X^+(z) = X(z)V,$$

where V is a certain constant nonsingular matrix.

Let U be a constant matrix related to the matrix V by the equality

$$V = \exp{(2\pi i U)}. \tag{70}$$

Then the matrix function $(z - a)^U$, after a single circuit along L, is carried into $(z - a)^U V$. Therefore, the matrix function

$$F(z) = X(z)(z - a)^{-U} \tag{71}$$

which is analytic in the domain G, is carried into itself (remains unchanged) [40] by analytic continuation along L. Therefore, the matrix function $F(z)$ is regular in G and can be expanded into a Laurent series

$$F(z) = \sum_{n=-\infty}^{+\infty} F_n (z - a)^n. \tag{72}$$

From (71) it follows that:

$$X(z) = F(z)(z - a)^U. \tag{73}$$

Thus, any integral function $X(z)$ can be represented in form (73), where the single-valued function $F(z)$ and the constant matrix U depend on the matrix of coefficients $P(z)$. However, it is a complicated problem constructively to determine the matrix U and the matrices F_n of coefficients in series (72) in terms of the coefficients P_n of series (69) in the general case.

In Section 10 we shall completely analyze the special case of this problem in which

$$P(z) = \sum_{n=-1}^{\infty} P_n (z - a)^n.$$

In this case, point a is called a *regular singular point* of system (55).

If expansion (69) has the form

$$P(z) = \sum_{n=-q}^{\infty} P_n (z - a)^n \quad (q > 1;\ P_{-q} \neq 0),$$

then the point a is called an *irregular singular point of pole type*.

[40] Hence it follows that the function $F(z)$ returns to its initial value when any closed circuit in G is traversed.

Finally, if series (69) has an infinite number of (matrix) coefficients P_n which are different from zero for negative values of n, then the point a is called an *essential singular point* of the differential system.

From formula (73) it follows that on traversing *any* circuit once in the positive direction (along a certain closed path L), the matrix integral $X(z)$ is multiplied on the right by the matrix

$$V = \exp(2\pi i U).$$

If this circuit originates (and terminates) at the point z_0, then according to (67),

$$V = X(z_0)^{-1} \oint_{z_0} \overline{(E + P \, dz)} X(z_0). \tag{74}$$

If in place of integral matrix $X(z)$ we consider any other integral matrix $X(z) = X(z) C$ (C is a constant matrix, $\det C \neq 0$), then, as seen from (74), the matrix V will be replaced by the similar matrix

$$\hat{V} = C^{-1} V C.$$

Thus, the "integral substitutions" V of the given system form a class of matrices which are mutually similar.

From formula (74) it also follows that the integral

$$\oint_{z_0} \overline{(E + P \, dz)} \tag{75}$$

is determined by the initial point of circuit z_0 and does not depend on the shape of the closed curve which makes the circuit.[41] If we change the point z_0, then the various values of integral (75) obtained are similar to each other.[42]

It is possible to prove these properties of integral (75) directly. In fact, let L and L' be two closed paths in G about the point $z = a$; let their initial points be z_0 and z_0' (see Figure 1). The doubly-connected domain contained between L and L' can be made simply-connected by making a cut from z_0 to z_0'.

---

[41] With the condition, of course, that the path of integration goes around point a once in the positive direction.

[42] This follows from formula (74), and also from formula (66).

We denote the integral along the cut by

$$T = \int_{z_0'}^{\overline{z_0}} (E + P \, dz).$$

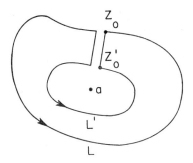

Fig. 1

Since the multiplicative integral along the closed contour of a simply-connected domain is equal to E, then

$$\overline{\int}_{L'} T \, \overline{\int}_{L}^{-1} T^{-1} = E$$

whence

$$\overline{\int}_{L'} = T \, \overline{\int}_{L} T^{-1}.$$

Thus, (as for the matrix V), the integral $\overline{\oint} (E + P \, dz)$ is determined to within a similarity transformation, and we will sometimes write equality (74) as:

$$V = \overline{\oint} (E + P \, dz),$$

where the sign of equality means that the elementary divisors of the matrices in the left and the right sides of the equality coincide.

As an example, let us consider a system with a regular singular point,

$$dX/dz = P(z)X$$

where

$$P(z) = \frac{P_{-1}}{z - a} + \sum_{n=0}^{+\infty} P_n(z - a)^n.$$

Let

$$Q(z) = \frac{P_{-1}}{z - a}.$$

Applying formula VIII' of the preceding section, we shall estimate the modulus of the difference

$$D = \overline{\oint} (E + P\,dz) - \oint (E + Q\,dz), \qquad (76)$$

where the path of integration is a circle of radius r ($r < R$) traversed in the positive direction. Then for

$$\text{mod } P_{-1} \leq p_{-1}I, \text{ mod } \sum_{\substack{|z-a|=r \\ n=0}}^{\infty} P_n(z-a)^n \leq d(r)I, \quad I = (1),$$

we can set

$$q = \frac{p_{-1}}{r}, \quad d = d(r), \quad l = 2\pi r,$$

in formula VIII', and obtain

$$\text{mod } D \leq \frac{1}{n} \exp\,(2\pi p_{-1})\,[\exp\,\{2\pi n r d(r)\} - 1]I.$$

Hence it is obvious that [43]

$$\lim_{r\to 0} D = 0. \qquad (77)$$

On the other hand, the system

$$dY/dz = QY$$

is a Cauchy system, and in this case, for any choice of the initial point z_0 of the circuit and for any $r < R$

$$\overline{\oint}_{z_0} (E + Q\,dz) = \exp\,(2\pi i P_{-1}).$$

---

[43] Here we note that for proper choice of $d(r)$,

$$\lim_{r\to 0} d(r) = d_0,$$

where d_0 is the maximum of the moduli of the elements of matrix P_0.

Therefore, from (76) and (77), the relation

$$\lim_{r \to 0} \overline{\oint}_{z_0} (E + P \, dz) = \exp (2\pi i P_{-1}) \tag{78}$$

follows. But the elementary divisors of the integral $\overline{\oint}_{z_0} (E + P \, dz)$ do not depend on z_0 and r and are the same as the elementary divisors of the substitution matrix V.

Hence, Volterra in his famous memoir (see [66]), and also in book [67] (pp. 117—120) draws the conclusion that the matrices V and $\exp (2\pi i P_{-1})$ are similar, and further that the substitution matrix V is determined by the matrix of "residues" P_{-1} to within similarity.

This assertion of Volterra is erroneous.

From (74) and (78), the only conclusion that can be drawn is that *the characteristic numbers of the integral substitution matrix V coincide with the characteristic numbers of the matrix* $\exp (2\pi i P_{-1})$. However, the elementary divisors of these matrices may be different. Thus, for example, the matrix

$$\begin{bmatrix} \alpha & r \\ 0 & \alpha \end{bmatrix}$$

has the one elementary divisor $(\lambda - \alpha)^2$ (for any $r \neq 0$), but the limit of this matrix for $r \to 0$, i.e., the matrix

$$\begin{bmatrix} \alpha & 0 \\ 0 & \alpha \end{bmatrix}.$$

has the two elementary divisors $\lambda - \alpha$, $\lambda - \alpha$.

Thus, the assertion of Volterra does not follow from (74) and (78). But in general it is not true, as shown by the following example.

Let $P(z)$ be defined as follows:

$$P(z) = \begin{bmatrix} 0 & 0 \\ 0 & -1 \end{bmatrix} \frac{1}{z} + \begin{bmatrix} 0 & 1 \\ 0 & 0 \end{bmatrix}$$

The corresponding system of differential equations has the form:

$$\frac{dx_1}{dz} = x_2, \qquad \frac{dx_2}{dz} = -\frac{x_2}{z}.$$

Integrating this system, we find that:

$$x_1 = c \ln z + d, \qquad x_2 = \frac{c}{z}.$$

The matrix integral

$$X(z) = \begin{bmatrix} \ln z & 1 \\ z^{-1} & 0 \end{bmatrix}$$

is multiplied on the right by the matrix

$$V = \begin{bmatrix} 1 & 0 \\ 2\pi i & 1 \end{bmatrix}$$

if the singular point $z = 0$ is encircled once in the positive direction. This matrix has the one elementary divisor $(\lambda - 1)^2$. On the other hand, the matrix

$$\exp{(2\pi i P_{-1})} = \exp{\left(2\pi i \begin{bmatrix} 0 & 0 \\ 0 & -1 \end{bmatrix}\right)} = \begin{bmatrix} 1 & 0 \\ 0 & 1 \end{bmatrix} = E$$

has the two elementary divisors $\lambda - 1$, $\lambda - 1$.

Now let us consider the case where the matrix $P(z)$ has a finite number of negative powers of $z - a$ (i.e., a is a regular singular point or an irregular singular point of pole type):

$$P(z) = \frac{P_{-q}}{(z-a)^q} + \ldots + \frac{P_{-1}}{z-a} + \sum_{n=0}^{\infty} P_n (z-a)^n \quad (q \geq 1;\ P_{-q} \neq 0).$$

Let us transform the given system

$$dX/dz = PX, \tag{79}$$

by means of the substitution

$$X = A(z)Y, \tag{80}$$

where $A(z)$ is a matrix function which is regular at the point $z = 0$ and assumes the value E at this point:

$$A(z) = E + A_1(z - a) + A_2(z - a)^2 + \ldots$$

the power series in the right side converging for, $|z - a| < r_1$.

The well-known American mathematician G. D. Birkhoff

published a theorem in 1913, (see [5]), which states that it is always possible to find a transformation (80) such that the matrix of coefficients of the transformed system

$$dY/dz = P^*(z)Y \qquad (79')$$

will contain only negative powers of $z - a$:

$$P^*(z) = \frac{P^*_{-q}}{(z-a)^q} + \ldots + \frac{P^*_{-1}}{z-a}.$$

Birkhoff's theorem, together with a complete proof, is presented in the book *Ordinary Differential Equations*, by E. L. Ince.[44] In the same book, an investigation of the behavior of a solution of an arbitrary system in the neighborhood of a singular point is made on the basis of the "canonical" systems (79').

However, Birkhoff's proof contains an error, and the theorem itself is not true. As a counter-example, we can take the example used above to refute the assertion of Volterra.[45] In this example, $q = 1$, $a = 0$ and

$$P_{-1} = \begin{bmatrix} 0 & 0 \\ 0 & -1 \end{bmatrix}, \quad P_0 = \begin{bmatrix} 0 & 1 \\ 0 & 0 \end{bmatrix}, \quad P_n = 0 \quad (n = 1, 2, \ldots).$$

Applying Birkhoff's theorem and substituting the product AY for X in (79), after replacing dY/dz by $z^{-1}P^*_{-1}Y$ and cancelling Y we obtain

$$A \frac{P_{-1}}{z} + \frac{dA}{dz} = PA.$$

Equating the coefficients of z^{-1} and the constant terms, we find:

$$P^*_{-1} = P_{-1}, \quad A_1 P_{-1} - P_{-1}A_1 + A_1 = P_0.$$

---

[44] See [29], pp. 470—474. Birkhoff and Ince formulate the theorem for the singular point $z = \infty$. This is not a restriction at all, since any singular point $z = a$ can be reduced to $z = \infty$ by means of the transformation $z' = (z - a)^{-1}$.

[45] In the case $q = 1$, Birkhoff's erroneous assertion is essentially that of Volterra (see p. 173).

Setting A_1 equal to $\begin{bmatrix} a & b \\ c & d \end{bmatrix}$, we obtain:

$$\begin{bmatrix} a & 0 \\ c & 0 \end{bmatrix} - \begin{bmatrix} 0 & 0 \\ -c & -d \end{bmatrix} = \begin{bmatrix} 0 & 1 \\ 0 & 0 \end{bmatrix}.$$

This is a contradictory equality.

In the following section, we will expound a canonical form to which system (79) can be transformed by means of transformation (80) for a regular singular point.

§ 10. Regular singular points

In order to investigate the behavior of a solution in the neighborhood of a singular point, we can assume without loss of generality that the singular point is the point $z = 0$.[46]

1. Let the system

$$dX/dz = P(z)X, \tag{81}$$

be given; let $P(z)$ be defined by

$$P(z) = \frac{P_{-1}}{z} + \sum_{m=0}^{\infty} P_m z^m \tag{82}$$

and let the series $\sum_{m=0}^{\infty} P_m z^m$ converge inside the circle $|z| < r$.

Let us set

$$X = A(z) Y, \tag{83}$$

where

$$A(z) = E + A_1 z + A_2 z^2 + \ldots. \tag{84}$$

Putting aside for the present the problem of the convergence of series (84), we will attempt to determine the matrix coefficients A_m of this series in such a way that the transformed system

$$dY/dz = P^*(z)Y, \tag{85}$$

where

---

[46] By the transformation $z' = z - a$ or $z' = z^{-1}$, any finite point $z = a$ or $z = \infty$, respectively, can be reduced to the point $z' = 0$.

$$P^*(z) = \frac{P^*_{-1}}{z} + \sum_{m=0}^{\infty} P^*_m z^m, \tag{86}$$

has a simplest possible ("canonical") form.[47]
Substituting the product AY for X in (81) and applying (85), we obtain:

$$A(z) P^*(z) Y + \frac{dA}{dz} Y = P(z) A(z) Y.$$

Multiplying both sides of this equality on the right by Y^{-1}, we find:

$$P(z)A(z) - A(z)P^*(z) = dA/dz.$$

If we substitute the series (82), (84), and (86) for $P(z)$, $A(z)$, and $P^*(z)$ and equate the coefficients of like powers of z in the left and right sides of the equality, we obtain an infinite system of matrix equations for the unknown coefficients A_1, A_2, ...:[48]

$$P_{-1} = P^*_{-1},$$

$$P_{-1}A_1 - A_1(P_{-1} + E) + P_0 = P^*_0,$$

$$P_{-1}A_2 - A_2(P_{-1} + 2E) + P_0 A_1 - A_1 P^*_0 + P_1 = P^*_1, \tag{87}$$

. . . .

$$P_{-1}A_{m+1} - A_{m+1}[P_{-1} + (m+1)E]$$
$$+ P_0 A_m - A_m P^*_0 + P_1 A_{m-1} - A_{m-1} P^*_1 + \ldots + P_m = P^*_m.$$

2. We consider several cases.
1. The matrix P_1 does not have distinct characteristic numbers which differ by an integer.
In this case, for any $k = 1, 2, 3, \ldots$ the matrices P_{-1} and $P_{-1} + kE$ do not have any characteristic numbers in common;

---

[47] We will attempt to arrange that a finite number (and as few as possible) of the coefficients P^*_m are different from zero in series (86).
[48] In all equations, starting with the second, we substituted the matrix P_{-1} for P^*_{-1} on the basis of the first equation.

therefore [49] the matrix equation

$$P_{-1}U - U(P_{-1} + kE) = T$$

has one and only one solution for any right member T.
We will denote this solution by

$$\Phi_k(P_{-1}, T).$$

Therefore, in equations (87) we can set all the matrices
P_m^* $(m = 0, 1, 2, \ldots)$ equal to zero and determine $A_1, A_2, \ldots$
successively by means of the equalities

$$A_1 = \Phi_1(P_{-1}, -P_0), \quad A_2 = \Phi_2(P_{-1}, -P_1 - P_0 A_1), \ldots.$$

Then the transformed system is a Cauchy system:

$$\frac{dY}{dz} = \frac{P_{-1}}{z} Y,$$

and for that reason the solution X of the initial system (81)
has the form [50]

$$X = A(z) z^{P_{-1}}. \tag{88}$$

2. *Included among the characteristic numbers of the matrix
P_{-1} are numbers which differ by a positive integer; but the matrix
P_{-1} has simple structure (P_{-1} is diagonable).*

---

[49] This can be proved as follows. The proposition is equivalent to the
assertion that the matrix equation

$$P_{-1}U = U(P_{-1} + kE) \tag{*}$$

has only the zero solution $U = 0$. Since the matrices P_{-1} and $P_{-1} + kE$
do not have common characteristic numbers, then there exists a polynomial $f(\lambda)$ for which

$$f(P_{-1}) = 0, \qquad f(P_{-1} + kE) = E.$$

But it follows from (*) that:

$$f(P_{-1})U = Uf(P_{-1} + kE).$$

Hence $U = 0$.

[50] Formula (88) determines one matrix integral of system (81). An
arbitrary matrix integral is obtained from (88) by multiplying on the right
by an arbitrary constant nonsingular matrix C.

Let us denote the characteristic numbers of the matrix P_{-1} by $\lambda_1, \lambda_2, \ldots, \lambda_n$ arranged so that the following inequalities hold:

$$\operatorname{Re} \lambda_1 \geqq \operatorname{Re} \lambda_2 \geqq \ldots \geqq \operatorname{Re} \lambda_n. \tag{89}$$

Without loss of generality, we can replace the matrix P_{-1} by any matrix which is similar to it in the following way. We multiply both sides of equation (81) on the left by the nonsingular matrix T, and on the right by T^{-1}. This has the effect of replacing all P_m by $T P_m T^{-1}$ ($m = -1, 0, 1, 2, \ldots$). (At the same time, X is replaced by TXT^{-1}.) Therefore, we can assume in the case under consideration that P_{-1} is a diagonal matrix:

$$P_{-1} = (\lambda_i \delta_{ik})_1^n. \tag{90}$$

Let us introduce symbols for the elements of the matrices P_m, P_m^* and A_m:

$$P_m = (p_{ik}^{(m)})_1^n, \; P_m^* = (p_{ik}^{(m*)})_1^n, \; A_m = (x_{ik}^{(m)})_1^n. \tag{91}$$

To determine A_1, we apply the second of equations (87). This matrix equation can be replaced by the scalar equations

$$(\lambda_i - \lambda_k - 1)x_{ik}^{(1)} + p_{ik}^{(0)} = p_{ik}^{(0*)} \quad (i, \, k = 1, 2, \ldots, n). \tag{92}$$

If none of the differences $\lambda_i - \lambda_k$ is equal to unity, we can set P_0^* equal to zero. Then from the second equation in (87),[51]

$$A_1 = \Phi_1(P_{-1}, \, -P_0).$$

In this case, the elements of matrix A_1 are uniquely determined by equations (92):

$$x_{ik}^{(1)} = -\frac{p_{ik}^{(0)}}{\lambda_i - \lambda_k - 1} \quad (i, \, k = 1, 2, \ldots, n). \tag{93}$$

If for some i, k [52]

$$\lambda_i - \lambda_k = 1$$

hen the corresponding $p_{ik}^{(0*)}$ is determined from (92):

[51] We are using the notation which was introduced in the discussion of case 1.

[52] As we see from (89), this is possible only for $i < k$.

$$p_{ik}^{(0*)} = p_{ik}^{(0)}$$

and the corresponding $x_{ik}^{(1)}$ is arbitrary.

For any i, k for which $\lambda_i - \lambda_k \neq 1$, we set:

$$p_{ik}^{(0*)} = 0,$$

and the corresponding $x_{ik}^{(1)}$ is found from formula (93).

Having determined A_1, we turn to the determination of A_2 from the third equation (87). We can replace this matrix equation by the system of n^2 scalar equations:

$$(\lambda_i - \lambda_k - 2)x_{ik}^{(2)} = p_{ik}^{(1*)} - p_{ik}^{(1)} - (P_0 A_1 - A_1 P_0^*)_{ik}. \quad (94)$$

Here we proceed just as we did in determining A_1.

If $\lambda_i - \lambda_k \neq 2$, then we set:

$$p_{ik}^{(1*)} = 0,$$

and then from (94) we find:

$$x_{ik}^{(2)} = - \frac{1}{\lambda_i - \lambda_k - 2} [p_{ik}^{(1)} - (P_0 A_1 - A_1 P_0^*)_{ik}].$$

If $\lambda_i - \lambda_k = 2$, then for these values of i and k, it follows from (94) that:

$$p_{ik}^{(1*)} = p_{ik}^{(1)} + (P_0 A_1 - A_1 P_0^*)_{ik}.$$

In this case, $x_{ik}^{(2)}$ is arbitrary.

Continuing this process, we can determine the matrices P_{-1}^*, P_0^*, P_1^*, ... and A_1, A_2, ... seriatim.

It is clear that only a finite number of the matrices P_m^* will be different from zero, and, as is easily seen, the matrix $P^*(z)$ will have the form [53]

---

[53] $P_m^* (m \geq 0)$ can be different from zero only when there exist characteristic numbers λ_i and λ_k of the matrix P_{-1} such that $\lambda_i - \lambda_k - 1 = m$ (and further, from (89), $i < k$). For a given m, some element $p_{ik}^{(m*)} = a_{ik}$ of the matrix P_m^* corresponds to each such equality; this element can be different from zero. All the remaining elements of the matrix P_m are equal to zero.

$$P^*(z) = \begin{bmatrix} \lambda_1 z^{-1}, & a_{12}z^{\lambda_1-\lambda_2-1}, & \ldots, & a_{1n}z^{\lambda_1-\lambda_n-1} \\ 0, & \lambda_2 z^{-1}, & , \ldots, & a_{2n}z^{\lambda_2-\lambda_n-1} \\ \multicolumn{4}{c}{\ldots\ldots\ldots\ldots\ldots\ldots\ldots\ldots} \\ 0, & 0, & , \ldots, & \lambda_n z^{-1} \end{bmatrix}, \tag{95}$$

where $a_{ik} = 0$, if $\lambda_i - \lambda_k$ is not a positive whole number, and

$$a_{ik} = p_{ik}^{(\lambda_i-\lambda_k-1*)},$$

if $\lambda_i - \lambda_k$ is a positive whole number.

Let us denote by m_i the integral part of the number Re λ_i:[54]

$$m_i = [\text{Re } \lambda_i] \quad (i = 1, 2, \ldots, n). \tag{96}$$

Then from (89)

$$m_1 \geq m_2 \geq \ldots \geq m_n.$$

Thus, if $\lambda_i - \lambda_k$ is a whole number, then

$$\lambda_i - \lambda_k = m_i - m_k.$$

Therefore, in the formula for the canonical matrix $P^*(z)$, given by (95), we can substitute $m_i - m_k$ for each difference $\lambda_i - \lambda_k$. Also, we set:

$$\tilde{\lambda}_i = \lambda_i - m_i \quad (i = 1, 2, \ldots, n), \tag{91'}$$

$$M = (m_i \delta_{ik})_1^n, \qquad U = \begin{bmatrix} \tilde{\lambda}_1 & a_{12} & \ldots & a_{1n} \\ 0 & \tilde{\lambda}_2 & \ldots & a_{2n} \\ \multicolumn{4}{c}{\ldots\ldots\ldots\ldots} \\ 0 & 0 & \ldots & \tilde{\lambda}_n \end{bmatrix}. \tag{97}$$

Then from (95) it follows that (see Formula I on p. 158):

$$P^*(z) = z^M \frac{U}{z} z^{-M} + \frac{M}{z} = D_z(z^M z^U).$$

Hence it follows that $Y = z^M z^U$ is a solution of equation (85), and

$$X = A(z)z^M z^U \tag{98}$$

is a solution of equation (81).[55]

---

[54] That is, m_i is the greatest integer not exceeding Re λ_i $(i = 1, 2, \ldots, n)$.

[55] The special form (97) corresponds to the case when the matrix P_{-1} is in canonical form. If the matrix P_{-1} is not in canonical form, then the matrices M and U in (98) are similar to the matrices (97).

3. Let us turn to the general case. As explained above, we can replace the matrix P_{-1} by any matrix that is similar to it, without loss of generality. We will assume that the matrix P_{-1} has the Jordan normal form [56]

$$P_{-1} = \{\lambda_1 E_1 + H_1,\ \lambda_2 E_2 + H_2, \ldots, \lambda_u E_u + H_u\}, \qquad (99)$$

where

$$\text{Re } \lambda_1 \geqq \text{Re } \lambda_2 \geqq \ldots \geqq \text{Re } \lambda_u. \qquad (100)$$

Here E denotes the identity matrix, and H is the matrix in which the elements of the first superdiagonal are equal to unity, and the remaining elements are equal to zero. In general, the orders of the matrices E_i and H_i in different diagonal cells will be different; these orders are the degrees of the corresponding elementary divisors of the matrix P_{-1}.[57]

In conformity with representation (99) of the matrix P_{-1}, we partition all the matrices P_m, P_m^*, A_m into blocks:

$$P_m = (P_{ik}^{(m)})_1^u,\ P_m^* = (P_{ik}^{(m*)})_1^u,\ A_m = (X_{ik}^{(m)})_1^u.$$

Then the second of equations (87) can be replaced by the system of equations

$$(\lambda_i E_i + H_i) X_{ik}^{(1)} - X_{ik}^{(1)}[(\lambda_k+1) E_k + H_k] + P_{ik}^{(0)} = P_{ik}^{(0*)} \qquad (101)$$
$$(i,\ k = 1, 2, \ldots, u),$$

which can be rewritten:

$$(\lambda_i - \lambda_k - 1) X_{ik}^{(1)} + H_i X_{ik}^{(1)} - X_{ik}^{(1)} H_k + P_{ik}^{(0)} = P_{ik}^{(0*)} \qquad (102)$$
$$(i,\ k = 1, 2, \ldots, u).$$

Let us set [58]

---

[56] See Appendix [II], p. 301.

[57] To simplify the notation, we omit the indices on E_i and H_i which indicate the orders of these matrices.

[58] To simplify the notation, we omit the indices i, k, in writing the elements of the matrices X_{ik}, $P_{ik}^{(0)}$, $P_{ik}^{(0*)}$.

$$X_{ik}^{(1)} = \begin{bmatrix} x_{11} & x_{12} & \cdots \\ x_{21} & x_{22} & \cdots \\ \cdot & \cdot & \cdot \cdot \cdot \\ \cdot & \cdot & \cdot \cdot \cdot \end{bmatrix} = (x_{st}), \quad P_{ik}^{(0)} = (p_{st}^{(0)}), \quad P_{ik}^{(0*)} = (p_{st}^{(0*)}).$$

Then matrix equation (102) (for fixed i and k) can be replaced by a system of scalar equations of the form [59]

$$(\lambda_i - \lambda_k - 1) x_{st} + x_{s+1, t} - x_{s, t-1} + p_{st}^{(0)} = p_{st}^{(0*)}$$

$$(s = 1, 2, \ldots, v; \; t = 1, 2, \ldots, w; \; x_{v+1, t} = x_{s,0} = 0), \quad (103)$$

where v and w are the orders of the matrices $\lambda_i E_i + H_i$ and $\lambda_k E_k + H_k$ in (99).

If $\lambda_i - \lambda_k \neq 1$, then all $p_{st}^{(0*)}$ in system (103) can be set equal to zero and all x_{st} are determined from recursive relations (103). In matrix form, this amounts to taking

$$P_{ik}^{(0*)} = 0$$

in equation (102), after which $X_{ik}^{(1)}$ is uniquely determined.

If $\lambda_i - \lambda_k = 1$, then relations (103) assume the form

$$x_{s+1, t} - x_{s, t-1} + p_{st}^{(0)} = p_{st}^{(0*)}$$

$$(s = 1, 2, \ldots, v; \; t = 1, 2, \ldots, w; \; x_{v+1, t} = x_{s,0} = 0). \quad (104)$$

It is easy to show that it is possible to determine the elements x_{st} of the matrix $X_{ik}^{(1)}$ from equations (104) in such a way that the matrix $P_{ik}^{(0*)}$ has one of the following forms (the dimensions being $v \times w$):

$$\begin{bmatrix} a_0 & 0 & \cdots & 0 \\ a_1 & a_0 & \cdots & 0 \\ \cdot & \cdot & & \cdot \\ \cdot & \cdot & \cdot & \cdot \\ \cdot & \cdot & \cdot & \cdot \\ \cdot & \cdot & \cdot & \cdot \\ a_{v-1} & a_{v-2} & \cdots a_1 & a_0 \end{bmatrix}, \qquad \begin{bmatrix} a_0 & 0 & \cdots & 0 & 0 & \cdots & 0 \\ a_1 & a_0 & \cdots & 0 & 0 & \cdots & 0 \\ \cdot & \cdot & & \cdot & & & \cdot \\ \cdot & \cdot & \cdot & \cdot & & & \cdot \\ \cdot & \cdot & \cdot & \cdot & & & \cdot \\ a_{v-1} & & a_1 & a_0 & 0 & \cdots & 0 \end{bmatrix},$$

$$(v = w) \qquad\qquad\qquad (v < w)$$

[59] It is suggested that the reader recall the properties of the matrix H, by forming for himself the matrices HA, AH.

$$\begin{bmatrix} 0 & 0 & \ldots & 0 \\ \cdot & \cdot & \cdot \cdot \cdot \cdot \cdot & \cdot \\ 0 & 0 & \ldots & 0 \\ a_0 & 0 & \ldots & 0 \\ a_1 & a_0 & \ldots & 0 \\ \cdot & & \cdot & \cdot \\ \cdot & & \cdot & \cdot \\ \cdot & & \cdot & \cdot \\ a_{w-1} & \cdots & a_1 & a_0 \end{bmatrix} . \qquad (105)$$

$$(v > w)$$

The matrices (105) are said to be properly lower triangular, or to have *proper lower triangular form*.[60]

From the third equation (87), we determine the matrix A_2. This equation can be replaced by the system of equations

$$(\lambda_i - \lambda_k - 2) X_{ik}^{(2)} + H_i X_{ik}^{(2)} - X_{ik}^{(2)} H_k + \{ P_0 A_1 - A_1 P_0^* \}_{ik} + P_{ik}^{(1)} = P_{ik}^{(1*)}$$

$$(i, \ k = 1, 2, \ldots, u). \qquad (106)$$

Arguing as we did when we determined A_1, we see that if $\lambda_i - \lambda_k \neq 2$, then the matrix $X_{ik}^{(2)}$ is uniquely determined from the corresponding equation (106) if we take $P_{ik}^{(1*)} = 0$. If $\lambda_i - \lambda_k = 2$, then the matrix $X_{ik}^{(2)}$ can be determined in such a way that the matrix $P_{ik}^{(i*)}$ has proper lower triangular form.

We can continue this process, determining all the matrix coefficients $A_1, A_2, \ldots$ and $P_{-1}^*, P_0^*, P_1^*, \ldots$ in succession. Thus, only a finite number of the coefficients P_m^* will be different from zero, and the matrix $P^*(z)$ will have the following block form:[61]

---

[60] Proper upper triangular matrices are defined in a similar manner. From equations (104) all the elements of the matrix $X_{ik}^{(1)}$ are not uniquely determined; there is a certain arbitrariness in selecting the elements x_{st}. This is seen directly from equation (102); for $\lambda_i - \lambda_k = 1$, it is possible to add to the matrix $X_{ik}^{(1)}$ an arbitrary matrix which is permutable with H, i.e., an arbitrary proper upper triangular matrix.

[61] The dimensions of the square matrices E_i, H_i and of the rectangular matrices B_{ik} are determined by the dimensions of the diagonal cells in the Jordan matrix P_{-1}, i.e., by the degrees of the elementary divisors of the matrix P_{-1}.

$$P^*(z) = \begin{bmatrix} \dfrac{\lambda_1 E_1 + H_1}{z}, & B_{12} z^{\lambda_1 - \lambda_2 - 1}, & \ldots, & B_{1u} z^{\lambda_1 - \lambda_u - 1} \\ 0, & \dfrac{\lambda_2 E_2 + H_2}{z}, & \ldots, & B_{2u} z^{\lambda_2 - \lambda_u - 1} \\ \multicolumn{4}{c}{\dotfill} \\ 0, & 0, & \ldots, & \dfrac{\lambda_u E_u + H_u}{z} \end{bmatrix}, \quad (107)$$

where

$$B_{ik} = \begin{cases} 0, & \text{if } \lambda_i - \lambda_k \text{ is not a positive integer;} \\ P_{ik}^{(\lambda_i - \lambda_k - 1*)}, & \text{if } \lambda_i - \lambda_k \text{ is a positive integer;} \\ & (i, k = 1, 2, \ldots, u). \end{cases}$$

All the matrices B_{ik} $(i, k = 1, 2, \ldots, u; i < k)$ have proper lower triangular form.

As in the preceding case, let m_i denote the integral part of Re λ_i

$$m_i = [\text{Re } \lambda_i] \qquad (i = 1, 2, \ldots, u) \qquad (108)$$

and let us set

$$\lambda_i = m_i + \tilde{\lambda}_i \qquad (i = 1, 2, \ldots, u). \qquad (108')$$

Again we replace $\lambda_i - \lambda_k$ throughout by the difference $m_i - m_k$ in expression (107) for $P^*(z)$. We define the block diagonal matrix M and the upper triangular matrix U as follows:[62]

$$M = (m_i E_i \delta_{ik})_1^u, \quad U = \begin{bmatrix} \tilde{\lambda}_1 E_1 + H_1, & B_{12}, & \ldots, & B_{1u} \\ 0, & \tilde{\lambda}_2 E_2 + H_2, & \ldots, & B_{2u} \\ \multicolumn{4}{c}{\dotfill} \\ 0, & 0, & \ldots, & \tilde{\lambda}_u E_u + H_u \end{bmatrix}. \quad (109)$$

Note that M has integral elements. By (107), we easily obtain the following representation for the matrix $P^*(z)$:

$$P^*(z) = z^M \frac{U}{z} \cdot z^{-M} + \frac{M}{z} = D_z(z^M z^U).$$

---

[62] Here the partitioning into blocks is conformal with the partitioning of the matrices P_{-1} and $P^*(z)$.

Hence it follows that the solution of equation (85) can be written in the form

$$Y = z^M z^U,$$

and the solution of equation (81) can be written

$$X = A(z) z^M z^U. \tag{110}$$

Here $A(z)$ is matrix series (84), M is a diagonal matrix with constant integral elements, and U is a constant triangular matrix. The matrices M and U are defined by equalities (108), (108′) and (109).[63]

3. It remains to prove the convergence of the series

$$A(z) = E + A_1 z + A_2 z^2 + \ldots.$$

We need the following lemma, which is of interest in itself.

LEMMA. *If the series*

$$x = a_0 + a_1 z + a_2 z^2 + \ldots \tag{111}$$

is a formal solution of the system [64]

$$dx/dz = P(z)x, \tag{112}$$

for which $z = 0$ is a regular singular point, then series (111) converges in any neighborhood of the point $z = 0$ in which the series expansion (82) for the matrix of coefficients $P(z)$ converges.

Proof. Let us set

$$P(z) = \frac{P_{-1}}{z} + \sum_{q=0}^{\infty} P_q z^q,$$

where the series $\sum P_m z^m$ converges for $|z| < r$. Then there exist positive constants p_{-1} and p, such that [65]

$$\text{mod } P_{-1} \leq p_{-1} I, \ \text{mod } P_m \leq \frac{p}{r^m} I, \ I = (1) \ (m = 0, 1, 2, \ldots). \tag{113}$$

---

[63] See footnote 54 on p. 181.

[64] Here $x = (x_1, x_2, \ldots, x_n)$ is a column of unknown functions; $a_0, a_1, a_2, \ldots$ are constant columns; $P(z)$ is the square matrix of coefficients.

[65] See p. 153 for the definition of the modulus of a matrix.

If we substitute series (111) for x into (112) and equate coefficients of like powers of x on both sides of equality (112), we obtain the following infinite system of vector (column) equations

$$P_{-1}a_0 = 0,$$
$$(E - P_{-1})a_1 = P_0 a_0,$$
$$(2E - P_{-1})a_2 = P_0 a_1 + P_1 a_0, \tag{114}$$
$$\cdots\cdots\cdots\cdots\cdots\cdots$$
$$(mE - P_{-1})a_m = P_0 a_{m-1} + P_1 a_{m-2} + \ldots + P_{m-1}a_0,$$
$$\cdots\cdots\cdots\cdots\cdots\cdots\cdots$$

It is sufficient to prove that the remainders

$$x^{(k)} = a_k z^k + a_{k+1} z^{k+1} + \ldots \tag{115}$$

of series (111) approach 0 in the neighborhood of the point $z = 0$. Suppose that the number k satisfies the inequality

$$k > n p_{-1}.$$

Then k will exceed the moduli of all the characteristic numbers of the matrix [66] P_{-1} and therefore, for $m \geq k$ we will have $\det (mE - P_{-1}) \neq 0$, and

$$(mE - P_{-1})^{-1} = \frac{1}{m}\left(E - \frac{P_{-1}}{m}\right)^{-1} = \frac{1}{m}E + \frac{1}{m^2}P_{-1} + \frac{1}{m^3}P_{-1}^2 + \ldots \tag{116}$$

$$(m = k,\ k + 1, \ldots).$$

The third member of this equality is a convergent matrix series. By means of this series and (114), we can express all the coefficients of series (115) in terms of $a_0, a_1, \ldots, a_{k-1}$, by using the recursion

---

[66] If λ_0 is a characteristic number of the matrix $A = (a_{ik})_1^n$, then $|\lambda_0| \leq n \cdot \max_{1 \leq i, k \leq n} |a_{ik}|$. Indeed, let A_x equal $\lambda_0 x$, where $x = (x_1, x_2, \ldots, x_n) \neq 0$. Then

$$\lambda_0 x_i = \Sigma_k a_{ik} x_k \qquad (i = 1, 2, \ldots, n).$$

Let $|x_j|$ equal $\max \{|x_1|, |x_2|, \ldots, |x_n|\}$. Then

$$|\lambda_0| |x_j| \leq \sum_{k=1}^{n} |a_{jk}| |x_k| \leq |x_j| n \max_{1 \leq i, k \leq n} |a_{ik}|.$$

Cancelling by $|x_j|$, we obtain the necessary inequality.

relations

$$a_m = \left(\frac{1}{m} E + \frac{1}{m^2} P_{-1} + \frac{1}{m^3} P_{-1}^2 + \ldots \right) (f_{m-1} + P_0 a_{m-1} + \ldots + P_{m-k-1} a_k)$$

$$(m = k, \; k+1, \ldots), \quad (117)$$

where

$$f_{m-1} = P_{m-k} a_{k-1} + \ldots + P_{m-1} a_0 \quad (m = k, \; k+1, \ldots). \quad (118)$$

Let us note that series (115) is a formal solution of the differential equation

$$dx^{(k)}/dz = P(z)x^{(k)} + f(z), \quad (119)$$

where

$$f(z) = \sum_{m=k-1}^{\infty} f_m z^m = P(z)(a_0 + a_1 z + \ldots + a_{k-1} z^{k-1})$$
$$\quad (120)$$
$$-a_1 - 2a_2 z - \ldots - (k-1)a_{k-1} z^{k-2}.$$

From (120) it follows that the series

$$\sum_{m=k-1}^{\infty} f_m z^m$$

converges for $|z| < r$, and therefore a number $N > 0$ exists with the property [67]

$$\mathrm{mod}\, f_m \leqq r^{-m} N \quad (m = k-1, \; k, \ldots). \quad (121)$$

From the form of recursive relations (117), it follows that, if we replace P_{-1}, P_q, f_{m-1} respectively by the matrices $p_{-1}I$, $r^{-q}pI$, $(r^{1-m}N)$ which dominate them, and if we replace the column a_m by the column (α_m),[68] $(m = k, \; k+1, \ldots; \; q = 0, 1, 2, \ldots)$, we obtain relations which justify the conclusion

$$\mathrm{mod}\, a_m \leqq (\alpha_m). \quad (122)$$

---

[67] Here $(r^{-m}N)$ denotes a column of elements all equal to one and the same number $r^{-m}N$.

[68] Here (α_m) denotes the column $(\alpha_m, \; \alpha_m, \ldots, \alpha_m)$ $(\alpha_m$ is a number; $m = k, \; k+1, \ldots)$.

Consequently, the series obtained by multiplying both members of

$$\xi^{(k)} = \alpha_k z^k + \alpha_{k+1} z^{k+1} + \cdots \tag{123}$$

by the column $(1, 1, \ldots, 1)$, will dominate series (115).

In (119), if we replace the matrices P_{-1}, P_q, f_m, $x^{(k)}$, defined by

$$P(z) = P_{-1} z^{-1} + \sum_0^\infty P_q z^q, \; f(z) = \sum_{k-1}^\infty f_m z^m,$$

respectively by the matrices $p_{-1} I$, $r^{-q} p I$, $(r^{-m} N)$, $(\xi^{(k)})$ which dominate them, we obtain a differential equation for $\xi^{(k)}$:

$$\frac{d\xi^{(k)}}{dz} = n \left(\frac{p_{-1}}{z} + \frac{p}{1 - \dfrac{z}{r}} \right) \xi^{(k)} + \frac{N \left(z^{k-1} / r^{k-1} \right)}{1 - \dfrac{z}{r}}. \tag{124}$$

This linear differential equation has the particular solution

$$\xi^{(k)} = \frac{N}{r^{k-1}} \frac{z^{n p_{-1}}}{\left(1 - \dfrac{z}{r} \right)^{npr-1}} \int_0^z z^{k-np_{-1}-1} \left(1 - \frac{z}{r} \right)^{np\,r} dz, \tag{125}$$

which is regular at the point $z = 0$ and which can be expanded about $z = 0$ into a power series (123) which is convergent for $|z| < r$.

Since the dominating series (123) converges, it follows that series (115) converges for $|z| < r$. The lemma is proved.

REMARK 1. The method of the above proof allows us to determine all the solutions of differential system (112) which are regular at a singular point, if such exist.

A necessary and sufficient condition that regular solutions (which are not identically equal to zero) exist, is that the matrix of residues P_{-1} have an integral nonnegative characteristic number.

Let s be the greatest such integral characteristic number of P_{-1}. Since the determinant $\varDelta$ of the system composed of the first $s + 1$ equations of (114) is zero, it is possible to find a nonnull set of columns a_0, a_1, $\ldots$, a_s which satisfy these first $s + 1$ equations.

From the remaining equations (114), the columns a_{s+1}, a_{s+2}, . . . can be expressed uniquely in terms of a_0, a_1, . . ., a_s. The series (111) converges according to the lemma. Thus, the linearly independent solutions of the first $s + 1$ equations (114) determine all the linearly independent solutions of the system (112) which are regular at the singular point $z = 0$.

If $z = 0$ is a singular point, then the initial value a_0 does not uniquely determine a solution for (111) which is regular at this point (if such exists). However, a solution which is regular at a regular singular point is uniquely determined when a_0, a_1, . . ., a_s are given, i.e., if the initial values of the solution itself for $z = 0$ and its first s derivatives are given (where s is the maximum nonnegative integral characteristic number of the matrix of residues P_{-1}).

REMARK 2. The theorem remains valid in the case $P_{-1} = 0$. In this case, p_{-1} can be taken as any positive number in the proof of the theorem. In the case $P_{-1} = 0$, the lemma proves again the well-known result concerning the existence of a regular solution in the neighborhood of a regular point of the system. In this case, the solution is uniquely determined from the initial value a_0.

4. Let the system

$$dX/dz = P(z)X, \qquad (126)$$

where

$$P(z) = \frac{P_{-1}}{z} + \sum_{m=0}^{\infty} P_m z^m$$

be such that the series in the right member converges for $|z| < r$.

Also, suppose that formal substitution in

$$X = A(z)Y \qquad (127)$$

of the series

$$A(z) = A_0 + A_1 z + A_2 z^2 + \ldots \qquad (128)$$

gives a system

$$dY/dz = P^*(z)Y, \qquad (129)$$

where

$$P*(z) = \frac{P^*_{-1}}{z} + \sum_{m=0}^{\infty} P^*_m z^m,$$

where the series in the right member also converges for $|z| < r$.

Under these hypotheses, we shall prove that series (128) also converges in the neighborhood $|z| < r$ of the point $z = 0$.

In the first place, it follows from (126), (127) and (129) that the series (128) is a formal solution of the following differential matrix equation:

$$dA/dz = P(z)A - AP*(z). \tag{130}$$

We will consider A as a vector (column) in the space of all matrices of nth order, i.e., in a space of n^2 dimensions. We can define a linear operator $\hat{P}(z)$, which operates on the matrix A in this space and which depends analytically on the parameter z, by means of the equality

$$\hat{P}(z)[A] = P(z)A - AP*(z); \tag{131}$$

then differential equation (130) can be written in the form

$$dA/dz = \hat{P}(z)[A]. \tag{132}$$

The right side of this equation can be thought of as the product of the matrix $\hat{P}(z)$ of order n^2 and the column A of n^2 elements. It is seen from formula (131) that the point $z = 0$ is a regular singular point for system (132). Series (128) is a formal solution of this system. Therefore, by the lemma, it follows that series (128) converges in the neighborhood $|z| < r$ of the point $z = 0$. In particular, the series for $A(z)$ in formula (110) also converges.

Thus, we have proved the following theorem.

THEOREM 2. *Every system*

$$dX/dz = P(z)X \tag{133}$$

with a regular singular point at $z = 0$

$$P(z) = \frac{P_{-1}}{z} + \sum_{m=0}^{\infty} P_m z^m$$

has a solution of the form

$$X = A(z) z^M z^U \tag{134}$$

where $A(z)$ is a matrix function which is regular for $z = 0$ and reduces to the identity matrix E at this point, and M and U are constant matrices; M is diagonable and has characteristic numbers which are integers; and the difference of any two different characteristic numbers of the matrix U is not an integer.

If the matrix P_{-1} can be reduced to Jordan form by transforming by the nonsingular matrix T

$$P_{-1} = T\{p_1 E_1 + H_1,\ \lambda_2 E_2 + H_2,\ \ldots,\ \lambda_s E_s + H_s\} T^{-1} \tag{135}$$
$$(\mathrm{Re}\ \lambda_1 \geqq \mathrm{Re}\ \lambda_2 \geqq \ldots \geqq \mathrm{Re}\ \lambda_s),$$

then M and U can be taken in the form

$$M = T\{m_1 E_1,\ m_2 E_2,\ \ldots,\ m_s E_s\} T^{-1}, \tag{136}$$

$$U = T \begin{bmatrix} \tilde{\lambda}_1 E_1 + H_1, & B_{12}, & \ldots, & B_{1s} \\ 0, & \tilde{\lambda}_2 E_2 + H_2, & \ldots, & B_{2s} \\ \cdots\cdots\cdots\cdots\cdots\cdots\cdots\cdots\cdots\cdots \\ 0, & 0, & \ldots, & \tilde{\lambda}_s E_s + H_s \end{bmatrix} T^{-1}, \tag{137}$$

where

$$m_i = [\lambda_i],\quad \tilde{\lambda}_i = \lambda_i - m_i \quad (i = 1, 2, \ldots, s), \tag{138}$$

B_{ik} *are proper* [69] *lower triangular matrices $(i, k = 1, 2, \ldots, s)$, and $B_{ik} = 0$, if $\lambda_i - \lambda_k$ is not a positive integer $(i, k = 1, 2, \ldots, s)$.*

In the special case, when none of the differences $\lambda_i - \lambda_k$ $(i, k = 1, 2, \ldots, s)$ is a positive integer, we can take M equal to 0 and U equal to P_{-1} in (134), i.e., the solution in this case can be written in the form

$$X = A(z) Z^{P_{-1}} \tag{139}$$

REMARK 1. We recall that earlier in this section we established an algorithm for determining the coefficients of the series $A(z) = \sum_m A_m z^m$ $(A_0 = E)$ in terms of the coefficients P_m of the series $P(z)$. In addition, the above theorem also gives the

---

[69] See (105), p. 183.

integral substitution V, by which solution (134) is multiplied when the singular point $z = 0$ is encircled once in the positive direction:

$$V = \exp{(2\pi i U)}.$$

REMARK 2. From the formulation of the theorem, it follows that

$$B_{ik} = 0$$

whenever the relation $\tilde{\lambda}_i \neq \tilde{\lambda}_k$ holds $(i,\ k = 1, 2, \ldots, s)$.
Therefore the matrices

$$\tilde{A} = T \operatorname{diag} (\tilde{\lambda}_1 E_1, \tilde{\lambda}_2 E_2, \ldots, \tilde{\lambda}_s E_s) T^{-1} \text{ and } \tilde{U} = T \begin{bmatrix} 0 & B_{12} \ldots B_{1s} \\ 0 & 0 \ \ \ldots B_{2s} \\ \cdot & \cdot \cdot \cdot \cdot \cdot \cdot \\ 0 & 0 \ \ \ldots 0 \end{bmatrix} T^{-1}$$

$$(140)$$

are permutable:

$$\tilde{A}\tilde{U} = \tilde{U}\tilde{A}.$$

Hence

$$z^M z^U = z^M z^{\tilde{A}+\tilde{U}} = z^M z^{\tilde{A}} z^{\tilde{U}} = z^A z^{\tilde{U}}, \tag{141}$$

where

$$A = M + \tilde{A} = T \operatorname{diag} (\lambda_1, \lambda_2, \ldots, \lambda_n) T^{-1} \tag{142}$$

where $\lambda_1, \lambda_2, \ldots, \lambda_n$ are the characteristic numbers of the matrix P_{-1}, arranged in such a way that the relations $\operatorname{Re} \lambda_1 \geqq \operatorname{Re} \lambda_2 \geqq \ldots \geqq \operatorname{Re} \lambda_n$ hold.
On the other hand,

$$z^{\tilde{U}} = h(\tilde{U}),$$

where $h(\lambda)$ is the Lagrange-Sylvester interpolation polynomial for the function $f(\lambda) = z^\lambda$.

Since all the characteristic numbers of the matrix $\tilde{U}$ are equal to zero, then $h(\lambda)$ is linearly dependent on $f(0), f'(0), \ldots, f^{(g-1)}(0)$, i.e., upon $1, \ln z, \ldots, (\ln z)^{g-1}$ (where g is the minimum index such that $\tilde{U}^g = 0$). Therefore

$$h(\lambda) = \sum_{j=0}^{g-1} h_j(\lambda) (\ln z)^j$$

hence

$$z^{\tilde{U}} = h(\tilde{U}) = \sum_{j=0}^{g-1} h_j(\tilde{U}) \, (\ln z)^j = T \begin{bmatrix} 1 & q_{12} \cdots q_{1n} \\ 0 & 1 & \cdots q_{2n} \\ \cdots \cdots \cdots \\ 0 & 0 & \cdots 1 \end{bmatrix} T^{-1} \qquad (143)$$

where q_{ij} $(i, j = 1, 2, \ldots, n; \; i < j)$ is a polynomial in $\ln z$ of degree less than g.

From (134), (141), (142), and (143), we see that a particular solution of system (126) can be written in the form

$$X = A(z) \begin{bmatrix} z^{\lambda_1} & 0 & \cdots 0 \\ 0 & z^{\lambda_2} & \cdots 0 \\ \cdots \cdots \cdots \cdots \\ 0 & 0 & \cdots z^{\lambda_n} \end{bmatrix} \begin{bmatrix} 1 & q_{12} \cdots q_{1n} \\ 0 & 1 & \cdots q_{2n} \\ \cdots \cdots \cdots \\ 0 & 0 & \cdots 1 \end{bmatrix}. \qquad (144)$$

Here $\lambda_1, \lambda_2, \ldots, \lambda_n$ are the characteristic numbers of the matrix P_{-1}, arranged in the order $\operatorname{Re} \lambda_1 \geqq \operatorname{Re} \lambda_2 \geqq \ldots \geqq \operatorname{Re} \lambda_n$, and q_{ij} $(i, j = 1, 2, \ldots, n; i < j)$ is a polynomial in $\ln z$ of degree not exceeding $g - 1$, where g is the maximum number of characteristic numbers λ_i which differ by an integer; $A(z)$ is a matrix function which is regular at the point $z = 0$, and $A(0) = T$ is invertible. If the matrix P_{-1} has Jordan canonical form, then $T = E$.

§ 11. Reducible analytic systems

As an application of the theorem of the preceding section, let us ask when the system

$$dX/dt = Q(t)X, \qquad (145)$$

(where

$$Q(t) = \sum_{m=1}^{\infty} \frac{Q_m}{t^m} \qquad (146)$$

is a series convergent for $t > t_0$), is reducible (in the sense of Lyapunov), i.e., when the system has a solution of the form

$$X = L(t)e^{Bt}, \qquad (147)$$

where $L(t)$ is a Lyapunov matrix (i.e., $L(t)$ satisfies conditions

1—3 on p. 139), and B is a constant matrix.[70] Here X, Q are matrices with complex elements, and t is a real argument. Let us make the substitution $z = t^{-1}$. The system (145) becomes

$$dX/dz = P(z)X, \qquad (148)$$

where

$$P(z) = -z^{-2}Q\left(\frac{1}{z}\right) = -\frac{Q_1}{z} - \sum_{m=0}^{\infty} Q_{m+2} z^m. \qquad (149)$$

The series in the right member converges for $|z| < t_0^{-1}$. Two cases are possible:

(i) $Q_1 = 0$. In this case, the point $z = 0$ is not a singular point of the system (148). This system has a solution which is regular and normalized at the point $z = 0$. This solution is given by the convergent power series

$$X(z) = E + X_1 z + X_2 z^2 + \dots \quad (|z| < t_0^{-1}).$$

The substitutions

$$L(t) = X(t^{-1}), \ B = 0$$

lead to the form (147). The system is reducible.

(ii) $Q_1 \neq 0$. In this case, system (148) has a regular singular point at the point $z = 0$.

Without loss of generality, we assume the matrix of residues $P_{-1} = -Q_1$ to be in Jordan form, where the diagonal elements $\lambda_1, \lambda_2, \dots, \lambda_n$ are arranged in the order

$$\operatorname{Re} \lambda_1 \geqq \operatorname{Re} \lambda_2 \geqq \dots \geqq \operatorname{Re} \lambda_n.$$

Then the matrix T of formula (144) is equal to the identity matrix, and therefore system (148) has the solution

$$X = A(z) \begin{bmatrix} z^{\lambda_1} & 0 & \dots & 0 \\ 0 & z^{\lambda_2} & \dots & 0 \\ \multicolumn{4}{c}{\dotfill} \\ 0 & 0 & \dots & z^{\lambda_n} \end{bmatrix} \begin{bmatrix} 1 & q_{12} & \dots & q_{1n} \\ 0 & 1 & \dots & q_{2n} \\ \multicolumn{4}{c}{\dotfill} \\ 0 & 0 & \dots & 1 \end{bmatrix}$$

[70] If equation (147) holds, then the Lyapunov transformation $X = L(t)Y$ carries the system (145) into the system $dY/dt = BY$.

where the function $A(z)$ is regular for $z = 0$ and takes the value E at this point, and q_{ik} $(i, k = 1, 2, \ldots, n; \ i < k)$ are polynomials in $\ln z$. Substituting t^{-1} for z, we have:

$$
X = A\left(\frac{1}{t}\right)
\begin{bmatrix}
\left(\frac{1}{t}\right)^{\lambda_1} & 0 & \cdots & 0 \\
0 & \left(\frac{1}{t}\right)^{\lambda_2} & \cdots & 0 \\
\multicolumn{4}{c}{\cdots\cdots\cdots\cdots\cdots} \\
0 & 0 & \cdots & \left(\frac{1}{t}\right)^{\lambda_n}
\end{bmatrix}
\begin{bmatrix}
1 & q_{12}\left(\ln\frac{1}{t}\right) & \cdots & q_{1n}\left(\ln\frac{1}{t}\right) \\
0 & 1 & \cdots & q_{2n}\left(\ln\frac{1}{t}\right) \\
\multicolumn{4}{c}{\cdots\cdots\cdots\cdots\cdots} \\
0 & 0 & \cdots & 1
\end{bmatrix}.
$$

$$(150)$$

Since the transformation $X = A(t^{-1})Y$ is a Lyapunov transformation, then system (145) will be reducible to a certain system with constant coefficients if and only if the product

$$
L_1(t) =
\begin{bmatrix}
t^{-\lambda_1} & 0 & \cdots & 0 \\
0 & t^{-\lambda_2} & \cdots & 0 \\
\multicolumn{4}{c}{\cdots\cdots\cdots\cdots\cdots} \\
0 & 0 & \cdots & t^{-\lambda_n}
\end{bmatrix}
\begin{bmatrix}
1 & q_{12}\left(\ln\frac{1}{t}\right) & \cdots & q_{1n}\left(\ln\frac{1}{t}\right) \\
0 & 1 & \cdots & q_{2n}\left(\ln\frac{1}{t}\right) \\
\multicolumn{4}{c}{\cdots\cdots\cdots\cdots\cdots} \\
0 & 0 & \cdots & 1
\end{bmatrix}
e^{-Bt},
$$

$$(151)$$

is a Lyapunov matrix for some constant matrix B, i.e., if and only if the matrices $L_1(t)$, dL_1/dt and $L_1^{-1}(t)$ are bounded. Moreover it follows from the Erugin theorem (Section 4), that the matrix B can be taken to be a matrix the characteristic numbers of which are all real.

Since the matrices $L_1(t)$ and $L_1^{-1}(t)$ are bounded for $t > t_0$, it follows that all the characteristic numbers of the matrix B must be equal to zero. This follows from the expressions for e^{Bt} and e^{-Bt} obtained from (151). In addition, all numbers $\lambda_1, \lambda_2, \ldots, \lambda_n$ must be pure imaginaries. For, since the elements of the last row of $L_1(t)$ are bounded, from (151) we see that $\mathrm{Re}\,\lambda_n \geqq 0$.

Similarly, since the elements of the first column of $L_1^{-1}(t)$ are bounded, it follows that $0 \geqq \operatorname{Re} \lambda_1 \geqq \operatorname{Re} \lambda_n$.

But if all the characteristic numbers of the matrix P_{-1} are pure imaginaries, none of the differences between two unequal characteristic numbers of the matrix P_{-1} is equal to an integer. Therefore, formula (139) holds

$$X = A(z) z^{P_{-1}} = A\left(\frac{1}{t}\right) t^{Q_1}$$

and a necessary and sufficient condition that the system be reducible is that the matrix

$$L_2(t) = t^{Q_1} e^{-Bt} \tag{152}$$

and its inverse be bounded for $t > t_0$.

Since all the characteristic numbers of the matrix B must be equal to zero, the minimal polynomial for the matrix B has the form λ^d. Let us denote the minimal polynomial of the matrix Q_1 by

$$\psi(\lambda) = (\lambda - \mu_1)^{c_1}(\lambda - \mu_2)^{c_2} \dots (\lambda - \mu_u)^{c_u} \quad (\mu_i \neq \mu_k \text{ for } i \neq k).$$

Since $Q_1 = -P_{-1}$, the numbers $\mu_1, \mu_2, \dots, \mu_u$ are the negatives of the corresponding numbers λ_i and hence they are all pure imaginaries also. Thus [see formulas (12), (13) on p. 138]

$$t^{Q_1} = \sum_{k=1}^{u} [U_{k0} + U_{k1} \ln t + \dots + U_{k, c_k-1}(\ln t)^{c_k-1}] t^{\mu_k}, \tag{153}$$

$$e^{Bt} = V_0 + V_1 t + \dots + V_{d-1} t^{d-1}. \tag{154}$$

Substituting these expressions into the relation

$$L_2(t) e^{Bt} = t^{Q_1},$$

we obtain

$$[L_2(t) V_{d-1} + (*)] t^{d-1} = Z_0(t) (\ln t)^{c-1}, \tag{155}$$

where c is the maximum of the numbers $c_1, c_2, \dots, c_n$, (*) denotes a matrix which tends to zero as $t \to \infty$, and $Z_0(t)$ is a matrix bounded for $t > t_0$.

Since the matrices in the left and right sides of equality (155) must have the same order of growth for $t \to \infty$, the relation

$$d = c = 1$$

follows, so that

$$B = 0.$$

Moreover, the matrix Q_1 has simple elementary divisors.

Conversely, if the matrix Q_1 has simple elementary divisors and if its characteristic numbers $\mu_1, \mu_2, \ldots, \mu_n$ are pure imaginaries, then

$$X = A(z) z^{-Q_1} = A(z)(z^{-\mu_i} \delta_{ik})_1^n$$

is the solution of system (149). If we set z equal to $1/t$ here, we obtain

$$X = A\left(\frac{1}{t}\right)(t^{\mu_i} \delta_{ik})_1^n.$$

The function $X(t)$, its derivative $dX(t)/dt$, and the inverse matrix $X^{-1}(t)$ are bounded for $t > t_0$. Therefore, the system is reducible $(B = 0)$. We have proved the following theorem.[71]

THEOREM 3. *If* $Q(t) = t^{-1}Q_1 + t^{-2}Q_2 + \cdots$ *is a series which converges for* $t > t_0$, *then the system*

$$dX/dt = Q(t)X$$

is reducible in the sense of Lyapunov if and only if all the elementary divisors of the matrix of residues Q_1 *are simple and all the characteristic numbers are pure imaginaries.*

§ 12. Analytic functions of sets of matrices, and applications to the study of differential systems. Researches of I. A. Lappo-Danilevskiĭ

By an analytic function of m matrices $X_1, X_2, \ldots, X_m$ of order n, we understand a series

[71] See Erugin's work [17], pp. 21—23. In that work, the theorem is proved in case no two characteristic numbers of the matrix Q_1 differ by an integer.

$$F(X_1, X_2, \ldots, X_m) = \alpha_0 + \sum_{\nu=1}^{\infty} \overset{(1 \ldots m)}{\sum_{j_1, j_2, \ldots, j_\nu}} \alpha_{j_1 j_2 \ldots j_\nu} X_{j_1} X_{j_2} \ldots X_{j_\nu}, \quad (156)$$

which converges for all matrices of nth order X_j, which satisfy the inequalities

$$\mathrm{mod}\, X_j < R_j \quad (j = 1, 2, \ldots, m). \quad (157)$$

Here the coefficients

$$\alpha_0, \;\; \alpha_{j_1 j_2 \ldots j_\nu} \;\; (j_1, j_2, \ldots, j_\nu = 1, 2, \ldots, m; \; \nu = 1, 2, 3, \ldots)$$

are complex numbers, R_j $(j = 1, 2, \ldots, m)$ are constant matrices of order n with positive elements, and X_j $(j = 1, 2, \ldots, m)$ are matrices of the same order, but variable and with complex elements.

The theory of analytic functions of several matrices was developed by I. A. Lappo-Danilevskiĭ. On the basis of this theory, Lappo-Danilevskiĭ made researches of a fundamental nature into systems of linear differential equations with coefficients which are rational functions of the independent variable.

Such a system can always be reduced to the form

$$\frac{dX}{dz} = \sum_{j=1}^{m} \left\{ \frac{U_{j0}}{(z - a_j)^{s_j}} + \frac{U_{j1}}{(z - a_j)^{s_j - 1}} + \ldots + \frac{U_{j, s_j - 1}}{z - a_j} \right\} X, \quad (158)$$

by means of a suitable transformation of the independent variable. Here, U_{jk} are constant matrices of order n, a_j are complex numbers, and s_j are positive integers $(k = 0, 1, \ldots, s_j - 1; j = 1, 2, \ldots, m)$.[72]

We shall illustrate certain results of Lappo-Danilevskiĭ in the special case when the system is *regular*. A regular system is one in which the condition $s_1 = s_2 = \ldots = s_m = 1$ holds; that is, a system of the type

$$\frac{dX}{dz} = \sum_{j=1}^{m} \frac{U_j}{z - a_j} X. \quad (159)$$

---

[72] In system (158), all the coefficients are proper rational fractions in z. Any collection of rational coefficients can be reduced to this form, if some finite point $z = c$ (regular for all the coefficients) is carried to the point $z = \infty$ by means of a linear fractional transformation of the variable z.

Following Lappo-Danilevskiĭ, we introduce certain special analytic functions — hyperlogarithms — which are defined by the following recursive relations:

$$l_b(z;\ a_{j_1}) = \int_b^z \frac{dz}{z - a_{j_1}},$$

$$l_b(z;\ a_{j_1},\ a_{j_2},\ \ldots,\ a_{j_\nu}) = \int_b^z \frac{l_b(z;\ a_{j_2},\ a_{j_3},\ \ldots,\ a_{j_\nu})}{z - a_{j_1}}\, dz.$$

By taking the points a_1, a_2, ..., a_m, ∞ as branch points (of logarithmic type), we can construct the corresponding Reimann surface $S(a_1, a_2, \ldots, a_m;\ \infty)$. The hyperlogarithm will be a single-valued function on this surface. On the other hand, the matrizer Ω_b^z of system (159) (i.e., the solution normalized at the point $z = b$), can be continued analytically so as to be a single-valued function on $S(a_1, a_2, \ldots, a_m;\ \infty)$; and b can be taken as any finite point on S different from a_1, a_2, ..., a_m.

For the normalized solution Ω_b^z of system (159), Lappo-Danilevskiĭ gives an explicit expression in terms of the defining matrices U_1, U_2, ..., U_m, in the form of a series

$$\Omega_b^z = E + \sum_{\nu=1}^{\infty} \sum_{j_1,\ldots,j_\nu}^{(1\ldots m)} l_b(z;\ a_{j_1},\ a_{j_2},\ \ldots,\ a_{j_\nu}) U_{j_1} U_{j_2} \ldots U_{j_\nu}. \tag{160}$$

This expansion converges uniformly in z for any U_1, U_2, ..., U_m and represents Ω_b^z in any finite domain on the surface $S(a_1, a_2, \ldots, a_m;\ \infty)$, if only none of the points $a_1, \ldots, a_m$ lies in the interior or on the boundary of this domain.

If series (156) converges for arbitrary matrices X_1, X_2, ..., X_m, then the corresponding function $F(X_1,\ X_2, \ldots, X_m)$ is called entire. Ω_b^z is an entire function of the matrices U_1, U_2, ..., U_m.

If we modify (160) by allowing z to encircle the point a_j once in the positive direction in such a way that the contour does not enclose other points a_i $(i \neq j)$, we obtain an expression for the *integral substitution* V_j corresponding to the point $z = a_j$:

$$V_j = E + \sum_{\nu=1}^{\infty} \sum_{j_1,\ldots,j_\nu}^{(1\ldots m)} p_j(b;\ a_{j_1},\ a_{j_2},\ \ldots,\ a_{j_\nu}) U_{j_1} U_{j_2} \ldots U_{j_\nu} \tag{161}$$

$$(j = 1, 2, \ldots, m)$$

where the symbols p_j are defined by the contour integrals

$$p_j(b; a_{j_1}) = \int_{(a_j)} \frac{dz}{z - a_{j_1}}$$

$$p_j(b; a_{j_1}, a_{j_2}, \ldots, a_{j_\nu}) = \int_{(a_j)} \frac{L_b(z; a_{j_2}, a_{j_3}, \ldots, a_{j_\nu})}{z - a_{j_1}} dz$$

$$(j_1, j_2, \ldots, j_\nu, \ j = 1, 2, \ldots, m; \ \nu = 1, 2, 3, \ldots)$$

Series (161) is also an entire function of $U_1, U_2, \ldots, U_m$.

After first generalizing the theory of analytic functions to the case of an infinite, but countable set of matrix-arguments $X_1, X_2, X_3, \ldots$,[73] Lappo-Danilevskiĭ applied this theory to study the behavior of the solution of a system in the neighborhood of an irregular singular point.[74] We will state the main result.

The normalized solution Ω_b^z of the system

$$\frac{dX}{dz} = \sum_{j=-q}^{+\infty} P_j z^j X,$$

where the power series in the right side converges for[75] $|z| < r \ (r > 1)$ can be represented by the series

$$\Omega_b^z = E + \sum_{\nu=1}^{\infty} \sum_{j_1, j_2, \ldots, j_\nu = -q}^{\infty} P_{j_1} \ldots P_{j_\nu} \sum_{\mu=0}^{\infty} b^{j_\mu+1+\ldots+j_\nu+\nu-\mu} z^{j_1+\ldots+j_\mu+\mu}$$

$$\cdot \sum_{\lambda=0}^{n-\mu} \alpha_{j_{\mu+1}, \ldots, j_\nu}^{*(\lambda)} \ln^\lambda b \sum_{\chi=0}^{\mu} \alpha_{j_1, \ldots, j_\mu}^{(\chi)} \ln^\chi z. \qquad (162)$$

Here $\alpha_{j_{\mu+1}, \ldots, j}^{*(\lambda)}$ and $\alpha_{j_1, \ldots, j_\mu}^{(\chi)}$ are scalar coefficients which are defined by special formulae. Series (162) converges for arbitrary matrices $P_1, P_2, \ldots$ in the annulus $\rho < |z| < r$; where ρ is any positive number less than r. The point b must also be in the interior of the annulus $(\rho < |b| < r)$.

---

[73] See [37], Vol. I, Memoir 1.

[74] See [37], Vol. I, Memoir 3; see also [18, 19].

[75] The restriction $r > 1$ is not essential, since this condition can always be obtained by substituting αz for z, where α is a suitably chosen positive number.

Not having the opportunity to present the work of Lappo-Danilevskiĭ in any great detail in this book, we are forced to limit our treatment to the formulations of the basic results presented above and to refer the reader to the pertinent literature.

All the researches of Lappo-Danilevskiĭ dealing with differential equations were published posthumously [76] by the Academy of Sciences of the USSR in three volumes in 1934—1936.

[76] See [37].

CHAPTER V

The Routh-Hurwitz Problem and Related Questions

§ 1. Introduction

In Section 2 of Chapter II we explained how, according to Lyapunov's theorem, the null solution of the system of differential equations

$$\frac{dx_i}{dt} = \sum_{k=1}^{n} a_{ik} x_k + (**) \tag{1}$$

(where the a_{ik}'s $(i, k = 1, 2, \ldots, n)$ are constants) is stable for arbitrary terms $(**)$ of second and higher degrees in the variables x_i if all of the characteristic roots of the matrix $A = (a_{ik})_1^n$, i.e., all of the roots of the secular polynomial $\Delta(\lambda) \equiv \det(\lambda E - A)$ have negative real parts.

The problem of establishing necessary and sufficient conditions under which all of the roots of a given algebraic equation lie in the left half-plane is consequently one of fundamental importance for a number of practical fields in which the stability of mechanical and electrical systems is investigated.

The importance of this algebraic problem was made clear in the original theory of machine control developed by the English physicist J. Clerk Maxwell and the learned Russian research engineer J. Vyshnegradskiĭ who, in their works[1] devoted to the theory of control, arrived at conditions of the type described for equations of degree at most three, and made extensive use of them.

In 1868 Maxwell proposed the mathematical problem of finding the corresponding conditions for algebraic equations of arbitrary degree. This problem, however, had been essentially solved in a paper[2] published in 1856 by the French mathematician Hermite.

[1] Maxwell, [46] Vyshnegradskiĭ, [68] and [69]. See also [2].
[2] Hermite, [27].

In this paper a close connection had been established between the number of roots of a complex polynomial $f(z)$ lying within an arbitrary half-plane (or even within an arbitrary sector), and the signature of a certain quadratic form. However, Hermite's results were not given in a form suitable for application by specialists working in practical fields, and his paper was consequently not given the circulation it deserved.

In 1877 the English physicist Routh,[3] using Sturm's Theorem and Cauchy's theory of indices, established an algorithm for determining the number k of roots of a real polynomial lying in the right half-plane. In the particular case $k = 0$ this algorithm gives a stability criterion.

At the end of the nineteenth century the great Slovakian research engineer A. Stodola, the creator of the theory of steam and gas turbines, not knowing of Routh's work, again proposed the problem of finding conditions for all of the roots of an algebraic equation to have negative real parts, and in 1895 A. Hurwitz,[4] basing his work on Hermite's, gave a second solution of the problem, independently of Routh. The determinant inequalities obtained by Hurwitz are now known as the Routh-Hurwitz conditions.

Even before the work of Hurwitz had seen the light of day, however, A. M. Lyapunov, the founder of the modern theory of stability, had established in his famous dissertation [5] a theorem from which follow necessary and sufficient conditions for all of the roots of the characteristic equation of a real matrix to have negative real parts.

New stability criteria were discovered in 1914 by the French mathematicians Liénard and Chipart.[6] Making use of special quadratic forms, these authors obtained stability criteria possessing certain advantages over the Routh-Hurwitz criteria; e.g., the number of determinant inequalities in the Liénard-Chipart criteria

[3] Routh, [59].
[4] Hurwitz, [28].
[5] Lyapunov, [42], Section 20.
[6] Liénard and Chipart, [41].

is approximately half the number in the Routh-Hurwitz criteria. The famous Russian mathematicians **P. L.** Chebyshev and **A. A.** Markov proved two remarkable theorems in connection with the series expansion of continued fractions of a special type. These theorems, as will be shown in Section 16, have a direct relation to the Routh-Hurwitz problem.

In the set of problems just sketched, essential use is made of the theory of quadratic forms and, in particular, the theory of Hankel forms.

§ 2. Cauchy indices

We turn now to a consideration of the so-called Cauchy indices.

DEFINITION 1. *The* Cauchy index *of the real rational function* $R(x)$ *between the limits a and b (denoted by $I_a^b R(x)$; a and b are real numbers, possibly $\pm \infty$) is the difference between the number of points at which $R(x)$ jumps from $-\infty$ to $+\infty$ and the number of points at which $R(x)$ jumps from $+\infty$ to $-\infty$ as the independent variable ranges from a to b.* In calculating the number of infinite discontinuities of each type the behavior at a and b is to be disregarded.

According to this definition, if

$$R(x) = \sum_{i=1}^{p} \frac{A_i}{x - \alpha_i} + R_1(x),$$

where A_i, α_i $(i = 1, 2, \ldots, p)$ are real numbers and $R_1(x)$ is a rational function which has no real poles, then [7]

$$I_{-\infty}^{+\infty} R(x) = \sum_{i=1}^{p} \text{sign } A_i \qquad (2)$$

and in general

$$I_a^b R(x) = \sum_{a < \alpha_i < b} \text{sign } A_i \quad (a < b). \qquad (2')$$

In particular, if $f(x) = a_0(x - \alpha_1)^{n_1} \ldots (x - \alpha_m)^{n_m}$ is a real

---

[7] By sign a (a being a real number) we mean $+1$, -1, or 0, according as $a > 0$, $a < 0$, or $a = 0$.

polynomial $(\alpha_i \neq \alpha_k$ for $i \neq k$; i, $k = 1, 2, \ldots, m)$, and among the roots α_1, α_2, $\ldots$, α_m of this polynomial only the first p are real, then

$$\frac{f'(x)}{f(x)} = \sum_{j=1}^{m} \frac{n_j}{x - \alpha_j} = \sum_{i=1}^{p} \frac{n_i}{x - \alpha_i} + R_1(x),$$

where $R_1(x)$ is a real rational function with no real poles.

Thus according to (2') *the index*

$$I_a^b \frac{f'(x)}{f(x)} \quad (a < b)$$

is equal to the number of distinct real roots of the function $f(x)$ lying within the interval (a, b).

An arbitrary real rational function $R(x)$ can always be represented in the form

$$R(x) = \sum_{i=1}^{p} \left\{ \frac{A_1^{(i)}}{x - \alpha_i} + \ldots + \frac{A_{n_i}^{(i)}}{(x - \alpha_i)^{n_i}} \right\} + R_1(x),$$

where all of the numbers α and A are real $(A_{n_i}^{(i)} \neq 0)$ and $R_1(x)$ does not have real poles.

Then

$$I_{-\infty}^{+\infty} R(x) = \sum \text{sign } A_{n_i}^{(i)} \tag{3}$$

and in general

$$I_a^b R(x) = \sum_{a < \alpha_i < b} \text{sign } A_{n_i}^{(i)} \tag{3'}$$

where in both cases the sum is extended over values of i for which n_i is odd.

One of the methods of calculating the index $I_a^b R(x)$ is based on the classical *Sturm's Theorem.*

We consider a sequence of polynomials

$$f_1(x), \ f_2(x), \ \ldots, f_m(x), \tag{4}$$

satisfying the following pair of conditions involving an interval [8] (a, b):

[8] Here a may be $-\infty$ and b may be $+\infty$.

1. For any value of x ($a < x < b$) at which any one of the functions $f_k(x)$ vanishes, the two adjacent functions $f_{k-1}(x)$ and $f_{k+1}(x)$ have values different from zero and of opposite signs.
2. The last function $f_m(x)$ in the sequence (4) does not vanish within (a, b); i.e., $f_m(x) \neq 0$ for $a < x < b$.
Such a sequence of polynomials (4) is called a *Sturm sequence in the interval* (a, b).
We shall denote by $V(x)$ the number of changes in sign in the sequence (4) for a fixed value [9] of x. Then as x ranges from a to b the size of $V(x)$ can change only when x passes through a zero of one of the functions in the sequence (4). But according to condition *1* the value of $V(x)$ cannot change when x is a zero of one of the functions $f_k(x)$ ($k = 2, \ldots, m - 1$). When x passes through a zero of $f_1(x)$, the sequence (4) loses or gains one change of sign according as $f_2(x)/f_1(x)$ passes from $-\infty$ to $+\infty$ or the reverse. Thus there holds

THEOREM 1 (Sturm). *If* $f_1(x)$, $f_2(x)$, $\ldots$, $f_m(x)$ *is a Sturm sequence in* (a, b), *and* $V(x)$ *is the number of changes of sign in this sequence, then*

$$I_a^b \frac{f_2(x)}{f_1(x)} = V(a) - V(b). \tag{5}$$

REMARK. If all of the terms in a Sturm sequence are multiplied by the same arbitrary polynomial $d(x) \not\equiv 0$ the resulting sequence of polynomials is called a *generalized Sturm sequence*. Since multiplying all of the terms in the sequence (4) by the same polynomial changes the value of neither member of equation (5), Sturm's theorem is valid even for generalized Sturm sequences.
We remark that if two polynomials $f(x)$ and $g(x)$ are given,

---

[9] If $a < x < b$ and $f_1(x) \neq 0$, then because of condition *1*, in the determination of $V(x)$ zero values in the sequence (4) may be ignored or one may regard them as having either sign. If a is finite, $V(a)$ should be taken to mean $V(a + \varepsilon)$, where ε is a positive number so small that none of the functions $f_i(x)$ ($i = 1, 2, \ldots, m$) vanish on the half-closed interval (a, $a + \varepsilon]$. In the same way, if b is finite, $V(b)$ should be assigned the value of $V(b - \varepsilon)$, where ε is chosen analogously.

and the degree of $g(x)$ is not greater than that of $f(x)$, then one can always use the Euclidean algorithm to construct a generalized Sturm sequence which begins with the functions $f_1(x) = f(x)$, $f_2(x) = g(x)$. In fact, if we denote the remainder obtained upon dividing $f_1(x)$ by $f_2(x)$ by $-f_3(x)$, the remainder obtained upon dividing $f_2(x)$ by $f_3(x)$ by $-f_4(x)$, and so on, we obtain the chain of identities

$$f_1(x) = q_1(x)f_2(x) - f_3(x), \ldots, f_{k-1}(x) = q_{k-1}(x)f_k(x) - f_{k+1}(x),$$
$$\ldots, f_{m-1}(x) = q_{m-1}(x)f_m(x), \tag{6}$$

where the last remainder which is not identically zero, $f_m(x)$, is the highest common factor of $f(x)$ and $g(x)$, and also the highest common factor of all the functions in the sequence (4) so constructed. If $f_m(x) \neq 0$ $(a < x < b)$, then the sequence (4) defined by the identities (6) satisfies conditions 1 and 2 and is accordingly a Sturm sequence. If the polynomial $f_m(x)$ has roots within the interval (a, b), then the sequence (4) is a generalized Sturm sequence, since one obtains a Sturm sequence by dividing all of its terms by $f_m(x)$.

From this it follows that the index of an arbitrary rational function $R(x)$ may be determined by using Sturm's theorem. All one needs to do is to write $R(x)$ in the form $Q(x) + g(x)/f(x)$, where $Q(x)$, $f(x)$, and $g(x)$ are all polynomials and the degree of $g(x)$ is at most that of $f(x)$. Then, if one constructs the generalized Sturm sequence for $f(x)$ and $g(x)$,

$$I_a^b R(x) = I_a^b \frac{g(x)}{f(x)} = V(a) - V(b).$$

Using Sturm's theorem, one can determine the number of distinct roots of a polynomial $f(x)$ within an interval (a, b), since this number is equal to $I_a^b(f'(x)/f(x))$, as we have shown.

§ 3. Routh's algorithm

1. Routh's problem is that of determining the number k of roots of a real polynomial $f(z)$ lying in the right half-plane $(\operatorname{Re} z > 0)$.

We first consider the case in which $f(z)$ has no zeros on the imaginary axis. In the right half plane we construct the semicircle with radius R and center at 0 and consider the domain bounded by this semicircle and the imaginary axis (Fig. 2). For a suf-

Fig. 2.

ficiently large value of R all k zeros of the polynomial $f(z)$ with positive real parts will lie within the domain. Thus arg $f(z)$ will increase by $2k\pi$ as z traverses the boundary of the domain once in the positive direction.[10] On the other hand, the increase in arg $f(z)$ along the semicircle of radius R as $R \to \infty$ is the increase in the argument of the leading term $a_0 z^n$ and is thus equal to $n\pi$. Thus we obtain the formula

$$\Delta_{-\infty}^{+\infty} \arg f(i\omega) = (n - 2k)\pi \tag{7}$$

for the increase in arg $f(z)$ along the imaginary axis.

We shall now introduce a notation for the coefficients of the polynomial $f(z)$ which is not quite the usual one. Namely, we put:

$$f(z) = a_0 x^n + b_0 z^{n-1} + a_1 z^{n-2} + b_1 z^{n-3} + \ldots \quad (a_0 \neq 0).$$

Then

$$f(i\omega) = U(\omega) + iV(\omega) \tag{8}$$

where for even values of n

---

[10] In fact, if $f(z) = a_0 \prod_{i=1}^{n} (z - z_i)$ then

$$\Delta \arg f(z) = \sum_{i=1}^{n} \Delta \arg (z - z_i).$$

If z_i lies within the domain under consideration, $\Delta \arg (z - z_i) = 2\pi$.

$$U(\omega) = (-1)^{\frac{n}{2}} (a_0 \omega^n - a_1 \omega^{n-2} + a_2 \omega^{n-4} - \ldots),$$
$$V(\omega) = (-1)^{\frac{n}{2}-1} (b_0 \omega^{n-1} - b_1 \omega^{n-3} + b_2 \omega^{n-5} - \ldots), \tag{8'}$$

and for odd values of n

$$U(\omega) = (-1)^{\frac{n-1}{2}} (b_0 \omega^{n-1} - b_1 \omega^{n-3} + b_2 \omega^{n-5} - \ldots),$$
$$V(\omega) = (-1)^{\frac{n-1}{2}} (a_0 \omega^n - a_1 \omega^{n-2} + a_2 \omega^{n-4} - \ldots). \tag{8''}$$

Following Routh, we avail ourselves of the Cauchy index. Then

$$\frac{1}{\pi} \Delta_{-\infty}^{+\infty} \arg f(i\omega) = \begin{cases} I_{-\infty}^{+\infty} \dfrac{U(\omega)}{V(\omega)}, & \text{if } \lim\limits_{\omega \to \infty} \dfrac{U(\omega)}{V(\omega)} = 0, \\[2ex] I_{-\infty}^{+\infty} \dfrac{V(\omega)}{U(\omega)}, & \text{if } \lim\limits_{\omega \to \infty} \dfrac{V(\omega)}{U(\omega)} = 0. \end{cases} \tag{9}$$

The equations (8') and (8'') show that for even values of n the lower formula in (9) is valid, and for odd values of n the upper. Moreover, from (7), (8'), (8''), and (9) we may easily obtain that for any value of n (even or odd)

$$I_{-\infty}^{+\infty} \frac{b_0 \omega^{n-1} - b_1 \omega^{n-3} + \ldots}{a_0 \omega^n - a_1 \omega^{n-2} + \ldots} = n - 2k. \tag{10}$$

Here it is to be recalled that by assumption $f(z)$ has no roots on the imaginary axis.

2. In order to determine the index on the left side of equation (10) we shall apply Sturm's theorem (cf. the preceding section). Putting

$$f_1(\omega) = a_0 \omega^n - a_1 \omega^{n-2} + \ldots, \quad f_2(\omega) = b_0 \omega^{n-1} - b_1 \omega^{n-3} + \ldots, \tag{11}$$

we construct a generalized Sturm sequence

$$f_1(\omega), \ f_2(\omega), \ f_3(\omega), \ldots, f_m(\omega) \tag{12}$$

by use of the Euclidean algorithm.

We shall consider first the *regular case* in which $m = n + 1$.

In this case the degree of each term in the sequence (12) is one less than that of the preceding term, and the degree of the last function $f_m(w)$ is zero; moreover, the sequence (12) is in fact an ordinary (ungeneralized) Sturm sequence.

From the Euclidean algorithm (cf. (6)), it follows that

$$f_3(\omega) = \frac{a_0}{b_0} f_2(\omega) - f_1(\omega) = c_0 \omega^{n-2} - c_1 \omega^{n-4} + c_2 \omega^{n-6} - \cdots,$$

where

$$c_0 = a_1 - \frac{a_0}{b_0} b_1 = \frac{b_0 a_1 - a_0 b_1}{b_0}, \quad c_1 = a_2 - \frac{a_0}{b_0} b_2 = \frac{b_0 a_2 - a_0 b_2}{b_0}, \ldots \quad (13)$$

In exactly the same way,

$$f_4(\omega) = \frac{b_0}{c_0} f_3(\omega) - f_2(\omega) = d_0 \omega^{n-3} - d_1 \omega^{n-5} + \cdots,$$

where

$$d_0 = b_1 - \frac{b_0}{c_0} c_1 = \frac{c_0 b_1 - b_0 c_1}{c_0}, \quad d_1 = b_2 - \frac{b_0}{c_0} c_2 = \frac{c_0 b_2 - b_0 c_2}{c_0}, \ldots \quad (13')$$

The coefficients of the other polynomials in the sequence may be found analogously. The polynomials

$$f_1(\omega), \ f_2(\omega), \ldots, f_{n+1}(\omega) \quad (14)$$

are even and odd functions with the parity alternating.

Next, we construct the *Routh scheme*:

$$\begin{matrix} a_0, & a_1, & a_2, \ldots, \\ b_0, & b_1, & b_2, \ldots, \\ c_0, & c_1, & c_2, \ldots, \\ d_0, & d_1, & d_2, \ldots, \\ \cdot & \cdot & \cdot \cdot \cdot \cdot \end{matrix} \quad (15)$$

In this scheme, as the formulas (13) and (13') show, each line is determined by the two preceding ones according to the following rule:

From the numbers of the upper row we subtract the corresponding numbers of the lower row multiplied by a number such that the first difference is zero. If we discard this zero difference, we obtain the row sought.

The regular case is obviously characterized by the fact that in the sequence

$$b_0, \ c_0, \ d_0, \ \ldots$$

obtained by applying this rule repeatedly we encounter no numbers which are equal to zero.

In Figures 3 and 4 the skeleton of the Routh scheme is shown for an even value of n ($n = 6$) and an odd value of n ($n = 7$). Here the elements of the scheme are indicated by points.

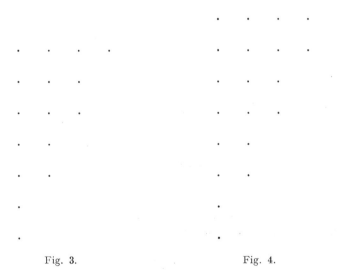

Fig. 3.   Fig. 4.

In the regular case the polynomials $f_1(\omega)$ and $f_2(\omega)$ have as highest common factor the nonzero constant $f_{n+1}(\omega)$. Thus these polynomials, and consequently $U(\omega)$ and $V(\omega)$ (cf. (8'), (8''), and (11)) do not vanish simultaneously, and the function $f(i\omega) = U(\omega) + iV(\omega) \neq 0$ for real values of ω. Thus *in the regular case the formula* (10) *is valid.*

Applying Sturm's theorem for the interval $(-\infty, +\infty)$ to the left member of this formula and making use of the sequence (14), we obtain, by (10):

$$V(-\infty) - V(+\infty) = n - 2k. \tag{16}$$

In the given case [11]

$$V(+\infty) = V(a_0, b_0, c_0, \ldots)$$

and

$$V(-\infty) = V(a_0, -b_0, c_0, -d_0, \ldots).$$

Hence

$$V(-\infty) = n - V(+\infty). \tag{17}$$

From the equations (16) and (17) we find:

$$k = V(a_0, b_0, c_0, d_0, \ldots). \tag{18}$$

This proves

THEOREM 2 (Routh). *The number of roots of a real polynomial $f(z)$ which lie in the right half-plane* Re $z > 0$ *is equal to the number of changes of sign in the first column of the Routh scheme.*

3. We consider now the important special case in which all of the roots of $f(z)$ have negative real parts (the "stable" case). If we construct the generalized Sturm sequence (12) for the polynomials (11) in this case, then since $k = 0$ the formula (16) becomes:

$$V(-\infty) - V(+\infty) = n. \tag{19}$$

But $0 \leq V(-\infty) \leq m - 1 \leq n$ and $0 \leq V(+\infty) \leq m - 1 \leq n$. Hence the equation (19) is possibly only when $m = n + 1$ (the regular case!) and $V(+\infty) = 0$, $V(-\infty) = m - 1 = n$. Then from formula (18) follows

THE ROUTH CRITERION. *In order for all of the roots of the real polynomial $f(z)$ to have negative real parts, it is necessary and sufficient that all of the elements in the first column of the Routh scheme be different from zero and of the same sign.*

---

[11] The sign of $f_k(\omega)$ for $\omega = +\infty$ is taken to be that of its leading coefficient, and for $\omega = -\infty$ is that of the leading coefficient after it has been multiplied by $(-1)^{n-k+1}$ ($k = 1, 2, \ldots, n + 1$).

4. In establishing Routh's theorem we operated with formula (10). In the sequel we shall need a generalization of this formula. Formula (10) was introduced on the assumption that the polynomial $f(z)$ has no roots on the imaginary axis. We shall show that in the general case, when $f(z)$ has k roots in the right half-plane and s roots on the imaginary axis, then formula (10) should be replaced by the formula

$$I_{-\infty}^{+\infty} \frac{b_0 \omega^{n-1} - b_1 \omega^{n-3} + b_2 \omega^{n-5} - \ldots}{a_0 \omega^n - a_1 \omega^{n-2} + a_2 \omega^{n-4} - \ldots} = n - 2k - s. \quad (20)$$

In fact

$$f(z) = d(z)f^*(z)$$

where the real polynomial $d(z) = z^s + \ldots$ has s roots on the imaginary axis, and the polynomial $f^*(z)$ of degree $n^* = n - s$ has no such roots.

For the sake of concreteness we shall consider the case in which s is an even number; the case in which s is odd can be disposed of in a completely analogous way.

Let

$$f(i\omega) = U(\omega) + iV(\omega) = d(i\omega)[U^*(\omega) + iV^*(\omega)].$$

Since in the case being considered $d(i\omega)$ is a real polynomial in ω,

$$\frac{U(\omega)}{V(\omega)} = \frac{U^*(\omega)}{V^*(\omega)}.$$

Since in this case n and n^* are of the same parity, applying the equations (8') and (8'') and the notation (11) we find:

$$\frac{f_2(\omega)}{f_1(\omega)} = \frac{f_2^*(\omega)}{f_1^*(\omega)}.$$

Since the formula (10) is applicable to the polynomial $f^*(z)$,

$$I_{-\infty}^{+\infty} \frac{f_2(\omega)}{f_1(\omega)} = I_{-\infty}^{+\infty} \frac{f_2^*(\omega)}{f_1^*(\omega)} = n^* - 2k = n - 2k - s,$$

which was to be shown.

§ 4. Singular cases. Examples

1. In the preceding section we analyzed the regular case, where in the Routh scheme none of the numbers b_0, c_0, d_0, ... turn out to be zero.

We shall turn now to the *singular* case where in calculating the sequence of numbers b_0, c_0, ... we encounter a number $h_0 = 0$. The Routh algorithm stops short on the line where h_0 occurs, since in order to obtain the numbers in later lines it would be necessary to divide by h_0.

Singular cases fall into two categories:

1. In the line where h_0 occurs there are nonzero numbers. This means that at some place in the sequence (12) the drop in degree is greater than one.

2. All of the numbers in the line containing h_0 are simultaneously zero. In this case the line in question must be the $(m + 1)^{st}$, where m is the number of terms in the generalized Sturm sequence (12). The degrees of the functions in the sequence (12) all drop one by one, but the degree of the last polynomial $f_m(\omega)$ is greater than zero.

In either case the number of functions in the sequence (12) is less than $n + 1$. Since the ordinary Routh algorithm breaks off in both cases, Routh gives special rules for completing the scheme.

2. In case *1*, following Routh, one substitutes a "small" quantity ε in place of $h_0 = 0$, where ε has a definite (but arbitrary) sign, and proceeds with the completion of the scheme. When this is done the subsequent elements in the first column of the scheme will be rational functions of ε. These elements will have definite signs, depending on the "smallness" and sign of ε. If any of these elements in identically zero relative to ε, we replace it by another small quantity η and proceed with the algorithm.

Example.

$$f(z) = z^4 + z^3 + 2z^2 + 2z + 1.$$

The Routh scheme (with a small parameter ε) is

$$1, \qquad\qquad 2, \quad 1$$
$$1, \qquad\qquad 2$$
$$\varepsilon, \qquad\qquad\quad 1 \qquad\qquad k = V(1,\ 1,\ \varepsilon,\ 2 - 1/\varepsilon,\ 1) = 2.$$
$$2 - 1/\varepsilon$$
$$1$$

The justification for this curious method of varying the elements of the scheme is this:

Since we have assumed that the case in question is not of type 2, the functions $f_1(\omega)$ and $f_2(\omega)$ must be relatively prime. From this it follows that the polynomial $f(z)$ can have no roots on the imaginary axis.

In the Routh scheme all of the elements are rational functions of the elements of the first two rows, i.e., of the coefficients of the given polynomial. But it is not hard to see from the formulas (13) and (13′) and the analogous formulas for succeeding rows that once arbitrary values are given for the elements of any two consecutive rows in the Routh scheme, and for the first element in each of the preceding rows, we may obtain all of the numbers in the first two rows, the coefficients of the given polynomial, as rational functions of the given numbers which, as functions of the elements of the given consecutive pair of rows, are entire. Thus, for instance, all of the a's and b's can be written as rational functions of

$$a_0,\ b_0,\ c_0,\ \ldots,\ h_0,\ h_1,\ \ldots,\ g_0,\ g_1,\ \ldots..$$

which are entire as functions of $h_0,\ h_1,\ \ldots,\ g_0,\ g_1,\ \ldots.$. Thus by changing $h_0 = 0$ to ε we in effect alter our original polynomial. Instead of the Routh scheme for $f(z)$ we obtain the Routh scheme for a polynomial $F(z,\ \varepsilon)$ which coincides with $f(z)$ when $\varepsilon = 0$. Since the roots of $F(z,\ \varepsilon)$ change continuously when ε changes, and when $\varepsilon = 0$ the function has no roots on the imaginary axis, it follows that when ε is sufficiently small in absolute value the polynomials $F(z,\ \varepsilon)$ and $F(z,\ 0) = f(z)$ have the same number k of roots in the right half-plane.

3.   Now we shall proceed to a consideration of singular cases of type 2. In the Routh scheme, let

$$a_0 \neq 0, \ b_0 \neq 0, \ \ldots, \ e_0 \neq 0, \ h_0 = 0, \ h_1 = 0, \ h_2 = 0, \ \ldots$$

In this case the last polynomial in the generalized Sturm sequence (16) has the form:

$$f_m(\omega) = e_0 \omega^{n-m+1} - e_1 \omega^{n-m-1} + \cdots$$

Routh suggested changing the vanishing polynomial $f_{m+1}(\omega)$ to $f'_m(\omega)$, i.e., writing the coefficients

$$(n - m + 1)e_0, \ (n - m - 1)e_1, \ldots$$

in place of the vanishing numbers $h_0, \ h_1, \ \ldots$, and proceeding with the algorithm.

The justification for this rule is as follows:

According to the formula at the end of Section 3,

$$I_{-\infty}^{+\infty} \frac{f_2(\omega)}{f_1(\omega)} = n - 2k - s$$

(the s roots of $f(z)$ on the imaginary axis are the same as the real roots of the polynomial $f_m(\omega)$). Hence, if these real roots are simple,

$$I_{-\infty}^{+\infty} \frac{f'_m(\omega)}{f_m(\omega)} = s$$

and, consequently,

$$I_{-\infty}^{+\infty} \frac{f_2(\omega)}{f_1(\omega)} + I_{-\infty}^{+\infty} \frac{f'_m(\omega)}{f_m(\omega)} = n - 2k.$$

This formula shows that the missing part of the Routh scheme should be supplied by the Routh scheme for the two polynomials $f_m(\omega)$ and $f'_m(\omega)$. The coefficients of the polynomial $f'_m(\omega)$ are used for the values of the elements of the zero row in the Routh scheme.

If the real roots of $f_m(\omega)$ are not simple, then if we denote by $d(\omega)$ the highest common factor of $f_m(\omega)$ and $f'_m(\omega)$, by $e(\omega)$ the highest common factor of $d(\omega)$ and $d'(\omega)$, etc., we will have:

$$I_{-\infty}^{+\infty} \frac{f'(\omega)}{f(\omega)} + I_{-\infty}^{+\infty} \frac{d'(\omega)}{d(\omega)} + I_{-\infty}^{+\infty} \frac{e'(\omega)}{e(\omega)} + \ldots = s.$$

Thus the desired number k may be obtained if the missing part of the Routh scheme is replaced by the Routh schemes for $f_m(\omega)$ and $f'_m(\omega)$, $d(\omega)$ and $d'(\omega)$, $e(\omega)$ and $e'(\omega)$, etc.

Example.

$$f(z) = z^{10} + z^9 - z^8 - 2z^7 + z^6 + 3z^5 + z^4 - 2z^3 - z^2 + z + 1.$$

The scheme is

ω^{10}	1	$-$ 1	1	1	$-$ 1	1
ω^9	1	$-$ 2	3	$-$ 2	1	
ω^8	1	$-$ 2	3	$-$ 2	1	

$$\omega^7 \begin{cases} 8 & -12 & 12 & -4 \\ 2 & -3 & 3 & -1 \end{cases}$$

ω^6	$-$ 1	3 $-$ 3	2

$$\omega^5 \begin{cases} 3 & -3 & 3 \\ 1 & -1 & 1 \end{cases}$$

$$\omega^4 \begin{cases} 2 & -2 & 2 \\ 1 & -1 & 1 \end{cases}$$

$$\omega^3 \begin{cases} 4 & -2 \\ 2 & -1 \end{cases}$$

ω^2	$-$ 1	2
ω	1	

$$\omega^0 \begin{cases} 2 \\ 1 \end{cases} \qquad k = V(1, 1, 1, 2, -1, 1, 1, 2, -1, 1, 1) = 4.$$

REMARK. One may multiply all of the elements of any row by the same positive number without changing the signs in the first scheme.

4. However, the application of both of Routh's rules does not make it possible to determine the value of k in all cases. The application of the first rule (the introduction of the small parameters ε, η, . . .) is justified only when the polynomial $f(z)$ has no roots on the imaginary axis.

If the polynomial $f(z)$ has roots on the imaginary axis, then changing the parameter ε may move some of these roots into the right half-plane and thus change the value of k.

Example.

$$f(z) = z^6 + z^5 + 3z^4 + 3z^3 + 3z^2 + 2z + 1.$$

The scheme is

ω^6	1	3	3	1
ω^5	1	3	2	
ω^4	ε	1	1	

$$\omega^3 \quad 3 - \frac{1}{\varepsilon} \quad 2 - \frac{1}{\varepsilon} \quad \left(u = 2 - \frac{1}{\varepsilon} - \frac{3 - \dfrac{1}{\varepsilon}}{1 - \dfrac{2\varepsilon - 1}{3 - \dfrac{1}{\varepsilon}}} = -\varepsilon + \ldots \right)$$

$$\omega^2 \quad 1 - \frac{2\varepsilon - 1}{3 - \dfrac{1}{\varepsilon}} \quad 1$$

$$\omega \quad u \qquad\qquad V\left(1, 1, \varepsilon, 3 - \frac{1}{\varepsilon}, 1, -\varepsilon, 1\right) = \begin{cases} 4 \text{ if } \varepsilon > 0, \\ 2 \text{ if } \varepsilon < 0. \end{cases}$$

$$\omega^0 \quad 1$$

The question as to which of these numbers is equal to k remains open.

In the general case, when $f(z)$ has roots on the imaginary axis, it is necessary to proceed as follows:

Putting $f(z) = F_1(z) + F_2(z)$, where

$$F_1(z) = a_0 z^n + a_1 z^{n-2} + \ldots, \quad F_2(z) = b_0 z^{n-1} + b_1 z^{n-3} + \ldots,$$

one must find the highest common factor $d(z)$ of the polynomials $F_1(z)$ and $F_2(z)$. Then $f(z) = d(z)f^*(z)$.

If $f(z)$ has a root z such that $-z$ is also a root (all roots on the imaginary axis have this property) then it follows from $f(z) = 0$ and $f(-z) = 0$ that $F_1(z) = 0$ and $F_2(z) = 0$, i.e., z is a root of $d(z)$. Hence the polynomial $f^*(z)$ has no root z such that $-z$ is also a root.

Then

$$k = k_1 + k_2,$$

where k_1 and k_2 are the numbers of roots in the right half-plane of $f^*(z)$ and $d(z)$ respectively; k_1 may be determined by Routh's algorithm, and $k_2 = (q - s)/2$, where q is the degree of $d(z)$ and s is the number of real roots of the polynomial $d(i\omega)$.[12]

In the last example,

$$d(z) = z^2 + 1, \quad f^*(z) = z^4 + z^3 + 2z^2 + 2z + 1.$$

Thus (cf. the first example in this section) $k_2 = 0$, $k_1 = 2$ and, consequently, $k = 2$.

§ 5. Lyapunov's theorem

From the investigations of A. M. Lyapunov published in 1892 in his monograph *The General Problem of the Stability of Motion*, there follows a theorem [13] which gives necessary and sufficient conditions for the roots of the characteristic equation $\det(\lambda E - A) = 0$ of the real matrix $A = (a_{ik})_1^n$ to have negative real parts. Since an arbitrary polynomial

$$f(\lambda) = a_0 \lambda^n + a_1 \lambda^{n-1} + \ldots + a_n \quad (a_0 \neq 0)$$

may be represented as a characteristic determinant [14] $\det(\lambda E - A)$, Lyapunov's theorem is of a general character and can be applied to any algebraic equation $f(\lambda) = 0$.

Let there be given the real matrix $A = (a_{ik})_1^n$ and a homogeneous polynomial of the mth order relative to the variables $x_1, x_2, \ldots, x_n$:

---

[12] $d(i\omega)$ is a real polynomial, or else becomes one upon division by i. One can use Sturm's theorem to find how many real roots it has.

[13] Cf. [42], Section 20.

[14] To this end it suffices, for example, to put

$$A = \begin{bmatrix} 0, & 0, & \ldots, & 0, & -a_n/a_0 \\ 1, & 0, & \ldots, & 0, & -a_{n-1}/a_0 \\ & \cdot & \cdot & & \\ & & \cdot & \cdot & \\ & & & \cdot & \cdot \\ 0, & 0, & \ldots, & 1, & -a_1/a_0 \end{bmatrix}.$$

$$V(\underbrace{x, \; x, \; \ldots, \; x}_{m}) \qquad [x = (x_1, \; x_2, \; \ldots, \; x_n)].$$

On the assumption that x is a solution of the vector differential equation

$$dx/dt = Ax$$

we calculate the total derivative of the function $V(x, \; x, \; .., \; x)$ with respect to t:

$$\frac{d}{dt} V(x, \; x, \; \ldots, \; x) = V(Ax, \; x, \; \ldots, \; x) \tag{21}$$

$$+ \; V(x, \; Ax, \; \ldots, \; x) + \ldots + V(x, \; x, \; \ldots, \; Ax) = W(x, \; x, \; \ldots, \; x),$$

where $W(x, \; x, \; \ldots, \; x)$ is again a homogeneous polynomial of the mth order relative to the variables $x_1, x_2, \ldots, x_n$. The equation (21) defines a linear operator $\mathscr{L}$ which assigns to each homogeneous polynomial of the mth order, $V(x, \; x, \; \ldots, \; x)$, some homogeneous polynomial $W(x, \; x, \; \ldots x)$ of the same order m:

$$W = \mathscr{L}(V).$$

We shall confine ourselves to the case [15] $m = 2$. In this case $V(x, \; x)$ and $W(x, \; x)$ are quadratic forms in the variables $x_1, x_2, \ldots, x_n$ and are connected by the equation

$$\frac{d}{dt} V(x, \; x) = V(Ax, \; x) + V(x, \; Ax) = W(x, \; x), \tag{22}$$

whence, since $V(x, \; y) = x'Vy$,

$$W = \mathscr{L}(V) = A'V + VA. \tag{23}$$

Here $V = ||v_{ik}||_1^n$ and $W = ||w_{ik}||_1^n$ are symmetric matrices made up of the coefficients of the forms $V(x, \; x)$ and $W(x, \; x)$ respectively. The linear operator $\mathscr{L}$ in the space of nth order matrices V is fully defined when the matrix A is given.

If $\lambda_1, \lambda_2, \ldots, \lambda_n$ are characteristic roots of the matrix A, then

---

[15] Lyapunov proved his theorem (cf. Theorem 3 below) for any positive integer m.

each characteristic number of the operator $\mathscr{L}$ can be represented in the form $\lambda_i + \lambda_k$ $(1 \leqq i,\ k \leqq n)$.[16]

Therefore, if the matrix A has neither zero as a characteristic root nor a pair of characteristic roots which add up to zero, the operator $\mathscr{L}$ is nonsingular. In this case if the matrix W is given the matrix V is uniquely defined in (23).

If V is a symmetric matrix, then the matrix W defined by the equation (23) is also symmetric. If $\mathscr{L}(V)$ is a nonsingular operator, the converse also holds: to an arbitrary symmetric matrix W there corresponds, by virtue of (23), a symmetric matrix V. In fact, if in this case we go over to the transposed matrix on both sides of (23) we find that the matrix V' as well as the matrix V satisfies the equation (23). By the uniqueness of the solution, it must then be true that $V = V'$.

In this manner we see that *if the matrix A does not have zero as a characteristic root, and has no pair of characteristic roots whose sum is zero, then to each quadratic form $W(x, x)$ there corresponds one and only one quadratic form $V(x, x)$ related to $W(x, x)$ by the equation* (22).

We are now in a position to formulate Lyapunov's theorem.

THEOREM 3 (Lyapunov). *If all characteristic roots of the real matrix A have negative real parts, then to an arbitrary negative definite quadratic form $W(x, x)$ there corresponds a positive definite quadratic form $V(x, x)$ such that if one takes*

$$dx/dt = Ax \qquad (24)$$

then $V(x, x)$ and $W(x, x)$ satisfy

$$\frac{d}{dt} V(x, x) = W(x, x). \qquad (25)$$

Conversely, if for some negative definite form $W(x, x)$ there exists a positive definite form $V(x, x)$ connected with $W(x, x)$ by the equations (24) *and* (25), *then all characteristic roots of the matrix A have negative real parts.*

[16] See Note 18, Chapter IV, p. 148.

Proof. (i). Let all of the characteristic roots of the matrix A have negative real parts. Then for an arbitrary solution $x = e^{At}x_0$ of the equation (24) we have: $\lim_{t \to \infty} x = 0$. Let the forms $V(x, x)$ and $W(x, x)$ be connected by the formula (25), and $W(x, x) < 0$ $(x \neq 0)$. (The form $W(x, x)$ is to be thought of as given, and $V(x, x)$ is then uniquely defined by (25), since under the present assumptions 0 is not a characteristic root of A, and no two characteristic roots of A can have 0 as their sum.)

We suppose that for some $x_0 \neq 0$

$$V_0 = V(x_0, x_0) < 0.$$

But

$$\frac{d}{dt} V(x, x) = W(x, x) < 0 \quad (x = e^{At}x_0).$$

Thus, for $t > 0$, the quantity $V(x, x)$ is negative and decreases as $t \to \infty$; but this contradicts the equation

$$\lim_{t \to \infty} V(x, x) = \lim_{x \to 0} V(x, x) = 0.$$

Consequently $V(x, x) > 0$ for $x \neq 0$; i.e., $V(x, x)$ is a positive definite quadratic form.

(ii). Conversely, let it be given that in the equation (25)

$$W(x, x) < 0, \quad V(x, x) > 0 \quad (x \neq 0).$$

From (25) it follows that

$$V(x, x) = V(x_0, x_0) + \int_0^t W(x, x)dt \quad (x = e^{At}x_0). \tag{25'}$$

We shall show that for an arbitrary $x_0 \neq 0$ the vector $x = e^{At}x_0$ comes arbitrarily near zero for certain arbitrarily large positive values of t. We assume the contrary. Then there exists a number $\nu > 0$ such that

$$W(x, x) < -\nu < 0 \quad (x = e^{At}x_0, \ x_0 \neq 0)$$

for all positive values of t. But then, from (25'),

$$V(x, x) < V(x_0, x_0) - \nu t$$

and, consequently, for all sufficiently large values of t, $V(x, x) < 0$, and this contradicts the assumption.

From what has been shown it follows that for some sufficiently large values of t the quantity $V(x, x)$ $(x = e^{At}x_0,\ x_0 \neq 0)$ will be arbitrarily near zero. But $V(x, x)$ decreases monotonically for $t > 0$, by virtue of

$$dV(x, x)/dt = W(x, x) < 0.$$

Hence $\lim_{t \to \infty} V(x, x) = 0$.

From this it follows that for an arbitrary $x_0 \neq 0$, $\lim_{t \to \infty} e^{At}x_0 = 0$, i.e., $\lim_{t \to \infty} e^{At} = 0$. This is possible only if all of the characteristic roots of the matrix A have negative real parts.

The theorem is completely proved.

For the form $W(x, x)$ in Lyapunov's theorem one may choose any negative definite quadratic form; in particular, one may choose the form $-x_1^2 - x_2^2 - \ldots - x_n^2$. In this case the theorem assumes the following formulation in terms of matrices:

THEOREM 3'. *In order that all the characteristic roots of the real matrix A have negative real parts it is necessary and sufficient that the matrix equation*

$$A'V + VA = -E \qquad (26)$$

has as a solution the matrix of coefficients of some positive definite quadratic form $V(x, x) > 0$.

From the theorems just proved there follows Lyapunov's well-known criterion for the determination of stability of a non-linear system in terms of its linear approximation.[17]

Suppose that one wishes to show that the null solution of the nonlinear system of differential equations (1) is asymptotically stable when the coefficients a_{ik} of the linear terms in the right hand members of the equations form a matrix A all of whose characteristic roots have negative real parts. Then if we define the positive definite form $V(x, x)$ by means of the matrix equation (26) and calculate its total derivative with respect to time on

---

[17] Cf. Lyapunov, [42], Section 26; Bellman [3], Ch. 4; Lefschetz [40], Ch. IV.

the assumption that $x = (x_1, x_2, \ldots, x_n)$ is a solution of the given system (1), we obtain

$$\frac{d}{dt} V(x, x) = - \sum_{i=1}^{n} x_i^2 + R(x_1, x_2, \ldots, x_n),$$

where $R(x_1, x_2, \ldots, x_n)$ is a series made up of terms of at least the third degree in $x_1, x_2, \ldots, x_n$. Thus in some sufficiently small neighborhood of the point $(0, 0, \ldots, 0)$ the inequalities

$$V(x, x) > 0, \quad \frac{d}{dt} V(x, x) < 0$$

hold simultaneously for any $x \neq 0$.

According to Lyapunov's general stability criterion,[18] this indicates that the null solution of the system of differential equations is asymptotically stable.

If one uses the equation (26) to express the elements of the matrix V in terms of the matrix A and substitutes the resulting expressions in the inequalities

$$v_{11} > 0, \quad \det \begin{bmatrix} v_{11} & v_{12} \\ v_{21} & v_{22} \end{bmatrix} > 0, \ldots, \quad \det \begin{bmatrix} v_{11} & v_{12} \cdots v_{1n} \\ v_{21} & v_{22} \cdots v_{2n} \\ \cdots \cdots \cdots \\ v_{n1} & v_{n2} \cdots v_{nn} \end{bmatrix} > 0,$$

then one obtains inequalities which the elements of the matrix A must satisfy in order for the characteristic roots of this matrix to have negative real parts. However, these inequalities may be obtained in a remarkably simpler way from the Routh-Hurwitz criterion, which is the subject of the next section.

REMARK. Lyapunov's theorems 3 and 3' can be directly generalized to cover the case of an arbitrary *complex* matrix A. In this case the quadratic forms $V(x, x)$ and $W(x, x)$ are replaced by the Hermitian forms

$$V(x, x) = \sum_{i, k=1}^{n} v_{ik} \bar{x}_i x_k, \quad W(x, x) = \sum_{i, k=1}^{n} w_{ik} \bar{x}_i x_k.$$

---

[18] Lyapunov [42], Section 16.

Correspondingly, the matrix equation (26) is replaced by the equation

$$A^*V + VA = -E \quad (A^* = \bar{A}').$$

§ 6. The Routh-Hurwitz theorem

In the preceding sections we have investigated Routh's method, unexcelled in its simplicity, for determining the number k of roots of a real polynomial which lie in the right half-plane, if the coefficients of the polynomial are given as specific numbers. But if the coefficients of the polynomial depend on certain parameters, and one wishes to determine for what values of the parameters the number k has a specific value, in particular the value 0 (the domain of stability!),[19] it is desirable to have concrete expressions for the quantities $c_0, d_0, \ldots$ in terms of the coefficients of the given polynomial. In the process of solving this problem, we shall obtain another method for determining the number k and, in particular, the stability criterion in the form in which it was obtained by Hurwitz.[20]

Again we consider the polynomial

$$f(z) = a_0 z^n + b_0 z^{n-1} + a_1 z^{n-2} + b_1 z^{n-3} + \ldots \quad (a_0 \neq 0).$$

The square matrix of order n

$$H = \begin{bmatrix} b_0, & b_1, & b_2, \ldots, b_{n-1} \\ a_0, & a_1, & a_2, \ldots, a_{n-1} \\ 0, & b_0, & b_1, \ldots, b_{n-2} \\ 0, & a_0, & a_1, \ldots, a_{n-2} \\ 0, & 0, & b_0, \ldots, b_{n-3} \\ \cdot & \cdot & \cdot \cdot \cdot \cdot \cdot \cdot \cdot \\ \cdot & \cdot & \cdot \cdot \cdot \cdot \cdot \cdot \cdot \end{bmatrix} \quad \left(\begin{matrix} a_k = 0 \text{ if } k > \left[\dfrac{n}{2} \right], \\ b_k = 0 \text{ if } k > \left[\dfrac{n-1}{2} \right] \end{matrix} \right) \quad (27)$$

will be called the *Hurwitz matrix*.

We shall transform this matrix by subtracting from the second, fourth, etc., rows the first, third, etc., respectively, first multi-

[19] This is precisely the situation that occurs in the designing of new mechanical or electrical control systems.
[20] Hurwitz [28].

plying the latter by a_0/b_0. We first confine our attention to the regular case, in which $b_0 \neq 0$, $c_0 \neq 0$, ... This yields the matrix

$$
\begin{bmatrix}
b_0 & b_1 & b_2 \dots b_{n-1} \\
0 & c_0 & c_1 \dots c_{n-2} \\
0 & b_0 & b_1 \dots b_{n-2} \\
0 & 0 & c_0 \dots c_{n-3} \\
0 & 0 & b_0 \dots b_{n-3} \\
\cdots\cdots\cdots \\
\cdots\cdots\cdots
\end{bmatrix}
$$

Here c_0, c_1, ... is the third row of the Routh scheme, filled out with zeros $(c_k = 0$ if $k > [n/2] - 1)$.

We again transform the matrix so obtained, subtracting from the third, fifth, etc., rows the second, fourth, etc., respectively, first multiplying the latter by b_0/c_0:

$$
\begin{bmatrix}
b_0 & b_1 & b_2 & b_3 \dots \\
0 & c_0 & c_1 & c_2 \dots \\
0 & 0 & d_0 & d_1 \dots \\
0 & 0 & c_0 & c_1 \dots \\
0 & 0 & 0 & d_0 \dots \\
0 & 0 & 0 & c_0 \dots \\
\cdots\cdots\cdots\cdots \\
\cdots\cdots\cdots\cdots
\end{bmatrix}
$$

Applying this process further, we ultimately arrive at a triangular nth order matrix

$$
R = \begin{bmatrix}
b_0 & b_1 & b_2 \dots \\
0 & c_0 & c_1 \dots \\
0 & 0 & d_0 \dots \\
\cdots\cdots\cdots
\end{bmatrix},
\tag{28}
$$

which we shall call the *Routh matrix*. It is obtained from the Routh scheme (cf. (15)) by (i) discarding the first row, (ii) shifting the rows to the right so that their first elements lie on the principal diagonal, and (iii) filling out an nth order square matrix by introducing zeros.

DEFINITION 2. *Two matrices A and B are said to be* equivalent *if and only if for any* $p \leq n$ *corresponding pth order minors on the first p rows of these matrices are equal:*

$$A \begin{bmatrix} 1, & 2, & \ldots, p \\ i_1, & i_2, & \ldots, i_p \end{bmatrix} = B \begin{bmatrix} 1, & 2, & \ldots, p \\ i_1, & i_2, & \ldots, i_p \end{bmatrix} \quad (1 \leq i_k \leq n; \, p = 1, 2, \ldots, n).$$

Since the pth order minors on the first p rows $(p = 1, 2, \ldots, n)$ do not change their values if one subtracts from any rows whatever any preceding rows multiplied by arbitrary constants, the Hurwitz and Routh matrices are equivalent according to Definition 2:

$$H \begin{bmatrix} 1, & 2, \ldots, p \\ i_1, & i_2, \ldots, i_p \end{bmatrix} = R \begin{bmatrix} 1, & 2, \ldots, p \\ i_1, & i_2, \ldots, i_p \end{bmatrix} \quad \begin{pmatrix} i_1, i_2, \ldots, i_p = 1, 2, \ldots, n, \\ p = 1, 2, \ldots, n \end{pmatrix}.$$

$$\tag{29}$$

The equivalence of the matrices H and R permits one to express all of the elements of R, i.e. the elements of the Routh scheme, in terms of the minors of the Hurwitz matrix H, and therefore in terms of the coefficients of the given polynomial. In fact, upon assigning the values 1, 2, 3, ... successively to p in (29), we obtain:

$$\left. \begin{array}{lll} H \begin{bmatrix} 1 \\ 1 \end{bmatrix} = b_0, & H \begin{bmatrix} 1 \\ 2 \end{bmatrix} = b_1, & H \begin{bmatrix} 1 \\ 3 \end{bmatrix} = b_2, \ldots, \\[2ex] H \begin{bmatrix} 1 & 2 \\ 1 & 2 \end{bmatrix} = b_0 c_0, & H \begin{bmatrix} 1 & 2 \\ 1 & 3 \end{bmatrix} = b_0 c_1, & H \begin{bmatrix} 1 & 2 \\ 1 & 4 \end{bmatrix} = b_0 c_2, \ldots, \\[2ex] H \begin{bmatrix} 1 & 2 & 3 \\ 1 & 2 & 3 \end{bmatrix} = b_0 c_0 d_0, & H \begin{bmatrix} 1 & 2 & 3 \\ 1 & 2 & 4 \end{bmatrix} = b_0 c_0 d_1, & H \begin{bmatrix} 1 & 2 & 3 \\ 1 & 2 & 5 \end{bmatrix} = b_0 c_0 d_2, \ldots \end{array} \right\}$$

$$\tag{30}$$

etc.

Hence we find the following expressions for the elements of the Routh scheme:

$$b_0 = H\begin{bmatrix}1\\1\end{bmatrix}, \qquad b_1 = H\begin{bmatrix}1\\2\end{bmatrix}, \qquad b_2 = H\begin{bmatrix}1\\3\end{bmatrix}, \dots,$$

$$c_0 = \frac{H\begin{bmatrix}1&2\\1&2\end{bmatrix}}{H\begin{bmatrix}1\\1\end{bmatrix}}, \qquad c_1 = \frac{H\begin{bmatrix}1&2\\1&3\end{bmatrix}}{H\begin{bmatrix}1\\1\end{bmatrix}}, \qquad c_2 = \frac{H\begin{bmatrix}1&2\\1&4\end{bmatrix}}{H\begin{bmatrix}1\\1\end{bmatrix}}, \dots,$$

$$d_0 = \frac{H\begin{bmatrix}1&2&3\\1&2&3\end{bmatrix}}{H\begin{bmatrix}1&2\\1&2\end{bmatrix}}, \quad d_1 = \frac{H\begin{bmatrix}1&2&3\\1&2&4\end{bmatrix}}{H\begin{bmatrix}1&2\\1&2\end{bmatrix}}, \quad d_2 = \frac{H\begin{bmatrix}1&2&3\\1&2&5\end{bmatrix}}{H\begin{bmatrix}1&2\\1&2\end{bmatrix}}, \dots,$$

$$\tag{31}$$

The successive principal minors of the matrix H are usually called the *Hurwitz determinants*. We shall denote them by

$$\Delta_1 = H\begin{bmatrix}1\\1\end{bmatrix} = b_0, \ \Delta_2 = H\begin{bmatrix}1&2\\1&2\end{bmatrix} = \det\begin{bmatrix}b_0 & b_1\\a_0 & a_1\end{bmatrix}, \dots$$

$$\dots, \Delta_n = H\begin{bmatrix}1,\ 2,\ \dots,\ n\\1,\ 2,\ \dots,\ n\end{bmatrix} = \det\begin{bmatrix}b_0 & b_1 & \dots & b_{n-1}\\a_0 & a_1 & \dots & a_{n-1}\\0 & b_0 & \dots & b_{n-2}\\0 & a_0 & \dots & a_{n-2}\\\multicolumn{5}{c}{\dots\dots\dots}\end{bmatrix}. \tag{32}$$

REMARK 1. According to formulas (30)

$$\Delta_1 = b_0, \ \Delta_2 = b_0 c_0, \ \Delta_3 = b_0 c_0 d_0, \dots \tag{33}$$

From $\Delta_1 \neq 0, \dots, \Delta_p \neq 0$ it follows that the first p of the numbers $b_0, c_0, \dots$ are different from zero, and conversely; in this case p successive rows, starting with the third, are defined in the Routh scheme, and the formulas (31) apply to them. If the coefficients of $f(x)$ are given numerically, formulas (32) provide the simplest means of calculating the Hurwitz determinants, for this calculation is reduced to the construction of the Routh scheme.

REMARK 2. The regular case (all of the quantities $b_0, c_0, \dots$ are defined and are different from zero) is characterized by the

inequalities
$$\Delta_1 \neq 0, \ \Delta_2 \neq 0, \ldots, \Delta_n \neq 0.$$

REMARK 3. The determination of the elements of the Routh scheme with the aid of formulas (31) is more general than their determination by Routh's algorithm. Thus, for example, if $b_0 = 0$, Routh's algorithm gives us nothing beyond the first two rows, which are made up of coefficients of the given polynomial. However, if while $\Delta_1 = 0$ the remaining determinants $\Delta_2, \Delta_3, \ldots$ are different from zero, we may skip the row of c's and then determine all subsequent rows in the Routh scheme by means of the formulas (31).

According to formulas (33)
$$b_0 = \Delta_1, \quad c_0 = \frac{\Delta_2}{\Delta_1}, \quad d_0 = \frac{\Delta_3}{\Delta_2}, \ldots,$$

and thus
$$V(a_0, b_0, c_0, \ldots) = V\left(a_0, \Delta_1, \frac{\Delta_2}{\Delta_1}, \frac{\Delta_3}{\Delta_2}, \ldots, \frac{\Delta_n}{\Delta_{n-1}}\right)$$
$$= V(a_0, \Delta_1, \Delta_3, \ldots) + V(1, \Delta_2, \Delta_4, \ldots).$$

Consequently Routh's theorem can be formulated in the following way:

THEOREM 4 (Routh-Hurwitz). *The number k of roots of the real polynomial $f(z) = a_0 z^n + \ldots$ which lie in the right half-plane is given by the formula*
$$k = V\left(a_0, \Delta_1, \frac{\Delta_2}{\Delta_1}, \frac{\Delta_3}{\Delta_2}, \ldots, \frac{\Delta_n}{\Delta_{n-1}}\right) \tag{34}$$

or equivalently
$$k = V(a_0, \Delta_1, \Delta_3, \ldots) + V(1, \Delta_2, \Delta_4, \ldots). \tag{34'}$$

REMARK. The formulation of the Routh-Hurwitz theorem just introduced is based on the assumption that we are dealing with the regular case characterized by the inequalities
$$\Delta_1 \neq 0, \ \Delta_2 \neq 0, \ldots, \Delta_n \neq 0.$$

In subsequent sections we shall show how this formula can be extended to singular cases in which some of the Hurwitz determinants are equal to zero.

We now consider the special case in which all of the roots of the polynomial $f(z)$ lie in the left half-plane $\operatorname{Re} z < 0$. In this case, according to the Routh criterion, all of the numbers $a_0, b_0, c_0, \ldots$ must differ from zero and have the same sign. Since we are dealing with the regular case, we obtain from (34) with $k = 0$

THE ROUTH-HURWITZ CRITERION. *In order for the roots of the real polynomial $f(z) = a_0 a^n + \ldots \ (a_0 \neq 0)$ all to have negative real parts, it is necessary and sufficient that the inequalities*

$$a_0 \Delta_1 > 0, \ \Delta_2 > 0, \ a_0 \Delta_3 > 0, \ \Delta_4 > 0, \ldots, \quad \begin{array}{l} a_0 \Delta_n > 0 \ (n \text{ odd}) \\ \Delta_n > 0 \ (n \text{ even}) \end{array} \quad (35)$$

should hold.

Note. If $a_0 > 0$, these conditions reduce to:

$$\Delta_1 > 0, \ \Delta_2 > 0, \ldots, \Delta_n > 0. \quad (36)$$

If one introduces the usual notation for the coefficients of the polynomial $f(z) = a_0 z^n + a_1 z^{n-1} + a_2 z^{n-2} + \ldots + a_n$, then if $a_0 > 0$ the Routh-Hurwitz conditions (36) may be written in the form of the following determinantal inequalities:

$$a_1 > 0, \ \det \begin{bmatrix} a_1 & a_3 \\ a_0 & a_2 \end{bmatrix} > 0, \ \det \begin{bmatrix} a_1 & a_3 & a_5 \\ a_0 & a_2 & a_4 \\ 0 & a_1 & a_3 \end{bmatrix} > 0, \ldots, \ \det \begin{bmatrix} a_1 & a_3 & a_5 \ldots & 0 \\ a_0 & a_2 & a_4 \ldots & 0 \\ 0 & a_1 & a_3 \ldots & 0 \\ 0 & a_0 & a_2 \ldots & 0 \\ \cdot & \cdot & \cdot & \cdot \cdot \\ \cdot & \cdot & \cdot & \cdot \ a_n \end{bmatrix} > 0.$$

$$(36')$$

A real polynomial $f(z)$ whose coefficients satisfy the conditions (35), i.e., a real polynomial all of whose roots have negative real parts, is usually called a *Hurwitz polynomial*.

In conclusion, we mention a remarkable property of the Routh scheme.

Let $f_0, f_1, \ldots$ and $g_0, g_1, \ldots$ be the $(m + 1)$th and $(m + 2)$th rows of the scheme $(f_0 = \Delta_m/\Delta_{m-1},\ g_0 = \Delta_{m+1}/\Delta_m)$. Since these two rows together with those which follow them form an independent Routh scheme, the elements of the $(m + p + 1)$th row (in the original scheme) can be expressed in terms of the elements of the $(m + 1)$th and $(m + 2)$th rows by the use of the same formulas that express the elements of the $(p + 1)$th row in terms of the elements of the first two rows $a_0, a_1, a_2, \ldots$ and $b_0, b_1, b_2, \ldots$ Putting

$$\tilde{H} = \begin{bmatrix} g_0 & g_1 & g_2 \cdots \\ f_0 & f_1 & f_2 \cdots \\ 0 & g_0 & g_1 \cdots \\ 0 & f_0 & f_1 \cdots \\ \cdot & \cdot & \cdot \cdots \end{bmatrix}$$

we obtain

$$\frac{H\begin{bmatrix} 1, \ldots, m+p-1, & m+p \\ 1, \ldots, m+p-1, & m+p+k-1 \end{bmatrix}}{H\begin{bmatrix} 1, \ldots, m+p-1 \\ 1, \ldots, m+p-1 \end{bmatrix}} = \frac{\tilde{H}\begin{bmatrix} 1, \ldots, p-1, & p \\ 1, \ldots, p-1, & p+k-1 \end{bmatrix}}{\tilde{H}\begin{bmatrix} 1, \ldots, p-1 \\ 1, \ldots, p-1 \end{bmatrix}}.$$
(37)

The Hurwitz determinant Δ_{m+p} is equal to the product of the first $m + p$ numbers in the sequence $b_0, c_0, \ldots$:

$$\Delta_{m+p} = b_0 c_0 \ldots f_0 g_0 \ldots l_0.$$

But [21]

$$\Delta_m = b_0 c_0 \ldots f_0, \quad \tilde{\Delta}_p = g_0 \ldots l_0.$$

Thus there holds the following important relation:

$$\Delta_{m+p} = \Delta_m \Delta_p.$$
(38)

The formula (38) is always valid, provided only that the numbers $f_0, f_1, \ldots$ and $g_0, g_1, \ldots$ are defined; i.e., provided that $\Delta_{m-1} \neq 0$ and $\Delta_m \neq 0$.

[21] Here $\tilde{\Delta}_p$ stands for the principal minor of order p in the matrix $\tilde{H}$.

The formulas (37) are meaningful if the condition $\Delta_{m+p-1} \neq 0$, as well as the conditions $\Delta_{m-1} \neq 0$ and $\Delta_m \neq 0$, is satisfied. From this condition it also follows that the denominator of the fraction in the right member of the equation (37) is not zero: $\tilde{\Delta}_{p-1} \neq 0$.

§ 7. Orlando's formula

When we consider the singular cases in which some of the Hurwitz determinants are zero, we need the following formula of Orlando, which expresses the determinant Δ_{n-1} in terms of the leading coefficient a_0 and the roots $z_1, z_2, \ldots, z_n$ of the polynomial $f(z)$:[22]

$$\Delta_{n-1} = (-1)^{\frac{n(n-1)}{2}} a_0^{n-1} \prod_{i<k}^{1\ldots n} (z_i + z_k). \tag{39}$$

When $n = 2$, this formula reduces to the well-known formula for the coefficient b_0 in the quadratic equation $a_0 z^2 + b_0 z + a_1 = 0$:

$$\Delta_1 = b_0 = -a_0(z_1 + z_2).$$

We shall now suppose that formula (39) is valid for a polynomial of degree n, $f(z) = a_0 z^n + b_0 z^{n-1} + \ldots$, and show that it is valid for the $(n+1)$-th-degree polynomial

$$F(z) = (z + h)f(z) = a_0 z^{n+1} + (b_0 + ha_0)z^n + (a_1 + hb_0)z^{n-1} + \ldots$$
$$(h = -z_{n+1}).$$

To this end we set up an auxiliary determinant of order $n + 1$:

$$D = \det \begin{bmatrix} b_0, & b_1, & \ldots, & b_{n-1}, & h^n \\ a_0, & a_1, & \ldots, & a_{n-1}, & -h^{n-1} \\ 0, & b_0, & \ldots, & b_{n-2}, & h^{n-2} \\ 0, & a_0, & \ldots, & a_{n-2}, & -h^{n-3} \\ \multicolumn{5}{c}{\cdots\cdots\cdots\cdots\cdots\cdots} \\ 0, & 0, & \ldots\ldots, & (-1)^n \end{bmatrix} \begin{pmatrix} a_k = 0 & \text{if} & k > \left[\dfrac{n}{2}\right], \\ & & \\ b_k = 0 & \text{if} & k > \left[\dfrac{n-1}{2}\right] \end{pmatrix}.$$

----

[22] Cf. Orlando [51]. In the present discussion the coefficients of the polynomial $f(z)$ may be arbitrary complex numbers.

We multiply the first row of D by a_0 and add to it the second row multiplied by $-b_0$, the third multiplied by a_1, the fourth multiplied by $-b_1$, etc. Then all of the elements of the first row but the last are reduced to zero, and the last element will be equal to $f(h)$. From this it is easy to conclude that

$$D = (-1)^n \, \Delta_{n-1} f(h).$$

On the other hand, if we add to each row but the last of the determinant D the next following row multiplied by h, we obtain $(-1)^n$ times the Hurwitz determinant Δ_n^* of order n for the polynomial $F(z)$:

$$D = (-1)^n \det \begin{bmatrix} b_0 + ha_0 & b_1 + ha_1 \dots \\ a_0 & a_1 + hb_0 \dots \\ 0 & b_0 + ha_0 \dots \\ 0 & a_0 \quad \dots \\ \dots \dots \dots \dots \dots \\ \dots \dots \dots \dots \dots \end{bmatrix} = (-1)^n \Delta_n^*.$$

Thus

$$\Delta_n^* = \Delta_{n-1} f(h) = a_0 \Delta_{n-1} \prod_{i=1}^{n} (h - z_i).$$

Now if we replace Δ_{n-1} by the equivalent expression given by (39) and put $h = -z_{n+1}$, we obtain:

$$\Delta_n^* = (-1)^{\frac{n(n+1)}{2}} a_0^n \prod_{i<k}^{1 \dots n+1} (z_i + z_k).$$

This establishes Orlando's formula for polynomials of arbitrary degree by mathematical induction.

It follows from Orlando's formula that $\Delta_{n-1} = 0$ *if and only if the sum of at least one pair of roots of the polynomial is zero.* In particular, $\Delta_{n-1} = 0$ if $f(z)$ has at least one pair of conjugate pure imaginary roots or has zero as a multiple root.

Since $\Delta_n = c \, \Delta_{n-1}$, where c is the constant term of the polynomial $f(z)$ $(c = (-1)^n a_0 z_1 z_2, \dots z_n)$, it follows from (39) that

$$\Delta_n = (-1)^{\frac{n(n+1)}{2}} a_0^n z_1 z_2 \dots z_n \prod_{i<k}^{1 \dots n} (z_i + z_k). \qquad (40)$$

The last formula shows that $\varDelta_n$ *vanishes if and only if* $f(z)$ *has a root* z *such that* $-z$ *is also a root.*

§ 8. Singular cases in the Routh-Hurwitz theorem

When we consider the singular cases in which some of the Hurwitz determinants are zero, we may assume that $\varDelta_n \neq 0$ (and, consequently, $\varDelta_{n-1} \neq 0$).

Indeed, if $\varDelta_n = 0$, then (as was explained at the end of the preceding section) the real polynomial $f(z)$ has a pair of roots z' and $-z'$ whose sum is zero. If we put $f(z) = F_1(z) + F_2(z)$, where

$$F_1(z) = a_0 z^n + a_1 z^{n-2} + \ldots, \quad F_2(z) = b_0 z^{n-1} + b_1 z^{n-3} + \ldots,$$

one may conclude from the equations $f(z') = f(-z') = 0$ that $F_1(z') = F_2(z') = 0$. It follows that z' is a root of the highest common factor $d(z)$ of the polynomials $F_1(z)$ and $F_2(z)$. Putting $f(z) = d(z)f^*(z)$, we reduce the Routh-Hurwitz problem for $f(z)$ to the same problem for the polynomial $f^*(z)$, for which the last Hurwitz determinant is not zero.[23]

1. We shall first consider the case in which

$$\varDelta_1 = \ldots = \varDelta_p = 0, \; \varDelta_{p+1} \neq 0, \ldots, \varDelta_n \neq 0.$$

From $\varDelta_1 = 0$ it follows that $b_0 = 0$; from

$$\varDelta_2 = \det \begin{bmatrix} 0 & b_1 \\ a_0 & a_1 \end{bmatrix} = -a_0 b_1 = 0$$

it follows that $b_1 = 0$. But then, automatically,

$$\varDelta_3 = \det \begin{bmatrix} 0 & b_1 & b_2 \\ a_0 & a_1 & a_2 \\ 0 & 0 & b_1 \end{bmatrix} = -a_0 b_1^2 = 0.$$

From

$$\varDelta_4 = \det \begin{bmatrix} 0 & 0 & b_2 & b_3 \\ a_0 & a_1 & a_2 & a_3 \\ 0 & 0 & 0 & b_2 \\ 0 & a_0 & a_1 & a_2 \end{bmatrix} = -a_0^2 b_2^2 = 0$$

[23] $d(z)$ causes no trouble.

it follows that $b_2 = 0$; but then $\Delta_5 = -a_0^2 b_2^3 = 0$, etc.

These considerations show that in (41) the number p must always be *odd*: $p = 2h - 1$. At the same time,

$$b_0 = b_1 = \ldots = b_{h-1} = 0, \ b_h \neq 0,$$

and [24]

$$\Delta_{p+1} = \Delta_{2h} = (-1)^{h(h+1)/2} a_0^h b_h^h,$$
$$\Delta_{p+2} = \Delta_{2h+1} = (-1)^{h(h+1)/2} a_0^h b_h^{h+1} = \Delta_{p+1} b_h.$$

We now change the coefficents b_0, b_1, ..., b_{h-1} very slightly, but in such a way that for the new values b_0^*, b_1^*, ..., b_{h-1}^* all of the modified Hurwitz determinants Δ_1^*, Δ_2^*, ..., Δ_n^* are different from zero, while the determinants Δ_{p+1}^*, ..., Δ_n^* retain their original signs. Moreover, we assign values of various degrees of "smallness" to b_0^*, ..., b_{h-1}^*; more precisely, we shall assume that b_{j-1}^* is so much smaller than b_j^* ($j = 1, 2, \ldots, h$; $b_h^* = b_h$) that in calculating the sign of a polynomial in the quantities b_j^* we may neglect the terms in which some of the b_j^* have indices $< i$ as compared with the terms in which all b_j^* have indices $\geq i$. Once this has been done, it is easy to find the "sign-determining" terms in

$$\Delta_k^* \ (k = 1, \ldots, p = 2h - 1):$$

$$\Delta_1^* = b_0^*, \ \Delta_2^* = -a_0 b_1^* + \ldots, \ \Delta_3^* = -a_0 b_1^{*2} + \ldots, \ \Delta_4^* = a_0^2 b_2^{*2} + \ldots,$$
$$\Delta_2^* = -a_0^2 b_2^{*2} + \ldots, \ \Delta_6^* = a_0^3 b_3^{*2} + \ldots,$$

etc.; in general,

$$\Delta_{2j}^* = (-1)^{j(j+1)/2} a_0^j b_j^{*j} + \ldots \qquad (j = 1, 2, \ldots, h - 1),$$
$$\Delta_{2j+1}^* = (-1)^{j(j+1)/2} a_0^j b_j^{*j+1} + \ldots \qquad (j = 0, 1, \ldots, h - 1).$$ (43)

If we choose the numbers b_0^*, ..., b_{h-1}^* to be positive, then the

---

[24] From (42) it follows that if h is odd,

$$\text{sign } \Delta_{p+2} = (-1)^{(h+1)/2} \text{ sign } a_0,$$

while if h is even

$$\text{sign } \Delta_{p+1} = (-1)^{h/2}.$$

signs of the determinants $\varDelta_i^*$ are given by the formula

$$\text{sign } \varDelta_i^* = (-1)^{j(j+1)/2} \text{sign } a_0^j \quad \left(j = \left[\frac{i}{2}\right], \; i = 1, 2, \ldots, p.\right) \quad (44)$$

For a sufficiently small change in the coefficients the number k remains unchanged, since the polynomial $f(z)$ has no roots on the imaginary axis. Thus, by (44), we determine the number of roots in the right half-plane by means of the formula

$$k = V\left[a_0, \varDelta_1^*, \frac{\varDelta_2^*}{\varDelta_1^*}, \ldots, \frac{\varDelta_{p+1}}{\varDelta_p^*}, \frac{\varDelta_{p+2}}{\varDelta_{p+1}}\right] + V\left[\frac{\varDelta_{p+2}}{\varDelta_{p+1}}, \ldots, \frac{\varDelta_n}{\varDelta_{n-1}}\right]. \quad (45)$$

An elementary calculation based on the fundamental formulas (42) and (44) shows that

$$V\left[a_0, \varDelta_1^* \frac{\varDelta_2^*}{\varDelta_1^*}, \ldots, \frac{\varDelta_{p+1}}{\varDelta_p^*}, \frac{\varDelta_{p+2}}{\varDelta_{p+1}}\right] = h + \frac{1-(-1)^h \varepsilon}{2} \left(\begin{array}{c} p = 2h - 1, \\ \varepsilon = \text{sign}\left(a_0 \frac{\varDelta_{p+2}}{\varDelta_{p+1}}\right) \end{array}\right).$$

$$(46)$$

We note that the quantity occurring on the left side of equation (46) does not depend on the manner in which the modified coefficients are chosen, provided that they are sufficiently small. This follows from formula (45), since k does not change its value for small changes in the coefficients.

2. Now suppose that for some $s > 0$

$$\varDelta_{s+1} = \ldots = \varDelta_{s+p} = 0, \quad (47)$$

while all the other Hurwitz determinants are different from zero.

We shall denote by $\tilde{a}_0, \tilde{a}_1, \ldots$ and $\tilde{b}_0, \tilde{b}_1, \ldots$ the elements of the $(s+1)$th and $(s+2)$th rows of the Routh scheme, and denote the corresponding Hurwitz determinants by $\tilde{\varDelta}_1, \tilde{\varDelta}_2, \ldots, \tilde{\varDelta}_{n-s}$. By formula (38),

$$\varDelta_{s+1} = \varDelta_s \tilde{\varDelta}_1, \ldots, \varDelta_{s+p} = \varDelta_s \tilde{\varDelta}_p, \; \varDelta_{s+p+1} = \varDelta_s \tilde{\varDelta}_{p+1}, \; \varDelta_{s+p+2} = \varDelta_s \tilde{\varDelta}_{p+2}.$$

$$(48)$$

If we now apply the results of Part 1 of this section we may conclude that p is odd, i.e., $p = 2h - 1$.[25]

We subject the coefficients of $f(z)$ to a slight change such that all of the Hurwitz determinants become different from zero and those that were different from zero before the change preserve their original signs. Then by (48), since the formula (46) applies to the determinants $\tilde{\varDelta}$, we obtain:

$$V\left[\frac{\varDelta_s}{\varDelta_{s-1}}, \frac{\varDelta^*_{s+1}}{\varDelta_s}, \ldots, \frac{\varDelta_{s+p+1}}{\varDelta^*_{s+p}}, \frac{\varDelta_{s+p+2}}{\varDelta_{s+p+1}}\right]$$

$$= h + \frac{1 - (-1)^h \varepsilon}{2}\left(\begin{array}{c} p = 2h - 1, \\ \varepsilon = \operatorname{sign}\left(\dfrac{\varDelta_s}{\varDelta_{s-1}} \dfrac{\varDelta_{s+p+2}}{\varDelta_{s+p+1}}\right) \end{array}\right), \tag{49}$$

$$k = V\left[a_0, \varDelta_1, \ldots, \frac{\varDelta_s}{\varDelta_{s-1}}\right] + V\left[\frac{\varDelta_s}{\varDelta_{s-1}}, \frac{\varDelta^*_{s+1}}{\varDelta_s}, \ldots, \frac{\varDelta_{s+p+2}}{\varDelta_{s+p+1}}\right]$$

$$+ V\left[\frac{\varDelta_{s+p+2}}{\varDelta_{s+p+1}}, \ldots, \frac{\varDelta_n}{\varDelta_{n-1}}\right].$$

The value of the left side of (49) is again independent of the manner in which the coefficients are changed.

3. We now suppose that among the Hurwitz determinants there are ν groups of consecutive vanishing determinants. We shall show that for each such group (47) the quantity on the left side of (49) is independent of the manner in which the coefficients are changed and is determined by this formula.[26] We have already shown that this is true if $\nu = 1$. We shall suppose that it is true for $\nu - 1$ or fewer groups, and show that it is true for ν groups.

[25] As in Note 24, if $p = 2h - 1$ and h is odd then

$$\operatorname{sign} \varDelta_{s+p+2} = (-1)^{(h+1)/2} \operatorname{sign} \varDelta_{s-1},$$

while if h is even

$$\varDelta_{s+p+1} = (-1)^{h/2} \operatorname{sign} \varDelta_s.$$

[26] From (47) and the inequalities $\varDelta_s \neq 0$, $\varDelta_{s+p+1} \neq 0$ it follows, by virtue of (48) and (42), that $\varDelta_{s-1} \neq 0$.

Let (47) be the second of the v groups; we define the set of determinants $\tilde{\varDelta}_1$, $\tilde{\varDelta}_2$, ... just as in Part **2**; then when the coefficients are changed slightly, we have

$$V\left[\frac{\varDelta_s^*}{\varDelta_{s-1}^*}, \ldots, \frac{\varDelta_n^*}{\varDelta_{n-1}^*}\right] = V\left[\tilde{a}_0^*, \tilde{\varDelta}_1^*, \ldots, \frac{\tilde{\varDelta}_{n-s}^*}{\varDelta_{n-s-1}^*}\right].$$

Since in the right side of this equation there are only $v - 1$ groups of consecutive vanishing determinants, our assertion holds for the right side, and hence also for the left side, of this equation. On the other hand, formula (49) is valid for the second, ..., vth group of vanishing Hurwitz determinants. But then from the formula

$$k = V\left[a_0^*, \varDelta_1^*, \frac{\varDelta_2^*}{\varDelta_1^*}, \ldots, \frac{\varDelta_n^*}{\varDelta_{n-1}^*}\right]$$

it follows that the quantity

$$V\left[\frac{\varDelta_s}{\varDelta_{s-1}}, \frac{\varDelta_{s+1}^*}{\varDelta_s}, \frac{\varDelta_{s+2}^*}{\varDelta_{s+1}^*}, \ldots, \frac{\varDelta_{s+p+2}}{\varDelta_{s+p+1}}\right]$$

is independent of the manner in which the coefficients are changed, and since (49) holds for the first group of vanishing determinants, it also holds for this one.

THEOREM 5. *If some of the Hurwitz determinants equal zero, but $\varDelta_n$ is not zero ($\varDelta_n \neq 0$), then the number of roots of the real polynomial $f(z)$ in the right half-plane is determined by the formula*

$$k = V\left(a_0, \varDelta_1, \frac{\varDelta_2}{\varDelta_1}, \ldots, \frac{\varDelta_n}{\varDelta_{n-1}}\right),$$

where in calculating the value of V for each group of p consecutive vanishing determinants (p is always an odd number!)

$$(\varDelta_s \neq 0) \qquad \varDelta_{s+1} = \ldots = \varDelta_{s+p} = 0 \qquad (\varDelta_{s+p+1} \neq 0)$$

one should put:

$$V\left[\frac{\varDelta_s}{\varDelta_{s-1}}, \frac{\varDelta_{s+1}}{\varDelta_s}, \ldots, \frac{\varDelta_{s+p+2}}{\varDelta_{s+p+1}}\right] = h + \frac{1 - (-1)^h \varepsilon}{2}, \qquad (50)$$

where [27]

$$p = 2h - 1 \;\; and \;\; \varepsilon = \text{sign} \left(\frac{\Delta_s}{\Delta_{s-1}} \frac{\Delta_{s+p+2}}{\Delta_{s+p+1}} \right).$$

§ 9. The method of quadratic forms. The determination of the number of distinct real roots of a polynomial

Routh obtained his algorithm by applying Sturm's theorem to the calculation of the Cauchy index of a proper rational function of a certain special type. (See Formula (10).) In this fraction one of the terms was of even degree in z, the other odd. In the present section and in subsequent sections we shall investigate the deeper and more instructive method of applying Hermitian quadratic forms to the Routh-Hurwitz problem. By means of this method we shall obtain an expression for the index of an arbitrary rational function in terms of the coefficients occurring in numerator and denominator. The method of quadratic forms makes it possible to apply to the Routh-Hurwitz problem Frobenius' ingenious investigations in the theory of Hankel forms [28] and to establish a close connection between some remarkable theorems of P. L. Chebyshev and A. A. Markov and the problem of stability.

We shall first acquaint the reader with the method of quadratic forms by considering the relatively simple problem of determining the number of distinct real roots of a polynomial.

In solving this problem we may restrict ourselves to the case in which $f(z)$ is a real polynomial. Indeed, let there be given a complex polynomial $f(z) = u(z) + iv(z)$ ($u(z)$ and $v(z)$ are real polynomials). Each real root of $f(z)$ makes $u(z)$ and $v(z)$ vanish simultaneously. Thus the complex polynomial $f(z)$ has the same real roots as the real polynomial $d(z)$ defined as the highest common factor of the polynomials $u(z)$ and $v(z)$.

---

[27] If $s = 1$ the ratio Δ_s/Δ_{s-1} should be changed to Δ_1, and if $s = 0$, to a_0.

[28] A quadratic form $\Sigma_{i,k} \, a_{ik} \, x_i \, x_k$ is said to be a *Hankel form* if the general coefficient depends only on the sum of the indices: $a_{ik} = f(i + k)$ ($i, k = 1, \ldots, n$); likewise, the coefficient matrix of a Hankel form is called a *Hankel matrix*.

Let $f(z)$ be a real polynomial, then. Let its distinct roots $\alpha_1, \alpha_2, \ldots, \alpha_q$ have multiplicities $n_1, n_2, \ldots, n_q$ respectively:

$$f(z) = a_0(z - \alpha_1)^{n_1}(z - \alpha_2)^{n_2} \ldots (z - \alpha_q)^{n_q}$$

$$[a_0 \neq 0; \ \alpha_i \neq \alpha_k \ \text{if} \ i \neq k \quad (i, \ k = 1, 2, \ldots, q)].$$

We now define the Newton sums

$$s_p = \sum_{j=1}^{q} n_j \alpha_j^p \quad (p = 0, 1, 2, \ldots),$$

and use these sums as coefficients in the Hankel form

$$S_n(x, x) = \sum_{i, k=0}^{n-1} s_{i+k} x_i x_k,$$

where n is an arbitrary integer $\geq q$.

THEOREM 6. *The number of distinct roots of $f(z)$ is equal to the rank of the form $S_n(x, x)$, and the number of distinct real roots of $f(z)$ is equal to the signature of that form.*

Proof. From the definition of the form $S_n(x, x)$ the following representation for it is an immediate consequence:

$$S_n(x, x) = \sum_{j=1}^{q} n_j (x_0 + \alpha_j x_1 + \alpha_j^2 x_2 + \ldots + \alpha_j^{n-1} x_{n-1})^2. \quad (51)$$

Here to each root α_j of the polynomial $f(z)$ there corresponds the square of a linear form

$$Z_j = x_0 + \alpha_j x_1 + \alpha_j^2 x_2 + \ldots + \alpha_j^{n-1} x_{n-1}.$$

The forms $Z_1, Z_2, \ldots, Z_q$ are linearly independent, since the coefficients of these forms constitute the Vandermonde matrix (α_j^h), the rank of which is equal to the number of distinct α_j, i.e., to q. Consequently [29] the rank of the form $S_n(x, x)$ is q.

In the representation (51) there is a positive square term for each real root. For each pair of complex conjugate roots α_j and $\bar{\alpha}_j$ there are two complex conjugate linear forms:

$$Z_j = P_j + iQ_j, \ \bar{Z}_j = P_j - iQ_j;$$

[29] See, for example, Bôcher [6], p. 134, Theorem 1.

and (51) contains the square of each. On combining these squares in (51), we obtain one positive and one negative square:

$$n_j Z_j^2 + n_j \bar{Z}_j^2 = 2n_j P_j^2 - 2n_j Q_j^2.$$

From this it is easy to see that the signature of the form $S_n(x, x)$, i.e., the difference between the number of positive and the number of negative squares, is equal to the number of distinct real α_j; for the quadratic form is thus represented by a linear combination of q squares of the real forms Z_j (for real α_j), P_j, and Q_j. These forms are independent, since q is the rank of $S_n(x, x)$. The theorem is proved.

If we apply to the theorem just proved a well-known rule for determining the signature of a quadratic form [30] we obtain the

COROLLARY. *The number of distinct real roots of the real polynomial $f(z)$ is equal to the excess of the number of permanences in sign over the number of changes in sign in the sequence of numbers*

$$1, \ s_0, \ \det \begin{bmatrix} s_0 & s_1 \\ s_1 & s_2 \end{bmatrix}, \ \ldots, \ \det \begin{bmatrix} s_0 & s_1 \cdots s_{n-1} \\ s_1 & s_2 \cdots s_n \\ \cdots\cdots\cdots \\ s_{n-1} & s_n \cdots s_{2n-2} \end{bmatrix}, \quad (52)$$

where s_p ($p = 0, 1, 2, \ldots$) are the Newton sums for the polynomial $f(z)$ and n is any number greater than or equal to the number q of distinct roots of $f(z)$. (In particular, n may be chosen to be the degree of $f(z)$.)

This rule for the determination of the number of distinct real roots is directly applicable only if all of the numbers in the sequence (52) are different from zero. Nevertheless, the question is here

---

[30] The rule reads as follows: *If for a quadratic form $A(x, x) = \Sigma_{ik} a_{ik} x_i x_k$ of rank r the first r principal minors D_k ($k = 1, 2, \ldots, r$) of the matrix $A = (a_{ik})_1^\infty$ are different from zero, then the signature of the form $A(x, x)$ is obtained if one subtracts from the number of permanences of sign in the sequence $1, D_1, D_2, \ldots, D_r$ the number of changes of sign in this sequence; or, equivalently, the signature of $A(x, x)$ is $r - 2V(1, D_1, D_2, \ldots, D_r)$.* This follows at once from the Jacobi reduction formula for quadratic forms. Cf. Jacobi [30].

one of calculating the signature of a Hankel quadratic form, and there exist simple ways of doing so even when this condition is not satisfied. We may therefore say that this rule is, with the necessary qualifications, applicable to the general case. This question is taken up in greater detail in Section 11 of this chapter.

From Theorem 6 it follows that *all of the forms* $S_n(x, x)$ $(n = q, q + 1, \ldots)$ *have the same rank and the same signature.*

In applying Theorem 6 (or its corollary) to the problem of determining the number of distinct real roots we shall take n to be the degree of the polynomial $f(z)$.

The number of distinct real roots of the real polynomial $f(z)$ is equal to the index $I_{-\infty}^{+\infty} f'(z)/f(z)$ (cf. Section 2). Thus Theorem 5 gives us as a corollary the formula

$$I_{-\infty}^{+\infty} \frac{f'(z)}{f(z)} = n - 2V \left[1, s_0, \det \begin{bmatrix} s_0 & s_1 \\ s_1 & s_2 \end{bmatrix}, \ldots, \det \begin{bmatrix} s_0 & s_1 \ldots s_{n-1} \\ s_1 & s_2 \ldots s_n \\ \cdots \cdots \cdots \\ s_{n-1} & s_n \ldots s_{2n-2} \end{bmatrix} \right],$$

where $s_p = \sum_{j=1}^{q} n_j \alpha_j^p$ $(p = 0, 1, \ldots)$ are the Newton sums for the polynomial $f(z)$ and n is the degree of $f(z)$.

In Section 11 we shall establish an analogous formula for the index of an arbitrary rational function. The information about infinite Hankel matrices that will be needed for this purpose is given in the next section.

§ 10. Infinite Hankel matrices of finite rank

1. Let there be given a sequence of complex numbers

$$s_0, s_1, s_2, \ldots$$

This sequence of numbers defines an infinite symmetric matrix

$$S = \begin{bmatrix} s_0 & s_1 & s_2 \ldots \\ s_1 & s_2 & s_3 \ldots \\ s_2 & s_3 & s_4 \ldots \\ \cdots \cdots \cdots \end{bmatrix}$$

which may be called an infinite *Hankel* matrix. In connection with an infinite Hankel matrix one considers the finite Hankel matrices $S_n = (s_{i+k})_0^{n-1}$ and the corresponding Hankel forms

$$S_n(x,x) = \sum_{i,\,k=0}^{n-1} s_{i+k} x_i x_k.$$

The successive principal minors of the matrix S will be denoted by $D_1,\ D_2,\ D_3,\ \ldots$:

$$D_p = \det\,[s_{i+k}]_0^{p-1} \quad (p = 1, 2, \ldots).$$

An infinite matrix may have finite or infinite rank. In the latter case the infinite matrix has nonzero minors of arbitrarily large order. The following theorem gives a necessary and sufficient condition which the sequence $s_0,\ s_1,\ s_2,\ \ldots$ must satisfy in order for the Hankel matrix which it defines to have a finite rank.

THEOREM 7. *The infinite matrix* $S = (s_{i+k})_0^\infty$ *has finite rank* r, *if and only if there exist* r *numbers* $\alpha_1, \ldots, \alpha_r$ *such that*

$$s_q = \sum_{g=1}^{r} \alpha_g s_{q-g} \quad (q = r,\ r+1,\ \ldots), \tag{53}$$

and r *is the smallest number with this property.*

Proof. If the matrix $S = (s_{i+k})_0^\infty$ has finite rank r, then the first $r+1$ rows $\Gamma_1,\ \Gamma_2, \ldots, \Gamma_{r+1}$ of this matrix are linearly dependent. Thus there exists a number $h \leq r$ such that the rows $\Gamma_1,\ \Gamma_2, \ldots, \Gamma_h$ are linearly independent, but the row Γ_{h+1} is a linear combination of these rows:

$$\Gamma_{h+1} = \sum_{g=1}^{h} \alpha_g \Gamma_{h-g+1}.$$

We consider the rows $\Gamma_{q+1},\ \Gamma_{q+2}, \ldots, \Gamma_{q+h+1}$, where q is an arbitrary nonnegative integer. From the structure of the matrix S it is immediately evident that these rows may be obtained from the first $h+1$ rows by "shortening," that is by omitting the elements of their first q columns. Thus

$$\Gamma_{q+h+1} = \sum_{g=1}^{h} \alpha_g \Gamma_{q+h-g+1} \quad (q = 0, 1, 2, \ldots).$$

Accordingly, any row in the matrix S after the hth can be expressed as a linear combination of the h preceding rows and, therefore, of the first h rows, which are linearly independent. From this it follows that *the rank r of the matrix S is h.*[31] If h is replaced by r and the linear relation $\Gamma_{g+h+1} = \sum_{g=1}^{h} \alpha_g \Gamma_{q+h-g+1}$ is written out in detail the result is (53).

Conversely, if the condition (53) is satisfied, then any row (or column) of the matrix S is a linear combination of the first r rows (or columns) of S. Thus all minors of the matrix S whose orders are greater than r are equal to zero, and the matrix has a finite rank $h \leq r$. But this rank cannot be less than r, for then, as was just shown, relations of the form (53) would hold for a smaller value of r, and this would contradict the second part of the condition in the theorem. Thus the theorem is completely proved.

COROLLARY. *If an infinite Hankel matrix S has finite rank r, then*

$$D_r = \det \left[s_{i+k} \right]_0^{r-1} \neq 0.$$

In fact, from the relations (53) it follows that any row (or column) of the matrix S is a linear combination of the first r rows (or columns). Hence any minor of order r can be represented in the form αD_r, where α is some number. From this follows the inequality $D_r \neq 0$.

REMARK. For finite Hankel matrices of rank r the inequality $D_r \neq 0$ may fail to hold. Thus, for example, the matrix

$$S_2 = \begin{bmatrix} s_0 & s_1 \\ s_1 & s_2 \end{bmatrix}$$

with $s_0 - s_1 = 0$, $s_2 \neq 0$ has rank 1, but at the same time $D_1 = s_0 = 0$.

2. We shall now discuss a remarkable connection between infinite Hankel matrices and rational functions.

---

[31] The statement "the number of linearly independent rows in a rectangular matrix is equal to the rank of this matrix" is valid for infinite as well as finite rows.

Let there be given a proper rational function $R(z) = g(z)/h(z)$, where

$$h(z) = a_0 z^m + \ldots + a_m \ (a_0 \neq 0), \ g(z) = b_1 z^{m-1} + b_2 z^{m-2} + \ldots + b_m.$$

We now write the function $R(z)$ as a power series in negative powers of z:

$$R(z) = \frac{g(z)}{h(z)} = \frac{s_0}{z} + \frac{s_1}{z^2} + \frac{s_2}{z^3} + \ldots$$

If all of the poles of the function $R(z)$, i.e., all of the values of z for which $R(z)$ becomes infinite, lie in the circle $|z| \leq a$, then the above series converges for $|z| > a$. We multiply both sides of the last equation by the denominator $h(z)$:

$$(a_0 z^m + a_1 z^{m-1} + \ldots + a_m)\left(\frac{s_0}{z} + \frac{s_1}{z^2} + \frac{s_2}{z^3} + \ldots\right)$$

$$= b_1 z^{m-1} + b_2 z^{m-2} + \ldots + b_m.$$

Comparing the coefficients of like powers of z on the two sides of this identity, we obtain the following system of relations:

$$\left.\begin{aligned} a_0 s_0 &= b_1, \\ a_0 s_1 + a_1 s_0 &= b_2, \\ \cdot\ \cdot\ \cdot\ \cdot\ \cdot\ \cdot\ \cdot\ \cdot\ & \\ a_0 s_{m-1} + a_1 s_{m-2} + \ldots + a_{m-1} s_0 &= b_m, \end{aligned}\right\} \qquad (54)$$

$$a_0 s_q + a_1 s_{q-1} + \ldots + a_m s_{q-m} = 0 \quad (q = m, m+1, \ldots). \quad (54')$$

Putting $\alpha_g = -a_g/a_0$ $(g = 1, 2, \ldots, m)$, we can write the relations $(54')$ in the form (53) (with $r = m$). Thus by Theorem 7, the infinite Hankel matrix $S = (s_{i+k})_0^\infty$ with coefficients s_0, s_1, s_2, ... has finite rank $(\leq m)$.

Conversely, if the matrix S has finite rank r, then the relations (53) hold, and these may be rewritten in the form $(54')$ with $m = r$. Then if we define the numbers b_1, b_2, ..., b_m by use of the equations (54), we shall have the relation

$$\frac{b_1 z^{m-1} + \ldots + b_m}{a_0 z^m + a_1 z^{m-1} + \ldots + a_m} = \frac{s_0}{z} + \frac{s_1}{z^2} + \ldots$$

The smallest value of the degree m of the denominator for which this relation can hold is the smallest number m for which relations (53) hold. By Theorem 7 this least value of m is equal to the rank of the matrix S.

This proves the theorem:

THEOREM 8. *The matrix* $S = (s_{i+k})_0^\infty$ *has finite rank if and only if the sum of the series*

$$R(z) = \frac{s_0}{z} + \frac{s_1}{z^2} + \frac{s_2}{z^3} + \cdots$$

is a rational function of the variable z. *When this happens the rank of the matrix* S *is equal to the number of poles of the function* $R(z)$, *each counted according to its multiplicity.*

§ 11. The determination of the index of a rational function from the coefficients of its numerator and denominator

1. Let an arbitrary rational function be given. We expand it in a series in descending powers of z:

$$R(z) = s_{-u-1}z^u + \cdots + s_{-2}z + s_{-1} + s_0 z^{-1} + s_1 z^{-2} + \cdots \quad (55)$$

This series converges outside any circle (whose center is the origin) which contains all poles of the function $R(z)$.

The sequence of coefficients corresponding to negative powers of z, namely $s_0, s_1, s_2, \ldots$, defines a certain infinite Hankel matrix $S = (s_{i+k})_0^\infty$.

In this manner one sets up a correspondence

$$R(z) \sim S$$

between rational functions on the one hand and infinite Hankel matrices on the other.

Obviously, two rational functions that differ by an entire function correspond to the same matrix S. However, not every matrix S corresponds to a rational function; in the last section it was shown that the matrix S corresponds to a rational function if and only if this infinite matrix has finite rank. This rank was equal to the number of poles (multiplicity being taken into account) of the function $R(z)$, i.e. to the degree of the denominator $f(z)$ in any irreducible fraction $g(z)/f(z) = R(z)$. The relation (55) defines a one-to-one correpondence between proper rational functions $R(z)$ and infinite Hankel matrices S of finite rank.

We shall now point out certain properties of this correspondence:

1. If $R_1(z) \sim S_1$ and $R_2(z) \sim S_2$, then if c_1 and c_2 are any numbers,

$$c_1 R_1(z) + c_2 R_2(z) \sim c_1 S_1 + c_2 S_2.$$

Later we shall have occasion to deal with the case in which the coefficients in the numerator and denominator of $R(z)$ are polynomials in a parameter α; in this case R will be a rational function of z and α. From the relations (54) it follows that the numbers s_0, s_1, s_2, ..., the elements of the matrix S, will depend rationally on α. Differentiating the relation (55) termwise with respect to α, we obtain: [32]

2. If $R(z, \alpha) \sim S(\alpha)$, then $\partial R/\partial \alpha \sim \partial S/\partial \alpha$.

2. We shall now write the function $R(z)$ in partial fractions form:

$$R(z) = Q(z) + \sum_{j=1}^{q} \left\{ \frac{A_1^{(j)}}{z - \alpha_j} + \frac{A_2^{(j)}}{(z - \alpha_j)^2} + \ldots + \frac{A_{\nu_j}^{(j)}}{(z - \alpha_j)^{\nu_j}} \right\}, \quad (56)$$

where $Q(z)$ is a polynomial, and we shall show how the matrix S corresponding to the rational function $R(z)$ may be obtained from the numbers α and A.

To this end we first consider the simple rational function

$$\frac{1}{z - \alpha} = \sum_{p=0}^{\infty} \frac{\alpha^p}{z^{p+1}}.$$

It yields the matrix $S_\alpha = [\alpha^{i+k}]_0^\infty$. The form $S_{\alpha n}(x, x)$ corresponding to this matrix is

$$S_{\alpha n}(x, x) = \sum_{i, k=0}^{n-1} \alpha^{i+k} x_i x_k = (x_0 + \alpha x_1 + \ldots + \alpha^{n-1} x_{n-1})^2.$$

---

[32] If $S = (s_{i+k})_0^\infty$, $\partial S/\partial \alpha$ stands for the matrix $(\partial s_{i+k}/\partial \alpha)_0^\infty$.

If

$$R(z) = Q(z) + \sum_{j=1}^{q} \frac{A^{(j)}}{z - \alpha_j},$$

then by virtue of *1* the corresponding matrix S is defined by the formula

$$S = \sum_{j=1}^{q} A^{(j)} S_{\alpha_j} = [\sum_{j=1}^{q} A^{(j)} \alpha_j^{i+k}]_0^\infty,$$

and the corresponding quadratic form is

$$S_n(x, x) = \sum_{j=1}^{q} A^{(j)} (x_0 + \alpha_j x_1 + \ldots + \alpha_j^{n-1} x_{n-1})^2.$$

In order to proceed to the general case (56), we first differentiate the relation

$$\frac{1}{z - \alpha} \sim S_\alpha = [\alpha^{i+k}]_0^\infty$$

$h - 1$ times, term by term. According to *1* and *2*, we obtain [33]

$$\frac{1}{(z - \alpha)^h} \sim \frac{1}{(h - 1)!} \frac{\partial^{h-1} S_\alpha}{\partial \alpha^{h-1}} = [C_{h-1}^{i+k} \alpha^{i+k-h+1}]_0^\infty$$

$$(C_{h-1}^{i+k} = 0 \text{ if } i + k < h - 1).$$

Thus, again applying rule *1*, we find that in the general case, when $R(z)$ satisfies (56):

$$R(z) \sim S = \sum_{j=1}^{q} \left[A_1^{(j)} + A_2^{(j)} \frac{\partial}{\partial \alpha_j} + \ldots + \frac{1}{(\nu_j - 1)!} A_{\nu_j}^{(j)} \frac{\partial^{\nu_j - 1}}{\partial \alpha_j^{\nu_j - 1}} \right] S_{\alpha_j}. \quad (57)$$

Carrying out the differentiation, we obtain:

$$S = \left[\sum_{j=1}^{q} (A_1^{(j)} \alpha_j^{i+k} + A_2^{(j)} C_1^{i+k} \alpha_j^{i+k-1} + \ldots + A_{\nu_j}^{(j)} C_{\nu_j-1}^{i+k} \alpha_j^{i+k-\nu_j+1}) \right]_0^\infty. \quad (57')$$

The corresponding Hankel form will be

$$S_n(x, x) = \sum_{j=1}^{q} \left[A_1^{(j)} + A_2^{(j)} \frac{\partial}{\partial \alpha_j} + \ldots + \frac{1}{(\nu_j - 1)!} A_{\nu_j}^{(j)} \frac{\partial^{\nu_j - 1}}{\partial \alpha_j^{\nu_j - 1}} \right]$$
$$\times (x_0 + \alpha_j x_1 + \ldots + \alpha_j^{n-1} x_{n-1})^2. \quad (57'')$$

---

[33] Here and below C_h^d stands for the number of combinations of d things taken h at a time.

3. Now we are in a position to formulate and prove the fundamental theorem: [34]

THEOREM 9. *If*

$$R(z) \sim S$$

and m is the rank [35] *of the matrix S, then the Cauchy index $I_{-\infty}^{+\infty} R(z)$ is equal to the signature $\sigma[S_n(x, x)]$ of the form $S_n(x, x)$ for any $n \geq m$:*

$$I_{-\infty}^{+\infty} R(z) = \sigma[S_n(x, x)].$$

Proof. Suppose that the relation (56) holds. Then according to (57)

$$S = \sum_{j=1}^{q} T_{\alpha_j},$$

where each term has the form

$$T_\alpha = \left[A_1 + A_2 \frac{\partial}{\partial \alpha} + \ldots + \frac{1}{(\nu - 1)!} A_\nu \frac{\partial^{\nu-1}}{\partial \alpha^{\nu-1}} \right] S_\alpha, \quad S_\alpha = (\alpha^{i+k})_0^\infty$$

and

$$S_n(x, x) = \sum_{j=1}^{q} T_{\alpha_j}(x, x) = \sum_{\alpha_j \text{ real}} T_{\alpha_j}(x, x) + \sum_{\alpha_j \text{ complex}} [T_{\alpha_j}(x, x) + T_{\bar\alpha_j}(x, x)].$$

According to Theorem 8 the rank of the matrix T_{α_j} and, therefore, that of the quadratic form $T_{\alpha_j}(x, x)$ is equal to ν_j $(j = 1, 2, \ldots, q)$; at the same time, the rank of $S_n(x, x)$ is equal to $m = \nu_1 + \ldots + \nu_q$. But if the rank of the sum of certain real quadratic forms is equal to the sum of the ranks of the constituent forms, then the same relation holds true for the signatures. Applied to the present case, this gives:

$$\sigma[S_n(x,x)] = \sum_{\alpha_j \text{ real}} \sigma[T_{\alpha_j}(x,x)] + \sum_{\alpha_j \text{ complex}} \sigma[T_{\alpha_j}(x, x) + T_{\bar\alpha_j}(x,x)]. \quad (59)$$

[34] This theorem was proved by Hermite in 1856 for the simplest case, that in which $R(z)$ has only simple poles (Hermite [27]). The theorem was proved in the general case by Hurwitz [28]. The proof given in the text is different from that given by Hurwitz.

[35] Recall that m is equal to the degree of the denominator in any representation of $R(z)$ as an irreducible fraction (cf. Theorem 8).

We consider two cases separately:

(i) α is real. If the parameters A_1, A_2, ..., $A_{\nu-1}$ and α in

$$\frac{A_1}{z - \alpha} + \frac{A_2}{(z - \alpha)^2} + \ldots + \frac{A_\nu}{(z - \alpha)^\nu}$$

are changed in any way whatever, the rank of the corresponding matrix T_α remains unchanged $(=\nu)$, and therefore the signature of the form $T(x, x)$ will likewise be unchanged.[36] Thus $\sigma[T_\alpha(x, x)]$ is still the same if we put $A_1 = A_2 = \ldots = A_{\nu-1} = 0$ and $\alpha = 0$ in (59) and (60), or in other words if we choose the matrix

$$\frac{1}{(\nu - 1)!} \frac{\partial^{\nu-1} S_\alpha}{\partial \alpha^{\nu-1}} = \begin{bmatrix} \overbrace{0 \quad 0 \ldots 0}^{\nu - 1} & A_\nu & 0 & 0 & \ldots \\ 0 & & & & \\ \vdots & & & & \\ 0 & & & & \\ A_\nu & & & & \\ 0 & & & & \\ 0 & & & & \\ \vdots & & & & \end{bmatrix}$$

instead of T_α.

The corresponding quadratic form is equal to

$$2A_\nu (x_0 x_{\nu-1} + x_1 x_{\nu-2} + \ldots + x_{s-1} x_s) \text{ if } \nu = 2s,$$
$$A_\nu [2 (x_0 x_{\nu-1} + \ldots + x_{s-2} x_s) + x_{s-1}^2] \text{ if } \nu = 2s-1. \quad (s = 1, 2, 3, \ldots).$$

[36] This follows from the fact *that the rank of a form $A(x, x)$ is equal to the number of nonzero characteristic roots of the matrix A, while the signature is the difference between the number of positive characteristic roots of A and the number of negative characteristic roots of A*, which in turn is an immediate consequence of the principal axis representation for quadratic forms (cf. Courant-Hilbert, [11] Vol. 1, pp. 19–23). In fact, a continuous change in the coefficients of the form works a continuous change in the characteristic roots. The signature can change only if some characteristic root changes sign, but if this happens then at some intermediate moment this characteristic root must be zero, and the rank changes; but the rank is constant.

But the signature of the upper form is always equal to zero, and the signature of the lower form is equal to sign A_ν.[37] In this manner we obtain the result that if α is real,

$$\sigma[T_\alpha(x, x)] = 0 \text{ if } \nu \text{ is even, } = A_\nu \text{ if } \nu \text{ is odd.} \quad (61)$$

(ii) α is a complex number. Let

$$T_\alpha(x, x) = \sum_{k=1}^{\nu} (P_k + iQ_k)^2, \quad T_{\bar\alpha}(x, x) = \sum_{k=1}^{\nu} (P_k - iQ_k)^2,$$

where P_k, Q_k $(k = 1, \ldots, \nu)$ are real linear forms in the variables $x_0, x_1, \ldots, x_{n-1}$. Then

$$T_\alpha(x, x) + T_{\bar\alpha}(x, x) = 2 \sum_{k=1}^{\nu} P_k^2 - 2 \sum_{k=1}^{\nu} Q_k^2. \quad (62)$$

Since the rank of this quadratic form is equal to 2ν, it must be that P_k, Q_k, $(k = 1, 2, \ldots, \nu)$ are linearly independent, and by (62)

$$\sigma[T_\alpha(x, x) + T_{\bar\alpha}(x, x)] = 0 \quad (63)$$

when α is not real.

From (59), (61), and (63) it follows that

$$\sigma[S_n(x, x)] = \sum \text{sign } A_{\nu_j}$$

the summation being extended over the values of j for which α_j is real and ν_j is odd. However, in Section 2 it was shown that the sum on the right side of this equation is equal to $I_{-\infty}^{+\infty} R(z)$. Thus the theorem is proved.

This theorem implies:

COROLLARY 1. *If* $R(z) \sim S = (s_{i+k})_0^\infty$ *and* m *is the rank of the matrix* S, *then all of the quadratic forms*

$$S_n(x, x) = \sum_{i, k=0}^{n-1} s_{i+k} x_i x_k \quad (n = m, m+1, \ldots)$$

have the same signature.

[37] Each product $x_k x_{\nu-k-1}$ $(k = 0, \ldots)$ can be written as a difference of squares,

$$\left(\frac{x_k + x_{\nu-k-1}}{2}\right)^2 - \left(\frac{x_k - x_{\nu-k-1}}{2}\right)^2,$$

and all of the linear forms occurring in these squares are independent.

Again using the rule for calculating the signature of a quadratic form,[38] and using also some results due to Frobenius which cover the singular cases,[39] we obtain a second corollary which shows how the Cauchy index may be explicitly calculated:

COROLLARY 2. *The index of an arbitrary rational function* $R(z)$, *which has corresponding matrix* $S = (s_{i+k})_0^\infty$ *of rank* m, *is given by the formula*

$$I_{-\infty}^{+\infty} R(z) = m - 2V\,(1,\,D_1,\,D_2,\,\ldots,\,D_m),\tag{64}$$

where

$$D_f = \det\,[s_{i+k}]_0^{f-1} = \det \begin{bmatrix} s_0 & s_1 \cdots s_{f-1} \\ s_1 & s_2 \cdots s_f \\ \cdots\cdots\cdots \\ s_{f-1} & s_f \cdots s_{2f-2} \end{bmatrix} \quad (f = 1,\,2,\,\ldots,\,m);\tag{65}$$

if among the determinants $D_1,\,D_2,\,\ldots,\,D_m$ *there is a group of consecutive determinants all equal to zero,[40]*

$$(D_n \neq 0)\ D_{h+1} = \ldots = D_{h+p} = 0\ (D_{h+p+1} \neq 0),$$

then in calculating $V(D_h,\,D_{h+1},\,\ldots,\,D_{h+p+1})$ *one may take*

$$\operatorname{sign} D_{h+j} = (-1)^{j(j-1)/2} \operatorname{sign} D_h \ (j = 1,\,2,\,\ldots,\,p)$$

and this gives

$$V(D_h,\,D_{h+1},\,\ldots,\,D_{h+p+1})$$
$$= \tfrac{1}{2}(p+1) \text{ if } p \text{ is odd,}$$
$$= \tfrac{1}{2}(p+1-\varepsilon) \text{ if } p \text{ is even, where } \varepsilon = (-1)^{\frac{1}{2}p} \operatorname{sign} D_{h+p+1}/D_h.$$

In order to express the index of a rational function in terms of the coefficients of its numerator and denominator, we need some auxiliary relations.

First of all, we can always represent $R(z)$ in the form

$$R(z) = Q(z) + g(z)/h(z),$$

[38] See Note 29 above, p. 241.
[39] Cf. Frobenius [23].
[40] Here always $D_m \neq 0$ (cf. the corollary to Theorem 7).

where $Q(z)$, $g(z)$, and $h(z)$ are polynomials, and

$$h(z) = a_0 z^m + a_1 z^{m-1} + \ldots + a_m \quad (a_0 \neq 0),$$
$$g(z) = b_0 z^m + b_1 z^{m-1} + \ldots + b_m.$$

Obviously,

$$I_{-\infty}^{+\infty} R(z) = I_{-\infty}^{+\infty} g(z)/h(z).$$

Let

$$g(z)/h(z) = s_{-1} + s_0 z^{-1} + s_1 z^{-2} + \ldots$$

Now if we multiply through by the denominator $h(z)$ and then compare the respective coefficients of like powers of z on the two sides of the equation, we obtain:

$$
\begin{aligned}
&a_0 s_{-1} = b_0, \\
&a_0 s_0 + a_1 s_{-1} = b_1, \\
&\cdots \cdots \cdots \cdots \\
&a_0 s_{m-1} + a_1 s_{m-2} + \ldots + a_m s_{-1} = b_m, \\
&a_0 s_t + a_1 s_{t-1} + \ldots + a_m s_{t-m} = 0 \quad (t = m,\ m+1, \ldots).
\end{aligned}
\tag{67}
$$

Making use of the relations (67), we obtain an expression for the following determinant of order $2p$:

$$
\begin{vmatrix}
a_0 & a_1 & a_2 & \ldots & a_{2p-1} \\
b_0 & b_1 & b_2 & \ldots & b_{2p-1} \\
0 & a_0 & a_1 & \ldots & a_{2p-2} \\
0 & b_0 & b_1 & \ldots & b_{2p-2} \\
\cdot & \cdot & \cdot & & \cdot \\
\cdot & \cdot & \cdot & & \cdot
\end{vmatrix}
=
\begin{vmatrix}
1 & 0 & 0 & \ldots & 0 \\
s_{-1} & s_0 & s_1 & \ldots & s_{2p-2} \\
0 & 1 & 0 & \ldots & 0 \\
0 & s_{-1} & s_0 & \ldots & s_{2p-3} \\
\cdot & \cdot & \cdot & & \cdot
\end{vmatrix}
\cdot
\begin{vmatrix}
a_0 & a_1 & a_2 & \ldots & a_{2p-1} \\
0 & a_0 & a_1 & \ldots & a_{2p-2} \\
0 & 0 & a_0 & \ldots & a_{2p-3} \\
\cdot & \cdot & \cdot & & \cdot \\
\cdot & \cdot & \cdot & & \cdot \\
0 & 0 & 0 & \ldots & a_0
\end{vmatrix}
$$

$$
= (-1)^{\frac{p(p-1)}{2}} a_0^{2p}
\begin{vmatrix}
s_{p-1} & s_p & \ldots & s_{2p-2} \\
s_{p-2} & s_{p-1} & \ldots & s_{2p-3} \\
\cdot & \cdot & & \cdot \\
s_0 & s_1 & \ldots & s_{p-1}
\end{vmatrix}
= a_0^{2p}
\begin{vmatrix}
s_0 & s_1 & \ldots & s_{p-1} \\
s_1 & s_2 & \ldots & s_p \\
\cdot & \cdot & & \cdot \\
s_{p-1} & s_p & \ldots & s_{2p-2}
\end{vmatrix}
= a_0^{2p} D_p
\tag{68}
$$

a_j and b_j being put equal to zero when $j > m$.

We now introduce the abbreviation

$$\nabla_{2p} = \det \begin{bmatrix} a_0 & a_1 & \ldots & a_{2p-1} \\ b_0 & b_1 & \ldots & b_{2p-1} \\ 0 & a_0 & \ldots & a_{2p-2} \\ 0 & b_0 & \ldots & b_{2p-2} \\ \multicolumn{4}{c}{\cdots\cdots\cdots} \end{bmatrix} \quad (p=1, 2, \ldots; \; a_j=b_j=0 \text{ if } j > m).$$

(69)

Then formula (68) becomes

$$\nabla_{2p} = a_0^{2p} D_p \quad (p = 1, 2, \ldots).$$

(68')

Using this formula and Corollary 2 to Theorem 9 we arrive at the theorem:

THEOREM 10. If [41] $\nabla_{2m} \neq 0$, $then$

$$I_{-\infty}^{+\infty} \frac{b_0 z^m + b_1 z^{m-1} + \ldots + b_m}{a_0 z^m + a_1 z^{m-1} + \ldots + a_m} = m - 2V(1, \nabla_2, \nabla_4, \ldots, \nabla_{2m}) \quad (a_0 \neq 0),$$

(70)

$where$ ∇_{2p} $(p = 1, 2, \ldots, m)$ is $defined$ by $formula$ (60); $here$ it is to be $understood$ $that$ if $there$ is a $block$ of $successive$ $vanishing$ $determinants$

$$(\nabla_{2h} \neq 0) \quad \nabla_{2h+2} = \ldots = \nabla_{2h+2p} = 0 \quad (\nabla_{2h+2p+2} \neq 0),$$

$then$ in the $calculation$ of $V(\nabla_{2h}, \ldots, \nabla_{2h+2p+2})$ one $must$ $take$

$$\text{sign } \nabla_{2h+2j} = (-1)^{\frac{j(j-1)}{2}} \text{ sign } \nabla_{2h} \quad (j = 1, 2, \ldots, p),$$

$or,$ $equivalently,$

$$V(\nabla_{2h}, \ldots, \nabla_{2h+2p+2}) = \tfrac{1}{2}(p + 1) \text{ if } p \text{ is odd,}$$
$$or \; = \tfrac{1}{2}(p + 1 - \varepsilon) \text{ if } p \text{ is even,}$$

$where$

$$\varepsilon = (-1)^{\frac{1}{2}p} \text{ sign } \nabla_{2h+2p+2}/\nabla_{2h}.$$

REMARK. If $\nabla_{2m} = 0$, i.e., if the fraction occurring after the index sign in (70) is reducible, then it is necessary to replace

---

[41] This condition means that $D_m \neq 0$ and, consequently, that the fraction following the index sign in (70) is irreducible.

formula (70) by the formula

$$I_{-\infty}^{+\infty} \frac{b_0 z^m + b_1 z^{m-1} + \ldots + b_m}{a_0 z^m + a_1 z^{m-1} + \ldots + a_m} = r - 2V (1, \nabla_2, \nabla_4, \ldots, \nabla_{2r}), \quad (70')$$

where r is the number of poles (counted with their multiplicities) of the rational function following the index sign. In other words, r is the degree of the denominator after the fraction is reduced to lowest terms.

Indeed, in this case the index with which we are concerned is equal to

$$r - 2V(1, D_1, D_2, \ldots, D_r),$$

since the number r is the rank of the corresponding matrix $S = (s_{i+k})_0^\infty$. But equation (68') is of a formal character and is also valid for reducible fractions. Thus

$$V(1, D_1, D_2, \ldots, D_r) = V(1, \nabla_2, \nabla_4, \ldots, \nabla_{2r}),$$

and we arrive at formula (70').

Formula (70') makes it possible to express the index of any rational function in which the degree of the numerator does not exceed that of the denominator in terms of the coefficients of the numerator and denominator.

§ 12. A second proof of the Routh-Hurwitz theorem

In Section 6 we proved the Routh-Hurwitz theorem by making use of Sturm's theorem and the Routh algorithm. In this section we shall give a proof of the Routh-Hurwitz theorem based on Theorem 10 of Section 11 and on the properties of the Cauchy index.

We shall first point out some properties of the Cauchy index that will be useful to us later.[42]

1. $I_a^b R(x) = - I_b^a R(x).$

2. $I_a^b R_1(x) R(x) = \operatorname{sign} R_1(x) \, I_a^b R(x)$ if $R_1(x)$ assumes neither of the values 0, ∞ on the interval (a, b).

---

[42] Here and subsequently the lower limit for the index may be $-\infty$, the upper limit $+\infty$.

3. *If $a < c < b$, then $I_a^b R(x) = I_a^c R(x) + I_c^b R(x) + \eta_c$, where $\eta_c = 0$ if $R(c)$ is finite, and $\eta_c = \pm 1$ if the function $R(x)$ has an infinite discontinuity at the point c; here $\eta_c = +1$ is to correspond to a change from $-\infty$ to $+\infty$ as x increases through c, and $\eta_c = -1$ is to correspond to a change from $+\infty$ to $-\infty$.*

4. *If $R(-x) = -R(x)$, then $I_{-a}^0 R(x) = I_0^a R(x)$. If $R(-x) = R(x)$, then $I_{-a}^0 R(x) = -I_0^a R(x)$.*

5. *$I_a^b R(x) + I_a^b 1/R(x) = \frac{1}{2}(\varepsilon_b - \varepsilon_a)$, where ε_a is the sign of $R(x)$ in (a, b) near a, and ε_b is the sign of $R(x)$ in (a, b) near b.*

The first four properties follow immediately from the definition of the Cauchy index (cf. Section 2). Property 5 follows from the fact that the sum of indices $I_a^b R(x) + I_a^b 1/R(x)$ is equal to the difference $n_1 - n_2$, where n_1 is the number of negative-to-positive changes in the sign of $R(x)$ as x varies from a to b, and n_2 is the number of positive-to-negative changes.

We shall consider the real polynomial (now using the usual notation for the coefficients)

$$f(z) = a_0 z^n + a_1 z^{n-1} + a_2 z^{n-2} + \ldots + a_{n-1} z + a_n \quad (a_0 > 0).$$

We may write it in the form

$$f(z) = h(z^2) + z g(z^2),$$

where

$$h(u) = a_n + a_{n-2} u + \ldots, \quad g(u) = a_{n-1} + a_{n-3} u + \ldots$$

We introduce the notation

$$\rho = I_{-\infty}^{+\infty} \frac{a_1 z^{n-1} - a_3 z^{n-3} + \ldots}{a_0 z^n - a_2 z^{n-2} + \ldots}. \tag{71}$$

In Section 3 we showed (cf. equation (20), p. 214) that

$$\rho = n - 2k - s, \tag{72}$$

where k is the number of roots of the polynomial $f(z)$ with positive real parts, and s is the number of roots of $f(z)$ lying on the imaginary axis.

We shall now obtain another expression for ρ.

We first consider the case in which n is even. Let $n = 2m$. Then

$$h(u) = a_0 u^m + a_2 u^{m-1} + \ldots + a_n,$$
$$g(u) = a_1 u^{m-1} + a_3 u^{m-2} + \ldots + a_{n-1}.$$

Applying properties *1—4* and putting $\eta = \pm 1$ if

$$\lim_{u \to -0} \frac{g(u)}{h(u)} = \pm \infty$$

and $\eta = 0$ in the remaining cases, we shall have:

$$\rho = -I_{-\infty}^{+\infty} \frac{zg(-z^2)}{h(-z^2)} = -(I_{-\infty}^0 + I_0^{+\infty} + \eta) = -2I_{-\infty}^0 \frac{zg(-z^2)}{h(-z^2)} - \eta$$

$$= 2I_{-\infty}^0 \frac{g(-z^2)}{h(-z^2)} - \eta = 2I_{-\infty}^0 \frac{g(u)}{h(u)} - \eta = I_{-\infty}^0 \frac{g(u)}{h(u)} - I_{-\infty}^0 \frac{ug(u)}{h(u)} - \eta$$

$$= I_{-\infty}^{+\infty} \frac{g(u)}{h(u)} - I_{-\infty}^{+\infty} \frac{ug(u)}{h(u)}.$$

In exactly the same way, if n is odd, $n = 2m + 1$, we have:

$$h(u) = a_1 u^m + a_3 u^{m-1} + \ldots + a_n, \; g(u) = a_0 u^m + a_2 u^{m-1} + \ldots + a_{n-1}.$$

Putting

$$\zeta = \text{sign} \left[\frac{g(u)}{h(u)} \right]_{u = -0}$$

if

$$\lim_{u \to 0} \frac{g(u)}{h(u)} = 0$$

and $\zeta = 0$ in the remaining cases, we find:

$$\rho = I_{-\infty}^{+\infty} \frac{h(-z^2)}{zg(-z^2)} = I_{-\infty}^0 + I_0^{+\infty} + \zeta = 2I_{-\infty}^0 \frac{h(-z^2)}{zg(-z^2)} + \zeta = 2I_{-\infty}^0 \frac{h(u)}{ug(u)} + \zeta$$

$$= I_{-\infty}^0 \frac{h(u)}{ug(u)} - I_{-\infty}^0 \frac{h(u)}{g(u)} + \zeta = I_{-\infty}^{+\infty} \frac{h(u)}{ug(u)} - I_{-\infty}^{+\infty} \frac{h(u)}{g(u)}.$$

Thus [43]

$$\rho = I_{-\infty}^{+\infty} \frac{g(u)}{h(u)} - I_{-\infty}^{+\infty} \frac{ug(u)}{h(u)} \quad (n = 2m), \qquad (73')$$

$$\rho = I_{-\infty}^{+\infty} \frac{h(u)}{ug(u)} - I_{-\infty}^{+\infty} \frac{h(u)}{g(u)} \quad (n = 2m + 1). \qquad (73'')$$

As before, $\Delta_1, \Delta_2, \ldots, \Delta_n$ will denote the Hurwitz determinants for the given polynomial $f(z)$. We shall suppose that $\Delta_n \neq 0.$[44]
(i) $n = 2m$. By formula (70),[45]

$$I_{-\infty}^{+\infty} \frac{g(u)}{h(u)} = m - 2V(1, \Delta_1, \Delta_3, \ldots, \Delta_{n-1}), \qquad (74)$$

$$I_{-\infty}^{+\infty} \frac{ug(u)}{h(u)} = m - 2V(1, -\Delta_2, +\Delta_4, -\Delta_6, \ldots)$$
$$= -m + 2V(1, \Delta_2, \Delta_4, \ldots, \Delta_n). \qquad (75)$$

But then, according to (73'),

$$\rho = n - 2V(1, \Delta_1, \Delta_3, \ldots, \Delta_{n-1}) - 2V(1, \Delta_2, \Delta_4, \ldots, \Delta_n),$$

which together with the equation $\rho = n - 2k$ gives:

$$k = V(1, \Delta_1, \Delta_3, \ldots, \Delta_{n-1}) + V(1, \Delta_2, \Delta_4, \ldots, \Delta_n). \qquad (76)$$

(ii) $n = 2m + 1$. By formula (70),

---

[43] If $a_1 \neq 0$, the two formulas (73') and (74'') may be combined into the single formula

$$\rho = I_{-\infty}^{+\infty} \frac{g(u)}{h(u)} + I_{-\infty}^{+\infty} \frac{h(u)}{ug(u)}$$

[44] In this case $s = 0$, so $\rho = n - 2k$. Moreover, $\Delta_n \neq 0$ indicates that the fractions following the index sign in formulas (73') and (73'') are in lowest terms.

[45] In calculating the values of the Hurwitz determinants here allowance must of course be made for the fact that the notation for the coefficients used here is different from that on which the formulas (32) (Section 6) were based.

$$I_{-\infty}^{+\infty}\frac{h(u)}{ug(u)} = m + 1 - 2V(1, \varDelta_1, \varDelta_3, \ldots, \varDelta_n), \qquad (77)$$

$$I_{-\infty}^{+\infty}\frac{h(u)}{g(u)} = m - 2V(1, -\varDelta_2, +\varDelta_4, -\ldots)$$
$$= -m + 2V(1, \varDelta_2, \varDelta_4, \ldots, \varDelta_{n-1}). \qquad (78)$$

The equation $\rho = 2m + 1 - 2k$ together with the equations (73''), (77), and (78) again gives us the formula (76).

The Routh-Hurwitz theorem is thus proved again (cf. (34'), 6).

REMARK 1. If in the formula

$$k = V(1, \varDelta_1, \varDelta_3, \ldots) + V(1, \varDelta_2, \varDelta_4, \ldots)$$

some of the intermediate Hurwitz determinants vanish, the formula nevertheless remains valid, provided that one assigns to the determinants in each group of consecutive vanishing determinants

$$(\varDelta_l \neq 0) \quad \varDelta_{l+2} = \varDelta_{l+4} = \ldots = \varDelta_{l+2p} = 0 \quad (\varDelta_{l+2p+2} \neq 0)$$

the sign given by

$$\mathrm{sign}\,\varDelta_{l+2j} = (-1)^{j(j-1)/2}\,\mathrm{sign}\,\varDelta_l \quad (j = 1, 2, \ldots, p),$$

in accordance with Theorem 7. This gives

$$V(\varDelta_l, \varDelta_{l+2}, \ldots, \varDelta_{l+2p+2}) = \begin{cases} \frac{1}{2}(p+1) & \text{if } p \text{ is odd,} \\ \frac{1}{2}(p+1-\varepsilon) & \text{if } p \text{ is even,} \\ \varepsilon = (-1)^{\frac{1}{2}p}\,\mathrm{sign}\,\varDelta_{l+2p+2}/\varDelta_l. \end{cases} \qquad (79)$$

A careful comparison of this rule for calculating k when some Hurwitz determinants vanish with the rule given in Theorem 5 will show that the two rules coincide.[46]

REMARK 2. If $\varDelta_n = 0$, the polynomials $ug(u)$ and $h(u)$ are not relatively prime. We denote by $d(u)$ the highest common factor of $g(u)$ and $h(u)$, and by $u^c d(u)$ the highest common factor of $ug(u)$ and $h(u)$ ($c = 0$ or 1). We shall denote the degree of $d(u)$ by δ and write

[46] Here it is necessary to take into account the remark made in Note 26 above (p. 238).

$$h(u) = d(u)h_1(u), \quad g(u) = d(u)g_1(u).$$

The irreducible rational function $g_1(u)/h_1(u)$ is always represented by some infinite Hankel matrix $S = (s_{i+k})_0^\infty$ of rank r, where r is the degree of $h_1(u)$. At the same time, the corresponding determinant $D_r \neq 0$, but $D_{r+1} = D_{r+2} = \ldots = 0$. By formula (68'),

$$\nabla_{2r} \neq 0, \quad \nabla_{2r+2} = \nabla_{2r+4} = \ldots = 0.$$

Moreover,

$$I_{-\infty}^{+\infty} \frac{g_1(u)}{h_1(u)} = r - 2V(1, \nabla_2, \ldots, \nabla_{2r}).$$

Applying all this to the fractions following the index signs in (74), (75), (77), and (78), we easily find that for arbitrary n (even or odd) and $\kappa = 2\delta + c$

$$\Delta_{n-\kappa-1} \neq 0, \quad \Delta_{n-\kappa} \neq 0, \quad \overbrace{\Delta_{n-\kappa+1} = \ldots = \Delta_n}^{\kappa} = 0$$

and that all of the formulas (74), (75), (77), and (78) remain valid in the case under consideration if one omits all of the Δ_i with $i > n - \kappa$ on the right sides of these formulas and changes the number m (in (77), the number $m + 1$) to the degree of the denominator of the fraction (after its reduction to lowest terms) following the index sign. Then, taking (73') and (73'') into account, we obtain:

$$\rho = n - \kappa - 2V(1, \Delta_1, \Delta_3, \ldots) - 2V(1, \Delta_2, \Delta_4, \ldots).$$

Together with the formula $\rho = n - 2k - s$ this gives:

$$k_1 = V(1, \Delta_1, \Delta_3, \ldots) + V(1, \Delta_2, \Delta_4, \ldots),$$

where $k_1 = k + \frac{1}{2}s - \frac{1}{2}\kappa$ is the number of roots of $f(z)$ lying in the right half plane, not counting those which are simultaneously roots of $f(-z)$.[47]

[47] This follows from the fact that κ is the degree of the highest common factor of $h(u)$ and $ug(u)$; κ is the number of "special" roots of the polynomial $f(z)$, i.e., of those roots z^* with the property that $-z^*$ is also a root of $f(z)$. This number equals the number of determinants in the last block of successive vanishing Hurwitz determinants $\Delta_{n-\kappa+1} = \ldots = \Delta_n = 0$.

§ 13. Some complements to the Routh-Hurwitz theorem The Liénard-Chipart stability criterion

Let there be given the polynomial with real coefficients

$$f(z) = a_0 z^n + a_1 z^{n-1} + \ldots + a_n \quad (a_0 > 0).$$

Then the Routh-Hurwitz conditions, necessary and sufficient for all roots of the polynomial $f(z)$ to have negative real parts, may be expressed by the inequalities

$$\Delta_1 > 0, \ \Delta_2 > 0, \ \ldots, \ \Delta_n > 0, \tag{81}$$

where

$$\Delta_i = \det \begin{bmatrix} a_1 & a_3 & a_5 & \ldots & \\ a_0 & a_2 & a_4 & \ldots & \\ 0 & a_1 & a_3 & \ldots & \\ 0 & a_0 & a_2 & a_4 & \\ & & & \cdot & \\ & & & & \cdot \\ & & & & a_n \end{bmatrix} \quad (a_k = 0 \text{ if } k > n)$$

is the Hurwitz determinant of order i $(i = 1, 2, \ldots, n)$.

If the conditions (81) are satisfied, the polynomial $f(z)$ may be written as a product of a_0 by factors of the form $z + u$, $z^2 + vz + w$ $(u > 0, \ v > 0, \ w > 0)$, so all coefficients of the polynomial $f(z)$ must be positive:

$$a_0 > 0, \ a_1 > 0, \ a_2 > 0, \ \ldots, a_n > 0. \tag{82}$$

In contrast to conditions (81), the conditions (82) are necessary but not sufficient for all of the roots of $f(z)$ to lie in the left half-plane.

However, once the conditions (82) are satisfied the conditions (81) are no longer independent. For instance, when $n = 4$ the Routh-Hurwitz conditions reduce to the single inequality $\Delta_3 > 0$, when $n = 5$ to the pair of inequalities $\Delta_2 > 0$, $\Delta_4 > 0$, and when $n = 6$ to the pair of inequalities $\Delta_3 > 0$, $\Delta_5 > 0$.[48]

[48] This fact was observed for the first few values of n in a series of papers on the theory of control independently of the general Liénard-Chipart criterion, with which the authors of these papers were evidently unacquainted.

This situation was investigated by the French mathematicians Liénard and Chipart, and it led them to the discovery in 1914 of stability criteria different from the Routh-Hurwitz criterion.[49]

THEOREM 11. (The Liénard-Chipart stability criteria.)

Necessary and sufficient conditions for the real polynomial $f(z) = a_0 z^n + a_1 z^{n-1} + \ldots + a_n$ $(a_0 > 0)$ *to have only roots with negative real parts may be expressed in any one of the four following forms:*

1. $a_n > 0, \; a_{n-2} > 0, \ldots; \; \Delta_1 > 0, \; \Delta_3 > 0, \ldots,$

2. $a_n > 0, \; a_{n-2} > 0, \ldots; \; \Delta_2 > 0, \; \Delta_4 > 0, \ldots,$

3. $a_n > 0, \; a_{n-1} > 0, \; a_{n-3} > 0, \ldots; \; \Delta_1 > 0, \; \Delta_3 > 0, \ldots,$

4. $a_n > 0, \; a_{n-1} > 0, \; a_{n-3} > 0, \ldots; \; \Delta_2 > 0, \; \Delta_4 > 0, \ldots.$

Conditions *1, 2, 3, 4* have an evident advantage over the Hurwitz conditions in that they involve about half as many determinant inequalities.

From Theorem 11 it follows that for a real polynomial in which all coefficients (or even only some of them: a_n, $a_{n-2}, \ldots$, or a_n, a_{n-1}, $a_{n-3}, \ldots$) are positive, the determinant inequalities of Hurwitz (81) are not independent; namely: *the positivity of the Hurwitz determinants of odd order implies that of the Hurwitz determinants of even order, and conversely.*

Conditions *1* were obtained by Liénard and Chipart by the use of special quadratic forms. We shall give a simpler derivation of conditions *1* (as well as of conditions *2, 3, 4*) based on Theorem 10 of Section 11 and the theory of the Cauchy index. They will be obtained as particular cases of a considerably more general theorem, to the discussion of which we now proceed.

We again consider the polynomials $h(u)$ and $g(u)$ which are connected with $f(z)$ by the identity

$$f(z) = h(z^2) + zg(z^2).$$

If n is even, $n = 2m$, then

$$h(u) = a_0 u^m + a_2 u^{m-1} + \ldots + a_n, \quad g(u) = a_1 u^{m-1} + a_3 u^{m-2} + \ldots + a_{n-1};$$

[49] Liénard and Chipart, [41].

and if n is odd, $n = 2m + 1$, then

$$h(u)=a_1u^m+a_3u^{m-1}+ \ldots +a_n, \ g(u)=a_0u^m+a_2u^{m-1}+ \ldots +a_{n-1}.$$

Thus the conditions $a_n > 0$, $a_{n-2} > 0, \ldots$ (or $a_{n-1} > 0$, $a_{n-3} > 0, \ldots$) may be replaced by the more general condition: $h(u)$ (or $g(u)$) does not change sign for positive values of u, i.e., either $h(u) \geqq 0$ for all $u > 0$ or else $h(u) \leqq 0$ for all $u > 0$ (similarly for $g(u)$).

With the aid of these conditions one can write down formulas for the number of roots of the polynomial $f(z)$ which lie in the right half-plane, using only the Hurwitz determinants of odd order or only those of even order.

THEOREM 12. *If the real polynomial*

$$f(z) = a_0z^n + a_1z^{n-1} + \ldots + a_n = h(z^2) + zg(z^2) \quad (a_0 > 0)$$

satisfies the conditions (a) $h(u)$ *(or* $g(u)$*) does not change sign for* $u > 0$, *and* (b) *the last Hurwitz determinant* $\Delta_n \neq 0$, *then* k, *the number of roots of* $f(z)$ *lying in the right half-plane, is given by the formulas*

	$n = 2m$	$n = 2m + 1$
$h(u)$ does not change sign for $u > 0$	$k=2V(1, \Delta_1, \Delta_3, \ldots, \Delta_{n-1})$ $=2V(1, \Delta_2, \Delta_4, \ldots, \Delta_n)$	$k=2V(1, \Delta_1, \Delta_3, \ldots, \Delta$ $-\tfrac{1}{2}(1-\varepsilon$ $=2V(1, \Delta_2, \Delta_4, \ldots, \Delta_{n-}$ $+\tfrac{1}{2}(1-\varepsilon$
$g(u)$ does not change sign for $u > 0$	$k=2V(1,\Delta_1,\Delta_3,\ldots,\Delta_{n-1})+\dfrac{\varepsilon_\infty-\varepsilon_0}{2}$ $=2V(1, \Delta_2, \Delta_4, \ldots, \Delta_n) -\dfrac{\varepsilon_\infty-\varepsilon_0}{2}$	$k=2V(1, \Delta_1, \Delta_3, \ldots, \Delta_n$ $-\tfrac{1}{2}(1-\varepsilon$ $=2V(1, \Delta_2, \Delta_4, \ldots, \Delta_{n-}$ $+\tfrac{1}{2}(1-\varepsilon$

(8

where [50]

$$\varepsilon_\infty = \text{sign}\left[\frac{g(u)}{h(u)}\right]_{u=+\infty}, \quad \varepsilon_0 = \text{sign}\left[\frac{g(u)}{h(u)}\right]_{u=+0} \tag{84}$$

Proof. Again we introduce the notation

$$\rho = I_{-\infty}^{+\infty}\frac{a_1 z^{n-1} - a_3 z^{n-3} + \cdots}{a_0 z^n - a_2 z^{n-2} + \cdots}.$$

We consider the four cases which correspond to the entries in the table (83).

(i) $n = 2m$; $h(u)$ does not change sign for $u > 0$. Then [51]

$$I_0^{+\infty}\frac{g(u)}{h(u)} = I_0^{+\infty}\frac{ug(u)}{h(u)} = 0,$$

and thus from the obvious equation

$$I_{-\infty}^0\frac{g(u)}{h(u)} = -I_{-\infty}^0\frac{ug(u)}{h(u)}$$

it follows that [52]

$$I_{-\infty}^{+\infty}\frac{g(u)}{h(u)} = -I_{-\infty}^{+\infty}\frac{ug(u)}{h(u)}.$$

---

[50] If $a_1 \neq 0$, then $\varepsilon_\infty = \text{sign } a_1$, and in general if

$$a_1 = a_3 = \ldots = a_{2\mu-1} = 0, \quad a_{2\mu+1} \neq 0,$$

then $\varepsilon_\infty = \text{sign } a_{2\mu+1}$; if $a_{n-1} \neq 0$, then

$$\varepsilon_0 = \text{sign } (a_{n-1}/a_n),$$

and in general if

$$a_{n-1} = a_{n-3} = \ldots = a_{n-2\mu+1} = 0, \quad a_{n-2\mu-1} \neq 0,$$

then

$$\varepsilon_0 = \text{sign } (a_{n-2\mu-1}/a_n).$$

[51] If $h(u_1) = 0$ $(u_1 > 0)$, then $g(u_1) \neq 0$, since $\Delta_n \neq 0$. Thus from $h(u) \gtreqless 0$ $(u > 0)$ it follows that $g(u)/h(u)$ does not change sign as u passes through the value u_1.

[52] Since $\Delta_n = a_n\Delta_{n-1} \neq 0$, it follows that $h(0) = a_n \neq 0$.

But then from (74) and (75) we find:

$$V(1, \Delta_1, \Delta_3, \ldots) = V(1, \Delta_2, \Delta_4, \ldots),$$

whence the Routh-Hurwitz formula (76) gives

$$k = 2V(1, \Delta_1, \Delta_3, \ldots, \Delta_{n-1}) = 2V(1, \Delta_2, \Delta_4, \ldots, \Delta_n).$$

(ii) $n = 2m$; $g(u)$ does not change sign for $u > 0$. In this case

$$I_0^{+\infty} \frac{h(u)}{g(u)} = I_0^{+\infty} \frac{h(u)}{ug(u)} = 0,$$

$$I_{-\infty}^0 \frac{h(u)}{g(u)} + I_{-\infty}^0 \frac{h(u)}{ug(u)} = 0$$

and, consequently, using the notation (84), we obtain:

$$I_{-\infty}^{+\infty} \frac{h(u)}{g(u)} + I_{-\infty}^{+\infty} \frac{h(u)}{ug(u)} - \varepsilon_0 = 0. \tag{85}$$

Replacing the functions following the index signs by their reciprocals and making use of 5 (Section 12) gives:

$$I_{-\infty}^{+\infty} \frac{g(u)}{h(u)} + I_{-\infty}^{+\infty} \frac{ug(u)}{h(u)} = \varepsilon_\infty - \varepsilon_0.$$

But this, by virtue of (74) and (75), yields:

$$V(1, \Delta_2, \Delta_4, \ldots) - V(1, \Delta_1, \Delta_3, \ldots) = \frac{\varepsilon_\infty - \varepsilon_0}{2}.$$

Whence, using the Routh-Hurwitz formula (76), we obtain:

$$k = 2V(1, \Delta_1, \Delta_3, \ldots) + \frac{\varepsilon_\infty - \varepsilon_0}{2} = 2V(1, \Delta_2, \Delta_4, \ldots) - \frac{\varepsilon_\infty - \varepsilon_0}{2}.$$

(iii) $n = 2m + 1$, $g(u)$ does not change sign for $u > 0$.

In this case, as in the preceding case, formula (85) holds. If in (85) one replaces the indices by the expressions given for them in (77) and (78), one obtains:

$$V(1, \Delta_1, \Delta_3, \ldots) - V(1, \Delta_2, \Delta_4, \ldots) = \frac{1 - \varepsilon_0}{2}.$$

In combination with the Routh-Hurwitz formula this equation gives:

$$k = 2V(1, \Delta_1, \Delta_3, \ldots) - \frac{1 - \varepsilon_0}{2} = 2V(1, \Delta_2, \Delta_4, \ldots) + \frac{1 - \varepsilon_0}{2}.$$

(iv) $n = 2m + 1$, $h(u)$ does not change sign for $u > 0$. From the equations

$$I_{-\infty}^{+\infty} \frac{g(u)}{h(u)} = I_0^{\infty} \frac{ug(u)}{h(u)} = 0, \quad I_{-\infty}^0 \frac{g(u)}{h(u)} + I_{-\infty}^0 \frac{ug(u)}{h(u)} = 0$$

we infer:

$$I_{-\infty}^{+\infty} \frac{g(u)}{h(u)} + I_{-\infty}^{+\infty} \frac{ug(u)}{h(u)} = 0.$$

Inverting the functions following the index signs give:

$$I_{-\infty}^{+\infty} \frac{h(u)}{g(u)} + I_{-\infty}^{+\infty} \frac{h(u)}{ug(u)} = \varepsilon_\infty.$$

Substituting in this the expressions for the indices given by (77) and (78), we obtain:

$$V(1, \Delta_1, \Delta_3, \ldots) - V(1, \Delta_2, \Delta_4, \ldots) = \frac{1 - \varepsilon_\infty}{2}.$$

From this and the Routh-Hurwitz formula there follows:

$$k = 2V(1, \Delta_1, \Delta_3, \ldots) - \frac{1 - \varepsilon_\infty}{2} = 2V(1, \Delta_2, \Delta_4, \ldots) + \frac{1 - \varepsilon_\infty}{2}.$$

Theorem 12 is completely proved.

Theorem 11 follows from this theorem as a special case.

COROLLARY. *If the real polynomial*

$$f(z) = a_0 z^n + a_1 z^{n-1} + \ldots + a_n \quad (a_0 > 0)$$

has positive coefficients, and if $\Delta_n \neq 0$, then the number k of roots of this polynomial which lie in the right half-plane is given by the formula

$$k = 2V(1, \Delta_1, \Delta_3, \ldots) = 2V(1, \Delta_2, \Delta_4, \ldots).$$

REMARK. If in the last formula or in the formulas (83) some of the intermediate Hurwitz determinants are zero, then in calculating the values of $V(1, \Delta_1, \Delta_3, \ldots)$ and $V(1, \Delta_2, \Delta_4, \ldots)$ one should follow the rules explained in Remark 1 in Section 12.

If $\Delta_n = \Delta_{n-1} = \ldots = \Delta_{n-k+1} = 0$, $\Delta_{n-k} \neq 0$, then upon omitting the determinants $\Delta_{n-k+1}, \ldots, \Delta_n$ from the formulas (83) we obtain from these formulas the number k_1 of "nonspecial" roots of $f(z)$ which lie in the right half-plane, if only $h(u) \neq 0$ for $u > 0$ or $g(u) \neq 0$ for $u > 0$.[53]

§ 14. Some properties of the Hurwitz polynomials Stieltjes' theorem
Representation of Hurwitz polynomials by continued fractions

1. Let there be given a real polynomial

$$f(z) = a_0 z^n + a_1 z^{n-1} + \ldots + a_n \quad (a_0 \neq 0).$$

We represent it in the form

$$f(z) = h(z^2) + z g(z^2).$$

We shall show what conditions must be imposed on the polynomials $h(u)$ and $g(u)$ in order for the polynomial $f(z)$ to be a Hurwitz polynomial.

Putting $k = s = 0$ in the formula (20), we obtain the result that a necessary and sufficient condition for $f(z)$ to be a Hurwitz polynomial is that the equation

$$\rho = n,$$

holds, where, as in the preceding sections,

$$\rho = I_{-\infty}^{+\infty} \frac{a_1 z^{n-1} - a_3 z^{n-3} + \ldots}{a_0 z^n - a_2 z^{n-2} + \ldots}.$$

Let $n = 2m$. According to formula (73'), this condition can be

---

[53] In this case the polynomials $h_1(u)$ and $g_1(u)$ obtained from $h(u)$ and $g(u)$ by dividing them by their highest common factor $d(u)$ satisfy the conditions of Theorem 12. Cf. the discussion at the end of Section 12.

written

$$n = 2m = I_{-\infty}^{+\infty} \frac{g(u)}{h(u)} - I_{-\infty}^{+\infty} \frac{ug(u)}{h(u)}. \tag{86}$$

Since the absolute value of the index of a rational function cannot exceed the degree of the denominator (m in the present case), equation (86) can be true if and only if we have simultaneously

$$I_{-\infty}^{+\infty} \frac{g(u)}{h(u)} = m, \quad I_{-\infty}^{+\infty} \frac{ug(u)}{h(u)} = -m. \tag{87}$$

If $n = 2m + 1$, the equation (73″) (with $\rho = n$) gives:

$$n = I_{-\infty}^{+\infty} \frac{h(u)}{ug(u)} - I_{-\infty}^{+\infty} \frac{h(u)}{g(u)}.$$

If we replace each of the fractions following an index sign here by its reciprocal (cf. 5, Section 12), and at the same time notice that $h(u)$ and $g(u)$ have the same degree, namely m, we obtain:

$$n = 2m + 1 = I_{-\infty}^{+\infty} \frac{g(u)}{h(u)} - I_{-\infty}^{+\infty} \frac{ug(u)}{h(u)} + \varepsilon_\infty. \tag{88}$$

If we again make use of the fact that the absolute value of the index of a fraction cannot exceed the degree of the denominator, we find that the equation (88) can hold true if and only if simultaneously

$$I_{-\infty}^{+\infty} \frac{g(u)}{h(u)} = m, \quad I_{-\infty}^{+\infty} \frac{ug(u)}{h(u)} = -m, \quad \varepsilon_\infty = 1. \tag{89}$$

If $n = 2m$, the first of the equations (87) indicates that the polynomial $h(u)$ has m distinct real roots $u_1 < u_2 < \ldots < u_m$ and that the proper fraction $g(u)/h(u)$ can be represented in the form

$$\frac{g(u)}{h(u)} = \sum_{i=1}^{m} \frac{R_i}{u - u_i}, \tag{90}$$

where

$$R_i = \frac{g(u_i)}{h'(u_i)} > 0 \quad (i = 1, 2, \ldots, m). \tag{90'}$$

From this representation of the fraction $g(u)/h(u)$ it follows that between any two roots u_i, u_{i+1} of the polynomial $h(u)$ there lies a real root u_i' of the polynomial $g(u)$ ($i = 1, 2, \ldots, m - 1$), and that the leading coefficients of the polynomials $h(u)$ and $g(u)$ have the same sign; i.e.,

$$h(u) = a_0(u - u_1) \ldots (u - u_m), \quad g(u) = a_1(u_1 - u_1') \ldots (u - u_{m-1}'),$$
$$u_1 < u_1' < u_2 < u_2' < \ldots < u_{m-1} < u_{m-1}' < u_m; \quad a_0 a_1 > 0.$$

The second of the equations (87) introduces only the one additional condition

$$u_m < 0.$$

From this condition it follows that all of the roots of $h(u)$ and $g(u)$ must be negative. If $n = 2m + 1$, then from the first of the equations (89) it follows that $h(u)$ has m distinct real roots $u_1, u_2, \ldots, u_m$ and that

$$\frac{g(u)}{h(u)} = s_{-1} + \sum_{i=1}^{m} \frac{R_i}{u - u_i} \qquad (s_{-1} \neq 0), \tag{91}$$

where

$$R_i = \frac{g(u_i)}{h'(u_i)} > 0 \qquad (i = 1, 2, \ldots, m). \tag{91'}$$

From the third equation of (89) it follows that

$$s_{-1} > 0, \tag{92}$$

i.e. that the leading coefficients a_0 and a_1 have the same sign. Moreover, from (91), (91'), and (92) it follows that $g(u)$ has m real roots $u_1' < u_2' < \ldots < u_m'$ lying respectively in the intervals $(-\infty, u_1)$, $(u_1, u_2). \ldots, (u_{m-1}, u_m)$. In other words

$$h(u) = a_1(u - u_1) \ldots (u - u_m), \quad g(u) = a_0(u - u_1') \ldots (u - u_m'),$$
$$u_1' < u_1 < u_2' < u_2 < \ldots < u_m' < u_m; \quad a_0 a_1 > 0.$$

The second of the equations (89), as for $n = 2m$, involves the single additional condition

$$u_m < 0.$$

DEFINITION 3. *We shall say that two polynomials $h(u)$ and $g(u)$ of the mth degree (or of degrees m, $m - 1$, respectively) form a positive pair if their roots u_1, u_2, ..., u_m and u_1', u_2', ..., u_m' (u_1', u_2', ..., u_{m-1}') are all distinct, real, negative, and interlock in the following manner*:

$$u_1' < u_1 < u_2' < u_2 < \ldots < u_m < 0$$
$$(\text{or } u_1 < u_1' < u_2 < \ldots < u_{m-1}' < u_m < 0),$$

while the leading coefficients have the same sign.[54]

Introducing the positive numbers $v_i = -u_i$, $v_i' = -u_i'$, and multiplying the two polynomials $h(u)$ and $g(u)$ of a positive pair by $+1$ or -1 so that the leading coefficients are left positive, we may write these polynomials in the form

$$h(u) = a_1 \prod_{i=1}^{m} (u + v_i), \qquad g(u) = a_0 \prod_{i=1}^{m} (u + v_i'), \qquad (93)$$

where

$$a_1 > 0, \ a_0 > 0, \ 0 < v_m < v_m' < v_{m-1} < v_{m-1}' < \ldots < v_1 < v_1',$$

if both of the polynomials $h(u)$ and $g(u)$ have the degree m, and in the form

$$h(u) = a_0 \prod_{i=1}^{m} (u + v_i), \qquad g(u) = a_1 \prod_{i=1}^{m-1} (u + v_i'), \qquad (93')$$

where

$$a_0 > 0, \ a_1 > 0, \ 0 < v_m < v_{m-1}' < v_{m-1} < \ldots < v_1' < v_1,$$

if the degree of $h(u)$ is m and that of $g(u)$ is $m - 1$.

The following two theorems summarize the discussions above.

THEOREM 13. *A necessary and sufficient condition that the polynomial $f(z) = h(z^2) + zg(z^2)$ be a Hurwitz polynomial, is that the polynomials $h(u)$ and $g(u)$ constitute a positive pair.*[55]

[54] If we omit the requirement that the roots be negative, we obtain a *real pair* of polynomials. On the use of this concept in connection with the Routh-Hurwitz problem, see I. G. Malkin, [44].

[55] This theorem is itself a special case of the so-called Hermite-Biehler theorem. Cf. Chebotarev and Meĭman, [8], p. 21.

THEOREM 14. *A necessary and sufficient condition that the two polynomials $h(u)$ (of degree m) and $g(u)$ (of degree $m-1$) constitute a positive pair is that the equations*

$$I^{+\infty}_{-\infty} \frac{g(u)}{h(u)} = m, \quad I^{+\infty}_{-\infty} \frac{ug(u)}{h(u)} = -m \qquad (94)$$

should be satisfied. If $h(u)$ and $g(u)$ have the same degree, there is the complementary condition

$$\varepsilon_\infty = \text{sign} \left[\frac{g(u)}{h(u)} \right]_{+\infty} = 1. \qquad (95)$$

2.   From the last theorem, derived from the properties of the Cauchy index, we may easily obtain Stieltjes' theorem on the representation of the fraction $g(u)/h(u)$ in the form of a continued fraction of a special type, provided that $h(u)$ and $g(u)$ constitute a positive pair of polynomials.

The proof of Stieltjes' theorem is based on the following lemma:

LEMMA. *If the polynomials $h(u)$ and $g(u)$ (the degree of $h(u)$ being m) form a positive pair, and*

$$\frac{g(u)}{h(u)} = c + \left(du + \frac{h_1(u)}{g_1(u)} \right)^{-1} \qquad (96)$$

where c, d are constants, and $h_1(u)$, $g_1(u)$ are polynomials of degree $\leq m-1$, then

1.   *$c \geq 0$, $d > 0$,*
2.   *the polynomials $h_1(u)$ and $g_1(u)$ have degree $m-1$,*
3.   *the polynomials $h_1(u)$ and $g_1(u)$ constitute a positive pair.*

Once $h(u)$ and $g(u)$ are given, $h_1(u)$ and $g_1(u)$ are uniquely determined up to a constant common factor, and the constants c and d are uniquely determined.

Conversely, it follows from (96) and 1, 2, 3, that the polynomials $h(u)$ and $g(u)$ form a positive pair, the degree of $h(u)$ being m and the degree of $g(u)$ being m or $m-1$ according as $c > 0$ or $c = 0$.

Proof.   Let $h(u)$, $g(u)$ be a positive pair. Then from (94) and (96) there follows:

$$m = I_{-\infty}^{+\infty} \frac{g(u)}{h(u)} = I_{-\infty}^{+\infty} \left(du + \frac{h_1(u)}{g_1(u)} \right)^{-1}. \tag{97}$$

From this equation it follows that the degree of $g_1(u)$ is equal to $m - 1$ and that $d \neq 0$.

Moreover, from (97) we find:

$$m = - I_{-\infty}^{+\infty} \left[du + \frac{h_1(u)}{g_1(u)} \right] + \operatorname{sign} d = - I_{-\infty}^{+\infty} \frac{h_1(u)}{g_1(u)} + \operatorname{sign} d.$$

From this it follows that $d > 0$ and that

$$I_{-\infty}^{+\infty} \frac{h_1(u)}{g_1(u)} = -(m - 1). \tag{98}$$

Now the second equation in (94) gives:

$$- m = I_{-\infty}^{+\infty} \frac{ug(u)}{h(u)} = I_{-\infty}^{+\infty} \left[cu + \left(d + \frac{h_1(u)}{ug_1(u)} \right)^{-1} \right] \tag{99}$$
$$= I_{-\infty}^{+\infty} \left(d + \frac{h_1(u)}{ug_1(u)} \right)^{-1} = - I_{-\infty}^{+\infty} \left[d + \frac{h_1(u)}{ug_1(u)} \right] = - I_{-\infty}^{+\infty} \frac{h_1(u)}{ug_1(u)}.$$

From this it follows that the degree of $h_1(u)$ is $m - 1$.

By virtue of (96), the condition (95) gives: $c > 0$. If the degree of $g(u)$ is less than that of $h(u)$, then (96) implies: $c = 0$.

From (98) and (99) we have:

$$I_{-\infty}^{+\infty} \frac{g_1(u)}{h_1(u)} = m - 1, \quad I_{-\infty}^{+\infty} \frac{ug_1(u)}{h_1(u)} = - m + \varepsilon_\infty^{(1)}, \tag{100}$$

where

$$\varepsilon_\infty^{(1)} = \operatorname{sign} \left[\frac{g_1(u)}{h_1(u)} \right]_{u = +\infty}.$$

Since the second of the indices (100) is at most $m - 1$ in absolute value,

$$\varepsilon_\infty^{(1)} = 1, \tag{101}$$

but then from (100) and (101) we may use Theorem 12 to conclude that the polynomials $h_1(u)$ and $g_1(u)$ form a positive pair.

From (96) there follows:

$$c = \lim_{u \to \infty} \frac{g(u)}{h(u)}, \quad \lim_{u \to \infty} \left[\frac{g(u)}{h(u)} - c \right] u = \frac{1}{d}.$$

Once c and d are determined, (96) determines the ratio $h_1(u)/g_1(u)$.

The relations (97), (98), (99), (100), and (101), applied in the reverse order, establish the second part of the lemma. Thus the lemma is completely proved.

Suppose we are given a positive pair of polynomials $g(u)$ and $h(u)$, where $h(u)$ has degree m. Then, dividing $g(u)$ by $h(u)$ and denoting the quotient by c_0, the remainder by $g_1(u)$, we obtain:

$$\frac{g(u)}{h(u)} = c_0 + \frac{g_1(u)}{h(u)} = c_0 + \left(\frac{h(u)}{g_1(u)} \right)^{-1}.$$

The ratio $h(u)/g_1(u)$ may be represented in the form $d_0 u + h_1(u)/g_1(u)$, where the degree of $h_1(u)$, as well as that of $g_1(u)$, is less than m. Then

$$\frac{g(u)}{h(u)} = c_0 + \left(d_0 u + \frac{h_1(u)}{g_1(u)} \right)^{-1}. \tag{102}$$

Thus for any positive pair $h(u)$, $g(u)$, there holds a relation (96). According to the lemma $c_0 \geqq 0$, $d_0 > 0$, while the polynomials $h_1(u)$ and $g_1(u)$ have the degree $m - 1$ and form a positive pair.

If we now apply these considerations to the positive pair $h_1(u)$, $g_1(u)$, we obtain an equation

$$\frac{g_1(u)}{h_1(u)} = c_1 + \left(d_1 u + \frac{h_2(u)}{g_2(u)} \right)^{-1},$$

where $c_1 > 0$, $d_1 > 0$, and the polynomials $h_2(u)$, $g_2(u)$ are of degree $m - 2$ and form a positive pair. Continuing this process further, we ultimately arrive at a positive pair h_m, g_m, these being constants with the same sign. If we put

$$g_m/h_m = c_m, \tag{102$^{(m)}$}$$

then from (102), $(102^{(1)})$, ..., $(102^{(m)})$ there follows:

$$\frac{g(u)}{h(u)} = c_0 + \cfrac{1}{d_0 u + \cfrac{1}{c_1 + \cfrac{1}{d_1 u + \cfrac{1}{c_2 + {\ddots}}}}}$$

$$+ \cfrac{1}{d_{m-1} u + \cfrac{1}{c_m}}.$$

Applying the second part of the lemma, we may show analogously that for any $c_0 \geqq 0$, $c_1 > 0$, ..., $c_m > 0$, $d_0 > 0$, $d_1 > 0$, ..., $d_{m-1} > 0$, the continued fraction written above defines uniquely (up to a constant common factor) a positive pair of polynomials $h(u)$ and $g(u)$, where $h(u)$ has the degree m and $g(u)$ has the degree m if $c_0 > 0$, $m - 1$ if $c_0 = 0$.

This proves

THEOREM 15 (Stieltjes). *If $h(u)$, $g(u)$ are a positive pair of polynomials and the degree of $h(u)$ is m, then*

$$\frac{g(u)}{h(u)} = c_0 + \cfrac{1}{d_0 u + \cfrac{1}{c_1 + \cfrac{1}{d_1 u + \cfrac{1}{c_2 + {\ddots}}}}} \qquad (103)$$

$$+ \cfrac{1}{d_{m-1} u + \cfrac{1}{c_m}},$$

where

$$c_0 \geqq 0, \; c_1 > 0, ..., c_m > 0, \; d_0 > 0, ..., d_{m-1} > 0.$$

Here $c_0 = 0$ if the degree of $g(u)$ is $m - 1$, and $c_0 > 0$ if the degree of $g(u)$ is m. The constants c_k, d_k are uniquely determined once $h(u)$ and $g(u)$ are given.

Conversely, for any $c_0 \geqq 0$ and any positive constants $c_1, \ldots, c_m$, $d_0, \ldots, d_{m-1}$, the continued fraction (103) *defines a positive pair of polynomials* $h(u)$, $g(u)$, *where* $h(u)$ *has the degree* m.

From Theorem 13 and Stieltjes' theorem there follows

THEOREM 16. *The real polynomial* $f(z) = h(z^2) + zg(z^2)$ *of degree* n *is a Hurwitz polynomial if and only if formula* (103) *holds with* c_0 *nonnegative and all of the constants* $c_1, \ldots, c_m$, $d_0, \ldots, d_{m-1}$ *positive. Moreover,* $c_0 > 0$ *when* n *is odd, and* $c_0 = 0$ *when* n *is even.*

§ 15. The domain of stability. Markov parameters

To every real polynomial of degree n there may be assigned a point of Euclidean n-space, the coordinates of which are the numbers obtained by dividing the leading coefficient into the other coefficients. In such a "coefficient space" the Hurwitz polynomials form a certain n-dimensional region which is defined (with $a_0 = 1$) by the Hurwitz inequalities $\varDelta_1 > 0$, $\varDelta_2 > 0$, $\ldots \varDelta_n > 0$ or, for instance, by the Liénard-Chipart inequalities $a_n > 0$, $a_{n-2} > 0, \ldots$; $\varDelta_1 > 0$, $\varDelta_3 > 0, \ldots$. This region will be called the *domain of stability*. If the coefficients are given as functions of p parameters, then the domain of stability can be regarded as lying in the space of these parameters.

The investigation of the domain of stability is a matter of great practical interest; thus, for instance, such an investigation is essential in the design of new control systems.[56]

In Section 16 we shall show that two remarkable theorems established by A. A. Markov and P. L. Chebyshev in connection with the expansion of continued fractions in power series in negative powers of the argument are closely related to the

[56] The study of the domain of stability, and also of the regions corresponding to various values of k (the number of roots in the right half-plane) has been the subject of a series of papers by Yu. I. Naĭmark. Cf. Naĭmark, [50].

investigation of the domain of stability. In order to formulate and prove these theorems we must regard the polynomials as being given not by their coefficients but by certain parameters which we shall call *Markov parameters*.

Let there be given a real polynomial

$$f(z) = a_0 z^n + a_1 z^{n-1} + \ldots + a_n \quad (a_0 \neq 0).$$

As before, we put it in the form

$$f(z) = h(z^2) + zg(z^2).$$

We shall suppose that the polynomials $h(u)$ and $g(u)$ are relatively prime $(\Delta_n \neq 0)$. The irreducible rational function $g(u)/h(u)$ can be expanded in a series of descending powers of u:[57]

$$\frac{g(u)}{h(u)} = s_{-1} + \frac{s_0}{u} - \frac{s_1}{u^2} + \frac{s_2}{u^3} - \frac{s_3}{u^4} + \ldots \quad (104)$$

The sequence of numbers $s_0, s_1, s_2, \ldots$ defines an infinite Hankel matrix $S = (s_{i+k})_0^\infty$. We define a rational function $R(v)$ by means of the equation

$$R(v) = -g(-v)/h(-v). \quad (105)$$

Then

$$R(v) = -s_{-1} + \frac{s_0}{v} + \frac{s_1}{v^2} + \frac{s_2}{v^3} + \ldots, \quad (106)$$

so that the relation

$$R(v) \sim S \quad (107)$$

holds (cf. Section 11).

Hence it follows, by Theorem 8, that the matrix S has rank $m = [n/2]$, since m is the degree of the polynomial $h(u)$ and, therefore, the number of poles of the function $R(v)$.

When $n = 2m$ (in this case $s_{-1} = 0$), a given matrix S uniquely determines an irreducible fraction $g(u)/h(u)$ and therefore determines a polynomial $f(z)$ up to a constant factor. When $n = 2m+1$, it is necessary to know s_{-1} as well as S to determine the polynomial $f(z)$.

[57] It is for the sake of convenience in what is to come that we denote the coefficients of even negative powers of u by $-s_1$, $-s_3$, etc.

On the other hand, in order to arrive at an infinite Hankel matrix S of rank m it is sufficient to give the first $2m$ numbers $s_0, s_1, \ldots, s_{2m-1}$. These numbers may be chosen arbitrarily, subject to the sole restriction

$$D_m = \det [s_{i+k}]_0^m \neq 0; \qquad (108)$$

all of the subsequent coefficients in the expansion (104) can be uniquely expressed (and indeed rationally) in terms of the first $2m$ coefficients. In fact, the elements of an infinite Hankel matrix S of rank m are related to one another by means of the recurrence relations (cf. Theorem 7, p. 244)

$$s_q = \sum_{g=1}^{m} \alpha_g s_{q-g} \qquad (q = m, \, m+1, \ldots). \qquad (109)$$

If the numbers $s_0, s_1, \ldots, s_{2m-1}$ satisfy the inequality (108), then the coefficients $\alpha_1, \ldots, \alpha_m$ are uniquely determined by the first m of the relations (109); then the other relations (109) define $s_{2m}, s_{2m+1}, \ldots$

Thus a real polynomial $f(z)$ of degree $n = 2m$ for which $\varDelta_n \neq 0$ is defined uniquely (except for a constant factor) by $2m$ numbers $s_0, s_1, \ldots, s_{2m-1}$ satisfying the inequality (108). If $n = 2m + 1$ it is necessary to adjoin s_{-1} to these numbers.

We shall call the n numbers $s_0, s_1, \ldots, s_{2m-1}$ (if $n = 2m$) or $s_{-1}, s_0, \ldots, s_{2m-1}$ (if $n = 2m + 1$) the *Markov parameters* for the polynomial $f(z)$. These parameters may be regarded as the coordinates of a point representing the given polynomial $f(z)$ in Euclidean n-space.

We shall show what conditions must be imposed on the Markov parameters in order for the coresponding polynomial $f(z)$ to be a Hurwitz polynomial. In other words, we shall determine the domain of stability in the space of Markov parameters.

Hurwitz polynomials are characterized by the conditions (94), with the supplementary condition (95) if $n = 2m + 1$. Introducing the function $R(v)$ defined by (105), we may rewrite the equations (94) as

$$I_{-\infty}^{+\infty} R(v) = m, \quad I_{-\infty}^{+\infty} v R(v) = m. \qquad (110)$$

The supplementary condition (95) for the case $n = 2m + 1$ gives:

$$s_{-1} > 0.$$

We now introduce the infinite Hankel matrix $S^{(1)} = (s_{i+k+1})_0^\infty$. The equation

$$vR(v) = -s_{-1}v + s_0 + \frac{s_1}{v} + \frac{s_2}{v^2} + \cdots,$$

which follows from (106), shows that the relation

$$vR(v) \sim S^{(1)} \tag{111}$$

holds.

The matrix $S^{(1)}$, like the matrix S, has finite rank m, since the function $vR(v)$, like $R(v)$ itself, has m poles. Thus the forms

$$S_m(x, x) = \sum_{i,k=0}^{m-1} s_{i+k} x_i x_k, \quad S_m^{(1)}(x, x) = \sum_{i,k=0}^{m-1} s_{i+k+1} x_i x_k$$

also have the rank m. But according to Theorem 9, and in view of relations (107) and (111), the signatures of these forms are equal to the indices (110), and thus likewise equal to m. Accordingly, conditions (110) show that the forms $S_m(x, x)$ and $S_m^{(1)}(x, x)$ are positive definite. We have established

THEOREM 17. *In order for the real polynomial* $f(z) = h(z^2) + zg(z^2)$ *of degree* $n = 2m$ *or* $n = 2m + 1$ *to be a Hurwitz polynomial, it is necessary and sufficient* [58] *that*

---

[58] We do not stipulate the special inequality $\Delta_n \neq 0$, since this inequality automatically follows from the conditions of the theorem. In fact, if $f(z)$ is a Hurwitz polynomial, then as we know, $\Delta_n \neq 0$. On the other hand, if the conditions *1, 2* are known to be satisfied, then from the positive definiteness of the form $S_m^{(1)}(x, x)$ it follows that

$$-I_{-\infty}^{+\infty} \frac{ug(u)}{h(u)} = I_{-\infty}^{+\infty} vR(v) = m,$$

and from this in turn it follows that the fraction $ug(u)/h(u)$ is in lowest terms; but this is equivalent to the inequality $\Delta_n \neq 0$.

In just the same way, it follows from the conditions of the theorem that

$$D_n = \det [s_{i+k}]_0^{m-1} \neq 0,$$

i.e., that the numbers $s_0, s_1, \ldots, s_{2m-1}$ and (if $n = 2m + 1$) the number s_{-1} are the Markov parameters of the polynomial $f(z)$.

1   the quadratic forms

$$S_m(x,\ x) = \sum_{i,\,k=0}^{m-1} s_{i+k} x_i x_k,\ \ S_m^{(1)}(x,\ x) = \sum_{i,\,k=0}^{m-1} s_{i+k+1} x_i x_k \quad (112)$$

be positive definite and
2   (if $n = 2m+1$)

$$s_{-1} > 0. \tag{113}$$

Here s_{-1}, s_0, s_1, . . ., s_{2m-1} are the coefficients in the expansion

$$\frac{g(u)}{h(u)} = s_{-1} + \frac{s_0}{u} - \frac{s_2}{u^2} + \frac{s_2}{u^3} - \frac{s_3}{u^4} + \cdots$$

We next introduce some further notations:

$$D_p = \det[s_{i+k}]_0^{p-1},\ \ D_p^{(1)} = \det[s_{i+k+1}]_0^{p-1} \quad (p = 1, 2, \ldots, m). \tag{114}$$

The condition *1* is equivalent to the system of determinantal inequalities:

$$\left.\begin{array}{l} D_1 = s_0 > 0,\ D_2 = \begin{vmatrix} s_0 & s_1 \\ s_1 & s_2 \end{vmatrix} > 0, \ldots, D_m = \begin{vmatrix} s_0 & s_1 & \cdots & s_{m-1} \\ s_1 & s_2 & \cdots & s_m \\ \cdot & \cdot & \cdots & \cdot \\ s_{m-1} & s_m & \cdots & s_{2m-2} \end{vmatrix} > 0, \\[2em] D_1^{(1)} = s_1 > 0,\ D_2^{(1)} = \begin{vmatrix} s_1 & s_2 \\ s_2 & s_3 \end{vmatrix} > 0, \ldots, D_m^{(1)} = \begin{vmatrix} s_1 & s_2 & \cdots & s_m \\ s_2 & s_3 & \cdots & s_{m+1} \\ \cdot & \cdot & \cdots & \cdot \\ s_m & s_{m+1} & & s_{2m-1} \end{vmatrix} > 0. \end{array}\right\} \tag{115}$$

In the case $n = 2m$ the inequalities (115) define the domain
of stability in the space of the Markov parameters. If $n = 2m+1$
one must adjoin the additional inequality

$$s_{-1} > 0. \tag{116}$$

In the next section we shall show what properties of the matrix
S follow from the inequalities (115) and thereby distinguish the
special class of infinite Hankel matrices S which correspond to
the Hurwitz polynomials.

§ 16. A connection with a moment problem

1. We shall first formulate the following *moment problem on the positive semi-axis* $0 < v < \infty$: [59]

Given a sequence of real numbers $s_0, s_1, \ldots$, one is required to find positive numbers

$$\mu_1 > 0, \quad \mu_2 > 0, \ldots, \mu_m > 0; \quad 0 < v_1 < v_2 < \ldots < v_m \quad (117)$$

such that the following equations hold true:

$$s_p = \sum_{j=1}^{m} \mu_j v_j^p \quad (p = 0, 1, 2, \ldots). \tag{118}$$

It can be seen without difficulty that the system of equations (118) is equivalent to the following expansion in negative powers of u:

$$\sum_{j=1}^{m} \frac{\mu_j}{u + v_j} = \frac{s_0}{u} - \frac{s_1}{u^2} + \frac{s_2}{u^3} - \ldots. \tag{119}$$

In this case the infinite Hankel matrix $S = (s_{i+k})_0^\infty$ has finite rank m, and by virtue of the inequalities (117) the polynomials $h(u)$ and $g(u)$ in the irreducible proper fraction

$$\frac{g(u)}{h(u)} = \sum_{j=1}^{m} \frac{\mu_j}{u + v_j} \tag{120}$$

(where we choose the leading coefficients of $h(u)$ and $g(u)$ to be positive) form a positive pair (cf. (91) and (91′)).

Thus, by Theorem 14, the moment problem we have formulated has a solution if and only if the sequence of numbers $s_0, s_1, \ldots$ defines (by (119) and (120)) a Hurwitz polynomial $f(z) = h(z^2) + zg(z^2)$ of degree $2m$.

The solution of the moment problem is unique, since the numbers v_j and μ_j $(j = 1, 2, \ldots, m)$ are uniquely defined by the expansion (119).

[59] This moment problem could be called the discrete moment problem, as distinguished from the general moment problem, in which the sums $\sum_{j=1}^{m} \mu_j v_j^p$ are replaced by the Stieltjes integrals $\int_0^\infty v^p \, d\mu(v)$. See Shohat and Tamarkin, [63].

Along with the "infinite" moment problem (118) we consider the "finite" moment problem given by the first $2m$ equations in (118):

$$s_p = \sum_{j=1}^{m} \mu_j v_j^p \quad (p = 0, 1, \ldots, 2m - 1). \tag{121}$$

From these relations one obtains the following expressions for the Hankel quadratic forms:

$$\sum_{i,\,k=0}^{m-1} s_{i+k} x_i x_k = \sum_{j=1}^{m} \mu_j (x_0 + x_1 v_j + \ldots + x_{m-1} v_j^{m-1})^2,$$

$$\sum_{i,\,k=0}^{m-1} s_{i+k+1} x_i x_k = \sum_{j=1}^{m} \mu_j v_j (x_0 + x_1 v_j + \ldots + x_{m-1} v_j^{m-1})^2. \tag{122}$$

Since the linear forms in the variables $x_0, x_1, \ldots, x_{m-1}$

$$x_0 + x_1 v_j + \ldots + x_{m-1} v_j^{m-1} \quad (j = 1, 2, \ldots, m)$$

are independent (the coefficients of these forms fill out a non-singular matrix of Vandermonde!), while $v_j > 0$, $\mu_j > 0$ $(j = 1, 2, \ldots, m)$, the quadratic forms (122) are positive definite. Then, according to Theorem 17, the numbers $s_0, s_1, \ldots, s_{2m-1}$ are the Markov parameters for some Hurwitz polynomial (119). Together with the remaining coefficients $s_{2m}, s_{2m+1}, \ldots$ they define a solvable infinite moment problem (118) which has the same solution as the finite problem (121).

Thus, we have proved

THEOREM 18.

1. A necessary and sufficient condition that

$$s_p = \sum_{j=1}^{m} \mu_j v_j^p \tag{123}$$

$(p = 0, 1, \ldots, 2m-1;\ \mu_1 > 0, \ldots, \mu_m > 0;\ 0 < v_1 < v_2 < \ldots < v_m)$, *be solvable, where the numbers s_p are given and the real numbers v_j and μ_j are to be found, is that the quadratic forms*

$$\sum_{i,\,k=0}^{m-1} s_{i+k} x_i x_k, \quad \sum_{i,\,k=0}^{m-1} s_{i+k+1} x_i x_k \tag{124}$$

be positive definite, i.e., that the numbers $s_0, s_1, \ldots, s_{2m-1}$ *be the Markov parameters of some Hurwitz polynomial of degree* $2m$.

2. *A necessary and sufficient condition that the infinite moment problem*

$$s_p = \sum_{j=1}^{m} \mu_j v_j^p \qquad (125)$$

$(p = 0, 1, \ldots, 2m - 1; \quad \mu_1 > 0, \ldots, \mu_m > 0; \quad 0 < v_1 \ldots < v_m)$, *be solvable, where the numbers* s_p *are given and the real numbers* v_j *and* μ_j *are to be found, is that* (i) *the quadratic forms* (124) *be positive definite and* (ii) *the infinite Hankel matrix* $S = (s_{i+k})_0^\infty$ *have rank* m, *i.e., that the series*

$$\frac{s_0}{u} - \frac{s_1}{u^2} + \frac{s_2}{u^3} - \ldots = \frac{g(u)}{h(u)} \qquad (126)$$

define a Hurwitz polynomial $f(z) = h(z^2) + zg(z^2)$ *of degree* $2m$.

3. *The solution of the moment problem, whether finite* (123) *or infinite* (124), *is always unique.*

2. We shall now use this theorem to investigate the minors of the infinite Hankel matrix $S = (s_{i+k})_0^\infty$ of rank m corresponding to some Hurwitz polynomial, i.e., of a matrix S for which the quadratic forms (124) are positive definite. In this case the numbers $s_0, s_1, s_2, \ldots$ which generate the matrix S can be represented in the form (123), so that for any minor of the matrix S of order $h \leq m$ we have:

$$\begin{bmatrix} s_{i_1+k_1} \cdots s_{i_1+k_h} \\ \cdots \cdots \cdots \\ s_{i_h+k_1} \cdots s_{i_h+k_h} \end{bmatrix} = \begin{bmatrix} \mu_1 v_1^{i_1} \; \mu_2 v_2^{i_1} \cdots \mu_m v_m^{i_1} \\ \cdots \cdots \cdots \cdots \cdots \\ \mu_1 v_1^{i_h} \; \mu_2 v_2^{i_h} \cdots \mu_m v_m^{i_h} \end{bmatrix} \cdot \begin{bmatrix} v_1^{k_1} \cdots v_1^{k_h} \\ v_2^{k_1} \cdots v_2^{k_h} \\ \cdots \cdots \\ \cdots \cdots \\ v_m^{k_1} \cdots v_m^{k_h} \end{bmatrix},$$

and, consequently, the determinant

$$S\begin{bmatrix} i_1 \; i_2 \ldots i_h \\ k_1 \; k_2 \ldots k_h \end{bmatrix}$$

$$= \sum_{1 \leq \alpha_1 < \alpha_2 < \ldots < \alpha_h \leq m} \mu_{\alpha_1} \mu_{\alpha_2} \cdots \mu_{\alpha_h} \begin{vmatrix} v_{\alpha_1}^{i_1} \; v_{\alpha_2}^{i_1} \cdots v_{\alpha_h}^{i_1} \\ v_{\alpha_1}^{i_2} \; v_{\alpha_2}^{i_2} \cdots v_{\alpha_h}^{i_2} \\ \cdots \cdots \cdots \\ v_{\alpha_1}^{i_h} \; v_{\alpha_2}^{i_h} \cdots v_{\alpha_h}^{i_h} \end{vmatrix} \begin{vmatrix} v_{\alpha_1}^{k_1} \; v_{\alpha_1}^{k_2} \cdots v_{\alpha_1}^{k_h} \\ v_{\alpha_2}^{k_1} \; v_{\alpha_2}^{k_2} \cdots v_{\alpha_2}^{k_h} \\ \cdots \cdots \cdots \\ v_{\alpha_h}^{k_1} \; v_{\alpha_h}^{k_2} \cdots v_{\alpha_h}^{k_h} \end{vmatrix}.$$

$$(127)$$

But from the inequalities

$$0 < v_1 < v_2 < \ldots < v_m,\ i_1 < i_2 < \ldots < i_h,\ k_1 < k_2 < \ldots < k_h$$

it follows that the generalized Vandermonde determinants (p. 118) are positive:

$$\det \begin{bmatrix} v_{\alpha_1}^{i_1} & v_{\alpha_2}^{i_1} & \ldots & v_{\alpha_h}^{i_1} \\ v_{\alpha_1}^{i_2} & v_{\alpha_2}^{i_2} & \ldots & v_{\alpha_h}^{i_2} \\ \cdot & \cdot & \cdot & \cdot \\ v_{\alpha_1}^{i_h} & v_{\alpha_2}^{i_h} & \ldots & v_{\alpha_h}^{i_h} \end{bmatrix} > 0, \quad \det \begin{bmatrix} v_{\alpha_1}^{k_1} & v_{\alpha_1}^{k_2} & \ldots & v_{\alpha_1}^{k_h} \\ v_{\alpha_2}^{k_1} & v_{\alpha_2}^{k_2} & \ldots & v_{\alpha_2}^{k_h} \\ \cdot & \cdot & \cdot & \cdot \\ v_{\alpha_h}^{k_1} & v_{\alpha_h}^{k_2} & \ldots & v_{\alpha_h}^{k_h} \end{bmatrix} > 0.$$

Thus, since the numbers μ_j $(i = 1, 2, \ldots, m)$ are also positive, it follows from (127) that

$$S\begin{bmatrix} i_1, & i_2, & \ldots, & i_h \\ k_1, & k_2, & \ldots, & k_h \end{bmatrix} > 0 \quad \left(0 \leqq \begin{matrix} i_1 < i_2 < \ldots < i_h \\ k_1 < k_2 < \ldots < k_h \end{matrix},\ h = 1, 2, \ldots, m \right).$$

(128)

Conversely, if all of the minors of arbitrary fixed order $h \leqq m$ in an infinite Hankel matrix S of rank m are positive, then the quadratic forms (127) are positive definite.

We now introduce

DEFINITION 4. *We shall say that an infinite matrix $A = (a_{i+k})_0^\infty$ is* totally positive of rank m *if and only if all of the minors of the matrix A of order $h \leqq m$ are positive, while all minors of order $h > m$ are zero.*

We can now reformulate the properties of the matrix S which were obtained above.[60]

THEOREM 19. *A necessary and sufficient condition that the infinite Hankel matrix $S = (s_{i+k})_0^\infty$ be totally positive of rank m, is that* (i) *the matrix S have rank m, and* (ii) *the quadratic forms*

$$\sum_{i,\,k=0}^{m-1} s_{i+k} x_i x_k,\ \sum_{i,\,k=0}^{m-1} s_{i+k+1} x_i x_k$$

be positive definite.

From this theorem and Theorem 17 follows

---

[60] Cf. Gantmacher and Kreĭn, [25].

THEOREM 20. *A real polynomial $f(z)$ of degree n is a Hurwitz polynomial if and only if the infinite Hankel matrix $S = (s_{i+k})_0^\infty$ corresponding to this polynomial is totally positive of rank $m = [n/2]$ and, in case n is odd, $s_{-1} > 0$.*

Here the elements $s_0, s_1, s_2, \ldots$ of the matrix S and the numbers s_{-1} are defined by the expansion

$$\frac{g(u)}{h(u)} = s_{-1} + \frac{s_0}{u} - \frac{s_1}{u^2} + \frac{s_2}{u^3} - \ldots \qquad (129)$$

where $f(z) = h(z^2) + zg(z^2)$.

§ 17. The theorems of Markov and Chebyshev

In his well-known memoir "On Functions Obtainable by the Inversion of Series of Continued Fractions," published in the *Journal of the St. Petersburg Academy of Sciences* for 1894, A. A. Markov proved two theorems, the second of which had been established by other methods and in a less general form by P. L. Chebyshev in 1892.

In this section we shall show that these theorems have a direct relation to the study of domains of stability in the space of Markov parameters, and shall give a comparatively simple proof of these theorems (in which continued fractions play no role). The proof is based on Theorem 19 of the preceding section.

The first theorem was formulated by A. A. Markov as follows:[61]

"On the basis of the preceding conclusions, it is not difficult to prove two remarkable theorems, with which we shall conclude our paper.

"One of them concerns the determinants [62]

$$\Delta_1, \Delta_2, \ldots, \Delta_m, \Delta^{(1)}, \Delta^{(2)}, \ldots, \Delta^{(m)},$$

and the other concerns the roots of the equation [63]

$$\psi_m(x) = 0.$$

---

[61] A. A. Markov, [45].

[62] In our notation, $D_1, D_2, \ldots, D_m, D_1^{(1)}, \ldots, D_m^{(1)}$.

[63] In our notation, $h(-x) = 0$.

"THEOREM ON THE DETERMINANTS. *If for the numbers*

$$s_0, \ s_1, \ s_2, \ \ldots, s_{2m-2}, \ s_{2m-1}$$

we have two sets of values

1) $s_0 = a_0, \quad s_1 = a_1, \quad s_2 = a_2, \ldots, s_{2m-2} = a_{2m-2}, \quad s_{2m-1} = a_{2m-1},$
2) $s_0 = b_0, \quad s_1 = b_1, \quad s_2 = b_2, \ldots, s_{2m-2} = b_{2m-2}, \quad s_{2m-1} = b_{2m-1},$

for which all of the determinants

$$\Delta_1 = s_0, \ \Delta_2 = \det \begin{bmatrix} s_0 & s_1 \\ s_1 & s_2 \end{bmatrix}, \ldots, \Delta_m = \det \begin{bmatrix} s_0 & s_1 \cdots s_{m-1} \\ s_1 & s_2 \cdots s_m \\ \cdots \cdots \cdots \\ s_{m-1} & s_m \quad s_{2m-2} \end{bmatrix},$$

$$\Delta^{(1)} = s_1, \ \Delta^{(2)} = \det \begin{bmatrix} s_1 & s_2 \\ s_2 & s_3 \end{bmatrix}, \ldots, \Delta^{(m)} = \det \begin{bmatrix} s_1 & s_2 \cdots s_m \\ s_2 & s_3 \cdots s_{m+1} \\ \cdots \cdots \cdots \\ s_m & s_{m+1} \quad s_{2m-1} \end{bmatrix}$$

are positive, and which satisfy the inequalities

$$a_0 \geqq b_0, \ b_1 \geqq a_1, \ a_2 \geqq b_2, \ b_3 \geqq a_3, \ldots, a_{2m-2} \geqq b_{2m-2}, \ b_{2m-1} \geqq a_{2m-1},$$

then our determinants

$$\Delta_1, \Delta_2, \ldots, \Delta_m; \ \Delta^{(1)}, \Delta^{(2)}, \ldots, \Delta^{(m)}$$

must remain positive for all values of $s_0, s_1, s_2, \ldots, s_{2m-1}$ satisfying the inequalities

$$a_0 \geqq s_0 \geqq b_0, \ b_1 \geqq s_1 \geqq a_1, \ a_2 \geqq s_2 \geqq b_2, \ldots,$$
$$a_{2m-2} \geqq s_{2m-2} \geqq b_{2m-2}, \ b_{2m-1} \geqq s_{2m-1} \geqq a_{2m-1}.$$

"Under the same conditions, the determinantal relations

$$\begin{vmatrix} a_0 & a_1 \cdots a_{k-1} \\ a_1 & a_2 \cdots a_k \\ \cdots \cdots \cdots \\ a_{k-1} & a_k \cdots a_{2k-2} \end{vmatrix} \geqq \begin{vmatrix} s_0 & s_1 \cdots s_{k-1} \\ s_1 & s_2 \cdots s_k \\ \cdots \cdots \cdots \\ s_{k-1} & s_k \cdots s_{2k-2} \end{vmatrix} \geqq \begin{vmatrix} b_0 & b_1 \cdots b_{k-1} \\ b_1 & b_2 \cdots b_k \\ \cdots \cdots \cdots \\ b_{k-1} & b_k \cdots b_{2k-2} \end{vmatrix}$$

and

$$
\begin{vmatrix} b_1 & b_2 & \ldots b_k \\ b_2 & b_3 & \ldots b_{k+1} \\ \cdot \cdot \cdot \cdot \cdot \cdot \cdot \cdot \\ b_k & b_{k+1} \ldots b_{2k-1} \end{vmatrix} \geqq \begin{vmatrix} s_1 & s_2 & \ldots s_k \\ s_2 & s_3 & \ldots s_{k+1} \\ \cdot \cdot \cdot \cdot \cdot \cdot \cdot \cdot \\ s_k & s_{k+1} \ldots s_{2k-1} \end{vmatrix} \geqq \begin{vmatrix} a_1 & a_2 & \ldots a_k \\ a_2 & a_3 & \ldots a_{k+1} \\ \cdot \cdot \cdot \cdot \cdot \cdot \cdot \cdot \\ a_k & a_{k+1} \ldots a_{2k-1} \end{vmatrix}
$$

must hold for $k = 1, 2, \ldots, m$."

In order to formulate this theorem in a way which more clearly shows its connection with the stability problem we shall first introduce some concepts and notations.

The Markov parameters $s_0, s_1, \ldots, s_{2m-1}$ (if $n = 2m$) or $s_{-1}, s_0, s_1, \ldots, s_{2m-1}$ (if $n = 2m + 1$) will be regarded as the coordinates of a point P in Euclidean n-space. The domain of stability in this space will be denoted by G. The domain G is defined by the inequalities (115), (116). We shall say that the point $P = \{s_i\}$ "precedes" the point $P^* = \{s_i^*\}$, and write $P < P^*$, if

$$ s_0 \leqq s_0^*, \ s_1^* \leqq s_1, \ s_2 \leqq s_2^*, \ s_3^* \leqq s_3, \ldots, s_{2m-1}^* \leqq s_{2m-1} \quad (130) $$

and (if $n = 2m + 1$)

$$ s_{-1} \leqq s_{-1}^* $$

the inequality being strict in at least one of these relations.

If only the relations (130) hold, without the last limitation, we shall write:

$$ P \leqq P^*. $$

We shall say that *the point Q lies "between" the points P and R* if $P < Q < R$.

To each point P there corresponds an infinite Hankel matrix of rank m: $S = (s_{i+k})_0^\infty$. This matrix will be denoted by S_P.

Now we repeat Markov's theorem, but in the following form:

THEOREM 21 (Markov). *If two points P and R belong to the domain of stability G, then any point Q lying between the points P and R also belongs to the domain G;* i.e.,

from $P, R \, \epsilon \, G, \ P \leqq Q \leqq R$ follows $Q \, \epsilon \, G$.

Proof. From $P \leqq Q \leqq R$ it follows that the two points P and R can be joined by an arc

$$s_i = (-1)^i \varphi_i(t) \qquad [\alpha \leqq t \leqq \gamma; \ i = 0, 1, \ldots, 2m - 1$$

$$\text{and (if } n = 2m + 1) \quad i = -1] \qquad (131)$$

passing through the point Q such that *1* the functions $\varphi_i(t)$ are continuous, monotone increasing, and differentiable with respect to t from $t = \alpha$ to $t = \gamma$, and *2* the values α, β, γ $(\alpha \leqq \beta \leqq \gamma)$ of the variable t correspond to the points P, Q, and R.

Using the values (131) we can set up an infinite Hankel matrix $S = S(t) = (s_{i+k})_0^\infty$ of rank m. We shall consider a part of this matrix, namely the rectangular matrix

$$\begin{bmatrix} s_0 & s_1 \cdots s_{m-1} & s_m \\ s_1 & s_2 \cdots s_m & s_{m+1} \\ \cdots & \cdots \cdots \cdots \cdots \\ s_{m-1} & s_m \cdots s_{2m-2} & s_{2m-1} \end{bmatrix}. \qquad (132)$$

According to the conditions of the theorem the matrix $S(t)$ is completely positive of rank m when $t = \alpha$ or γ; thus all minors of the matrix (132) of order $p = 1, 2, \ldots, m$ are positive.

We shall show that this property is preserved for any intermediate value of t $(\alpha < t < \gamma)$.

For $p = 1$ this is obvious. We shall show that the assertion is true for minors of order p on the supposition that it is true for minors of order $p - 1$. First consider minor of order p, taken from p consecutive rows and p consecutive columns of the matrix (132):

$$D_p^{(q)} = \begin{bmatrix} s_q & s_{q+1} \cdots s_{q+p-1} \\ s_{q+1} & s_{q+2} \cdots s_{q+p} \\ \cdots & \cdots \cdots \cdots \cdots \\ s_{q+p-1} & s_{q+p} \cdots s_{q+2p-2} \end{bmatrix} \quad (q = 0, 1, \ldots, 2(m-p)+1). \quad (133)$$

We shall calculate the derivative with respect to t of this minor,

$$\frac{d}{dt} D_p^{(q)} = \sum_{i,\,k=0}^{p-1} \frac{\partial D_p^{(q)}}{\partial s_{q+i+k}} \frac{ds_{q+i+k}}{dt}. \qquad (134)$$

The derivatives $\partial D_p^{(q)}/\partial s_{q+i+k}$ $(i,\ k = 0,\ 1,\ \ldots, p-1)$ are the algebraic complements (adjoints) of the elements of the determinant (133). Since by supposition all minors of this determinant are positive, then

$$(-1)^{i+k}\frac{\partial D_p^{(q)}}{\partial s_{q+i+k}} > 0 \quad (i,\ k = 0, 1, \ldots, p-1). \tag{135}$$

On the other hand, from (131) we find:

$$(-1)^{q+i+k}\frac{ds_{q+i+k}}{dt} = \frac{d\varphi_{q+i+k}}{dt} \geqq 0 \quad (i, k = 0, 1, \ldots, p-1). \tag{136}$$

From (134), (135), and (136), there follows:

$$(-1)^q \frac{d}{dt} D_p^{(q)} \geqq 0 \quad \begin{pmatrix} q = 0, 1, \ldots, 2(m-p)+1, \\ p = 1, 2, \ldots, m \quad \alpha \leqq t \leqq \gamma \end{pmatrix}. \tag{137}$$

Thus each minor (133), if q is even, is monotonically increasing (more precisely, nondecreasing) and if q is odd, is monotonically decreasing (more precisely, nonincreasing) as t increases from the value α to the value γ; and since this minor is positive for $t = \alpha$ and $t = \gamma$, it will be positive for any intermediate value of t $(\alpha \leqq t \leqq \gamma)$.

From the fact that the minors of order $p-1$ of the matrix (132) are positive, and that the minors of order p formed from successive rows and columns are positive, it follows [64] that *all* minors of order p of the determinant (132) are positive.

From what has been proved it follows that for any t $(\alpha \leqq t \leqq \gamma)$ the values of $s_0, s_1, \ldots, s_{2m-1}$ and (if $n = 2m+1$) s_{-1} satisfy the inequalities (115) and (116), i.e., that these numbers are the Markov parameters of some Hurwitz polynomial. In other words, the whole curve (131), and in particular the point Q, lies in the domain of stability G.

Markov's theorem is proved.

REMARK. Since it has been shown that each point of the curve (131) belongs to the domain G, then for any t $(\alpha \leqq t \leqq \gamma)$ the values (131) define a completely positive matrix $S(t) = (s_{i+k})_0^\infty$

---

[64] This by an identity for determinants due to Fekete. See [24].

of rank m. Thus the inequalities (135), and consequently also (137), hold for arbitrary t $(\alpha \leq t \leq \beta)$; as t increases any $D_p^{(q)}$ increases if q is even, decreases if q is odd $(q=0, 1, \ldots, 2(m-p)+1;$ $p = 1, \ldots, m)$. In other words, from $P \leq Q \leq R$ it follows that

$$(-1)^q D_p^{(q)}(P) \leq (-1)^q D_p^{(q)}(Q) \leq (-1)^q D_p^{(q)}(R)$$

$$[q = 0, 1, \ldots, 2(m - p)+1; \ p = 1, \ldots, m].$$

For $q = 0, 1$, these inequalities give the inequalities of Markov.

We shall now consider the theorem of Chebyshev and Markov mentioned at the beginning of this section. Again, we quote A. A. Markov: [65]

"THEOREM ON THE ROOTS. *If the numbers*

$$a_0, \ a_1, \ a_2, \ldots, a_{2m-2}, \ a_{2m-1},$$

$$s_0, \ s_1, \ s_2, \ldots, s_{2m-2}, \ s_{2m-1},$$

$$b_0, \ b_1, \ b_2, \ldots, b_{2m-2}, \ b_{2m-1}$$

satisfy all the conditions of the preceding theorems,[66] *then the equations*

$$\det \begin{bmatrix} a_0 & a_1 & \ldots a_{m-1} & 1 \\ a_1 & a_2 & \ldots a_m & x \\ a_2 & a_3 & \ldots a_{m+1} & x^2 \\ \cdot & \cdot & \cdot \cdot \cdot \cdot \cdot \cdot \cdot & \cdot \\ a_m & a_{m+1} & \ldots a_{2m-1} & x^m \end{bmatrix} = 0,$$

$$\det \begin{bmatrix} s_0 & s_1 & \ldots s_{m-1} & 1 \\ s_1 & s_2 & \ldots s_m & x \\ s_2 & s_3 & \ldots s_{m+1} & x^2 \\ \cdot & \cdot & \cdot \cdot \cdot \cdot \cdot \cdot \cdot & \cdot \\ s_m & s_{m+1} & \ldots s_{2m+1} & x^m \end{bmatrix} = 0,$$

$$\det \begin{bmatrix} b_0 & b_1 & \ldots b_{m-1} & 1 \\ b_1 & b_2 & \ldots b_m & x \\ b_2 & b_3 & \ldots b_{m+1} & x^2 \\ \cdot & \cdot & \cdot \cdot \cdot \cdot \cdot \cdot \cdot & \cdot \\ b_m & b_{m+1} & \ldots b_{2m-1} & x^m \end{bmatrix} = 0$$

[65] Markov, [45] (Note 61), p. 103.

[66] This refers to the preceding theorem of Markov, the "theorem on the determinants."

of degree m in the unknown x have neither multiple, imaginary, nor negative roots.

Moreover, the roots of the second equation are larger than the corresponding roots of the first equation and smaller than those of the last."

We shall first explain how this theorem is related to the domain of stability in the space of Markov parameters. We put $f(z) = h(z^2) + zg(z^2)$ and

$$h(-v) = c_0 v^m + c_1 v^{m-1} + \ldots + c_m \quad (c_0 \neq 0).$$

From the expansion (105)

$$R(v) = -\frac{g(-v)}{h(-v)} = -s_{-1} + \frac{s_0}{v} + \frac{s_1}{v^2} + \ldots$$

we obtain the identity

$$-g(-v) = \left(-s_{-1} + \frac{s_0}{v} + \frac{s_1}{v^2} + \ldots\right)(c_0 v^m + c_1 v^{m-1} + \ldots + c_m).$$

Setting the coefficients of the powers $v^{-1}, v^{-2}, \ldots, v^{-m}$ equal to zero, we find:

$$\left.\begin{aligned}
s_0 c_m + s_1 c_{m-1} + \ldots + s_m c_0 &= 0, \\
s_1 c_m + s_2 c_{m-1} + \ldots + s_{m+1} c_0 &= 0, \\
\cdots\cdots\cdots\cdots\cdots\cdots\cdots\cdots & \\
s_{m-1} c_m + s_m c_{m-1} + \ldots + s_{2m-1} c_0 &= 0;
\end{aligned}\right\} \tag{138}$$

To these relations we add the equation

$$h(-v) = 0, \tag{139}$$

written in the form

$$c_m + vc_{m-1} + \ldots v^m c_0 = 0. \tag{139'}$$

Eliminating the coefficients $c_0, c_1, \ldots, c_m$ from (138) and (139'), we may represent the equation (139) by

$$\det \begin{bmatrix}
s_0 & s_1 & \ldots & s_{m-1} & 1 \\
s_1 & s_2 & \ldots & s_m & v \\
s_2 & s_3 & \ldots & s_{m+1} & v^2 \\
\multicolumn{5}{c}{\cdots\cdots\cdots\cdots\cdots} \\
s_m & s_{m+1} & \ldots & s_{2m-1} & v^m
\end{bmatrix} = 0. \tag{139''}$$

Thus it appears that the algebraic equations in the Chebyshev-Markov theorem coincide with the equation (139), while the inequalities imposed on the values of s_0, s_1, . . ., s_{2m-1} coincide with the inequalities (115) which define the domain of stability in the space of Markov parameters.

The Chebyshev-Markhov theorem shows how the roots $u_1 = -v_1$, . . ., $u_m = -v_m$ of the polynomial $h(u)$ vary when the corresponding Markov parameters vary within the domain of stability.

The first part of the theorem asserts a fact that we already know (cf. Theorem 13), namely that when the inequalities (115) are satisfied all of the roots u_1, u_2, . . ., u_m of the polynomial $h(u)$ are simple, real, and negative. We shall denote these roots by

$$u_1(\boldsymbol{P}), \ u_2(\boldsymbol{P}), \ . . ., u_m(\boldsymbol{P}),$$

where $\boldsymbol{P}$ is the corresponding point of the domain $\boldsymbol{G}$.

Then the second (basic) part of the Chebyshev-Markov theorem may be stated as follows:

THEOREM 22 (Chebyshev-Markov). *If* $\boldsymbol{P}$ *and* $\boldsymbol{Q}$ *are two points of the domain* $\boldsymbol{G}$*, and the point* $\boldsymbol{P}$ *"precedes" the point* $\boldsymbol{Q}$*,*

$$\boldsymbol{P} < \boldsymbol{Q}, \tag{140}$$

then [67]

$$u_1(\boldsymbol{P}) < u_1(\boldsymbol{Q}), \ u_2(\boldsymbol{P}) < u_2(\boldsymbol{Q}), \ . . ., u_m(\boldsymbol{P}) < u_m(\boldsymbol{Q}). \tag{141}$$

Proof. The coefficients of the polynomial $h(u)$ may be expressed as rational functions of the parameters s_0, s_1, . . ., s_{2m-1} — for instance, by the use of the equations (138), where for the sake of concreteness one may put $c_0 = 1$.

Then from

$$h(u_i) = 0 \quad (i = 1, 2, . . ., m)$$

there follows:

$$\frac{\partial h(u_i)}{\partial s_l} + h'(u_i)\frac{du_i}{ds_l} = 0 \quad (i=1, 2, . . ., m; \ l=0, 1, . . ., 2m-1). \tag{142}$$

---

[67] In other words, the roots u_1, u_2, . . ., u_m increase when s_0, s_2, . . ., s_{2m-2} increase and s_1, s_3, . . ., s_{2m-1} decrease.

Here it is to be understood that

$$\frac{\partial h(u_i)}{\partial s_l} = \left[\frac{\partial h(u)}{\partial s_l}\right]_{u=u_i}.$$

On the other hand, differentiating termwise with respect to the parameter s_l in the expansion

$$\frac{g(u)}{h(u)} = s_{-1} + \frac{s_0}{u} - \frac{s_1}{u^2} + \frac{s_2}{u^3} - \ldots$$

gives

$$\frac{h(u)\dfrac{\partial g(u)}{\partial s_l} - g(u)\dfrac{\partial h(u)}{\partial s_l}}{h^2(u)} = \frac{(-1)^l}{u^{l+1}} + \frac{1}{u^{2m+1}} \quad (*). \qquad (143)$$

Multiplying both sides of this equation by the polynomial $h^2(u)/(u - u_i)$ and denoting the coefficient of the power u^l in this polynomial by C_{il}, we obtain:

$$\frac{h(u)}{u - u_i}\frac{\partial g(u)}{\partial s_l} - \frac{g(u)\dfrac{\partial h(u)}{\partial s_l}}{u - u_i} = \frac{(-1)^l C_{il}}{u} + \ldots. \qquad (144)$$

If we equate the coefficients of $1/u$ (the residues) on the left and right sides of this equation, we find:

$$(-1)^{l-1} g(u_i) \frac{\partial h(u_i)}{\partial s_l} = C_{il}, \qquad (145)$$

and this, in conjunction with (142), gives:

$$\frac{du_l}{ds_l} = \frac{(-1)^l C_{il}}{g(u_i) h'(u_i)}.$$

Introducing the quantities

$$R_i = \frac{g(u_i)}{h'(u_i)} \qquad (i = 1, 2, \ldots, m), \qquad (146)$$

we obtain the *Chebyshev-Markov formula*

$$\frac{du_i}{ds_l} = \frac{(-1)^l C_{il}}{R_i [h'(u_i)]^2} \quad (i = 1, 2, \ldots, m; \; l = 0, 1, \ldots, 2m - 1). \quad (147)$$

But in the domain of stability the quantities R_i are positive (cf. (90′)). The same may be said for the coefficients C_{il}. In fact,

$$\frac{h^2(u)}{u - u_i} = c_0^2 (u + v_1)^2 \ldots (u + v_{i-1})^2 (u + v_i)(u + v_{i+1})^2 \ldots (u + v_m)^2, \quad (148)$$

where

$$v_i = - u_i > 0 \qquad (i = 1, 2, \ldots, m).$$

From (148) one sees that all of the coefficients C_{il} in the expansion of $h^2(u)/(u - u_i)$ are positive. Thus, we obtain from the Chebyshev-Markov formula the inequality:

$$(-1)^l \frac{du_i}{ds_l} > 0. \qquad (149)$$

In proving Markov's theorem we showed that any two points $P < Q$ of the domain G may be joined by an arc $s_l = (-1)^l \varphi_l(t)$ $(l = 0, 1, \ldots, 2m - 1)$, where $\varphi_l(t)$ is a monotonically increasing differentiable function of t (t ranges from α to β $(\alpha < \beta)$, $t = \alpha$ corresponding to the point P, $t = \beta$ to the point Q). Then along this curve, because of (149),[68]

$$\frac{du_i}{dt} = \sum_{l=0}^{2m-1} \frac{\partial u_i}{\partial s_l} \frac{ds_l}{dt} \geqq 0, \quad \frac{du_i}{dt} \not\equiv 0 \quad (\alpha \leqq t \leqq \beta). \qquad (150)$$

Hence by integrating we obtain

$$u_{i(t=\alpha)} = u_i(P) < u_{i(t=\beta)} = u_i(Q) \qquad (i = 1, 2, \ldots, m).$$

The Chebyshev-Markov theorem is proved.

[68] Since

$$(-1)^l (ds_l/dt) = d\varphi_l/dt \geqq 0 \qquad (\alpha \leqq t \leqq \beta),$$

while for at least one l there exists a value of t for which $(-1)^l (ds_l/dt) > 0$.

18. The generalized Routh-Hurwitz problem

In this section we shall give a rule for determining the number of roots in the right half-plane of a polynomial $f(z)$ with *complex* coefficients.

Let

$$f(iz) = b_0 z^n + b_1 z^{n-1} + \ldots + b_n + i(a_0 z^n + a_1 z^{n-1} + \ldots + a_n), \quad (151)$$

where $a_0, a_1, \ldots, a_n, b_0, b_1, \ldots, b_n$ are real numbers. If n is the degree of the polynomial $f(z)$, then $b_0 + ia_0 \neq 0$. Without loss of generality we may suppose that $a_0 \neq 0$ (otherwise we could replace $f(z)$ by $if(z)$).

We shall assume that the real polynomials

$$a_0 z^n + a_1 z^{n-1} + \ldots + a_n \text{ and } b_0 z^n + b_1 z^{n-1} + \ldots + b_n \quad (152)$$

have a constant highest common factor, i.e., that the resultant of these two polynomials is different from zero:

$$\nabla_{2n} = \det \begin{bmatrix} a_0 & a_1 \ldots a_n & 0 & \ldots 0 \\ b_0 & b_1 \ldots b_n & 0 & \ldots 0 \\ 0 & a_0 \ldots a_{n-1} & a_n & \ldots 0 \\ 0 & b_0 \ldots b_{n-1} & b_n & \ldots 0 \\ \cdot & \cdot \cdot \cdot \cdot \cdot \cdot \cdot & \cdot & \cdot \cdot \cdot \\ \cdot & \cdot \cdot \cdot \cdot \cdot \cdot \cdot & \cdot & \cdot \cdot \cdot \end{bmatrix} \neq 0. \quad (153)$$

From this it follows, in particular, that since the polynomials (152) have no nonconstant common factor, the polynomial $f(z)$ has no root on the imaginary axis.

We shall again denote by k the number of roots of $f(z)$ having positive real parts. Considering the domain in the right half-plane bounded by the imaginary axis and a circle whose center is at the origin and whose radius is R ($R \to \infty$), and repeating word for word the discussion given in the first part of Section 3 for a real polynomial $f(z)$, we obtain as a formula for the increase of arg $f(z)$ along the imaginary axis

$$\Delta_{-\infty}^{+\infty} \arg f(z) = (n - 2k)\pi. \quad (154)$$

Hence, by virtue of (151) and the condition $a_0 \neq 0$, we obtain:

$$I_{-\infty}^{+\infty} \frac{b_0 z^n + b_1 z^{n-1} + \ldots + b_n}{a_0 z^n + a_1 z^{n-1} + \ldots + z_n} = n - 2k. \qquad (155)$$

Applying Theorem 10 of Section 11, we obtain from this that

$$k = V(1, \nabla_2, \nabla_4, \ldots, \nabla_{2n}), \qquad (156)$$

where

$$\nabla_{2p} = \det \begin{bmatrix} a_0 & a_1 \ldots a_{2p-1} \\ b_0 & b_1 \ldots b_{2p-1} \\ 0 & a_0 \ldots a_{2p-2} \\ 0 & b_0 \ldots b_{2p-2} \\ \cdot\ \cdot\ \cdot\ \cdot\ \cdot\ \cdot\ \cdot\ \cdot \\ \cdot\ \cdot\ \cdot\ \cdot\ \cdot\ \cdot\ \cdot\ \cdot \end{bmatrix} (p=1, 2, \ldots, n; a_k = b_k = 0 \text{ if } k > n). \quad (157)$$

We have arrived at the theorem:

THEOREM 23. *If there is given a complex polynomial $f(z)$ for which $f(iz) = b_0 z^n + b_1 z^{n-1} + \ldots + b_n + i(a_0 z^n + \ldots + a_n)$ $(a_0 \neq 0)$, where the polynomials $a_0 z^n + \ldots + a_n$ and $b_0 z^n + \ldots + b_n$ are relatively prime $(\nabla_{2n} \neq 0)$, then the number of roots of the polynomial $f(z)$ lying in the right half-plane is determined by formulas (156) and (157).*

Here it is to be understood that if among the determinants (157) there are some which equal zero, then in calculating $V(1, \nabla_2, \ldots, \nabla_{2n})$ one should put, for each block of successive vanishing determinants

$$(\nabla_{2h} \neq 0)\ \nabla_{2h+2} = \ldots = \nabla_{2h+2p} = 0 (\nabla_{2h+2p+2} \neq 0) \quad (158)$$

the values

$$\text{sign } \nabla_{2h+2j} = (-1)^{j(j-1)/2} \text{ sign } \nabla_{2h} \quad (j = 1, 2, \ldots, p), \quad (159)$$

or, equivalently, $V(\nabla_{2h}, \nabla_{2h+2}, \ldots, \nabla_{2h+2p+2}) = \frac{1}{2}(p + 1)$ if p is odd, $\frac{1}{2}(p + 1 - \varepsilon)$ if p is even, where

$$\varepsilon = (-1)^{p/2} \text{ sign } \frac{\nabla_{2h+2p+2}}{\nabla_{2h}}. \qquad (160)$$

We shall leave it to the reader to verify that in the particular case in which the polynomial $f(z)$ is real the Routh-Hurwitz Theorem (cf. Section 6) can be obtained from Theorem 23.

In conclusion we would remark that in this chapter we have considered the application of quadratic forms (in particular, Hankel forms) to a problem on the distribution of the roots of a polynomial in the complex plane, the Routh-Hurwitz problem. At the same time, quadratic and Hermitian forms have interesting applications to other problems on the distribution of roots. We would refer the reader who is interested in these questions to the survey by M. G. Kreĭn and M. A. Naĭmark, *The Method of Symmetric and Hermitian Forms in the Theory of the Isolation of Roots of Algebraic Equations*, Khar'kov, 1936.

APPENDIX I

The Theorem of Schur

Every matrix of complex numbers can be transformed into a triangular matrix T by a complex unitary transformation.

We are given A, a matrix of complex numbers. A must have a characteristic root λ and a corresponding unit eigenvector u, such that

$$Au = u\lambda$$

holds. We assume without proof that there is a unitary matrix U ($U^*U = UU^* = E$) which has u for a first column, and check that AU has first column $u\lambda$; i.e., U^*AU has first column $\{\lambda, 0, \ldots, 0\}$. The proof is completed by induction, to find T, V such that

$$V^*AV = T, \ V^*V = VV^* = E.$$

COROLLARY. *If A is normal, i.e., $AA^* = A^*A$, then T is diagonal. If $T = U^*AU$ is diagonal, $U^*U = UU^* = E$, then A is normal.*

See [49], p. 26.

APPENDIX II

Derivation of the Jordan Normal Form[1]

Jordan's researches led to the conclusion that, if A is a linear transformation on the vector space R (over complex numbers), it is possible to change the matrix of A by a similarity transformation so that it takes the form J pictured at the end of this appendix.

In the elementary theory of matrices it is shown that every linear transformation A possesses a minimal polynomial $m(\lambda)$ with the property that $m(A) = 0$. We consider a decomposition of the minimal polynomial into relatively prime factors:

$$m(\lambda) = p(\lambda)q(\lambda).$$

We define two subspaces R_1 and R_2 of R. By R_1 we mean the collection of vectors v for which $p(A)v = 0$, and by R_2 we mean the collection of vectors w for which $q(A)w = 0$:

$$R_1 \equiv \{v, \, p(A)v = 0\}; \quad R_2 \equiv \{w, q(A)w = 0\}.$$

Next we remark that R is the direct sum of these two subspaces:

$$R = R_1 \oplus R_2.$$

For, since p, q are relatively prime polynomials, there are polynomials r, s such that

$$1 = q(\lambda)r(\lambda) + p(\lambda)s(\lambda).$$

Thus, if z is any vector, we can write $z = z_1 + z_2$, where

$$z_1 = q(A)r(A)z, \; z_2 = p(A)s(A)z;$$

z_1 is in R_1, since $p(A)z_1 = m(A)[r(A)z] = 0$, and similarly z_2 is in R_2.

---

[1] The proof given here is essentially that in [31]. See also [6].

It is easy to show further that the space R can be decomposed into a direct sum of subspaces, each of which is annihilated by a power $(\lambda - \lambda_i)^a$ of a single binomial $\lambda - \lambda_i$.

The structure of such a subspace can be further investigated. Let S be annihilated by $(\lambda - \lambda_i)^a$. From each vector w_1 in S, we can form a chain

$$w_2 = (A - \lambda_i) w_1, \ w_3 = (A - \lambda_i)^2 w_1, \ldots,$$
$$w_s = (A - \lambda_i)^{s-1} w_1 \neq 0; \ (A - \lambda_i)^s w_1 = 0.$$

For various possible choices of w_1, the length of the chain $\{w_1, w_2, \ldots, w_s\}$ will vary; the length of the longest possible chain is a. Let w_1 be a fixed vector which gives rise to a chain of this length. From the relation $(A - \lambda_i)w_{p-1} = w_p$, the relations

$$Aw_1 = \lambda w_1 + w_2$$
$$Aw_2 = \qquad \lambda w_2 + w_3$$
$$\cdots \cdots \cdots \cdots \cdots$$
$$Aw_a = \qquad \qquad \lambda w_a$$

in the scheme above follow. By the method of *reductio ad absurdum*, we prove that $w_1, w_2, \ldots, w_s$ are linearly independent (multiply a putative linear relation by $(A - \lambda_i)^t$). Let S_1 be the subspace of S generated by $w_1, w_2, \ldots, w_s$. Now let v_1 be any vector in S, and form

$$v_p = (A - \lambda_i)^p v_1 \qquad (p = 1, 2, \ldots).$$

Suppose that for $p = 1, 2, \ldots, r$, $v_p \notin S_1$; $v_{r+1} \in S_1$. Pick v_1 so that r is as large as possible. By an inductive argument, we can show that, by subtracting from v_1 a suitable element w in $S_1 : v_1' = v_1 - w$, it will happen that the difference v_1' and its iterates $v_2' = (A - \lambda_i)v_1', \ldots, v_r'$ are not in S_1, but v_{r+1}' is zero. Moreover these new vectors v_p' are linearly independent, and no linear combination of them is in S_1. (We say that v_1' is obtained by reducing v_1 modulo S_1.)

Calling the subspace generated by $v_1', v_2', \ldots, v_r'$, S_2, the next step is to find a vector u_1 with as long a chain as possible mod $S_1 + S_2$, and to reduce it modulo $S_1 + S_2$. Eventually S is exhausted, and every element of S can be written in terms of $w_1, \ldots, w_s; v'_1, \ldots, v'_r; \ldots$ If the basis of S is changed to these last vectors, the matrix corresponding to the restriction of the transformation A to S becomes a block diagonal one, consisting of boxes like the one marked $\lambda_i E_s + H_s$ ranged along the main diagonal, and zeros elsewhere:

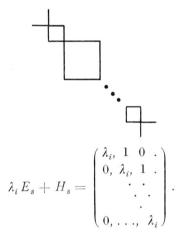

$$\lambda_i E_s + H_s = \begin{pmatrix} \lambda_i, & 1 & 0 & . \\ 0, & \lambda_i, & 1 & . \\ & \ddots & \ddots \\ & & & . \\ 0, & \ldots, & & \lambda_i \end{pmatrix}.$$

This block diagonal form, which is also written

$$J = \operatorname{diag}\,(\lambda_1 E_{r_{1,1}} + H_{r_{1,1}},\ \lambda_1 E_{r_{1,2}} + H_{r_{1,2}},\ \ldots,\ \lambda_i E_{r_{i,1}} + H_{r_{i,1}},\ \ldots\,)$$

is called the Jordan normal form of the matrix A. Since a change of basis is a similarity transformation, it follows that $J = RAR^{-1}$.

APPENDIX III

The Rational Canonical Form

The matrix R which transforms a fixed $n \times n$ matrix A into the Jordan form RAR^{-1} may have elements r_{ij} not all of which are rational functions of the elements of A. Into what form can a fixed matrix A be transformed if the elements of the transforming matrix are so restricted?

An exposition and solution of this problem appear in [31, 43] and standard texts on matrix theory. The circle of ideas can be explained very quickly by the consideration of a special case.

It is clear that the first n^2 powers of A cannot be linearly independent of E, the identity matrix; the polynomial

$$\lambda^p - a_1 \lambda^{p-1} - \ldots - a_{p-1}\lambda - a_p$$

in λ of lowest degree which is identically 0 in A is called the *minimal polynomial* of A. We suppose that the degree p of this polynomial is n:

$$p = n,$$

and show that A must in this case be similar to the matrices

$$
B = \begin{bmatrix}
0 & \cdots & & \cdots & a_n \\
1 & \cdots & & \cdots & a_{n-1} \\
0 & 1 & & \cdots & a_{n-2} \\
\cdot & \cdot & \cdot & \cdot & \cdot \\
0 & \cdots & 1 & 0 & a_2 \\
0 & \cdots & & 1 & a_1
\end{bmatrix}, \quad
C = \begin{bmatrix}
0 & 1 & 0 & \ldots & 0 \\
0 & 0 & 1 & \ldots & 0 \\
\cdot & & \cdot & \cdot & \\
0 & 0 & 0 & \ldots & 1 \\
a_n, & a_{n-1} & & \cdots & a_1
\end{bmatrix}.
$$

This conclusion is an easy consequence of the fact that there must be a basis (e_i) of the vector space (on which the transformation represented by A operates) with the property that

305

$$B \begin{bmatrix} e_1 \\ \cdot \\ \cdot \\ \cdot \\ e_n \end{bmatrix} = \begin{bmatrix} A e_1 \\ \cdot \\ \cdot \\ \cdot \\ A e_n \end{bmatrix}.$$

In attempting to establish this last assertion, it is natural to choose e_i so that the relations

$$e_{n-1} + a_1 \, e_n = A e_n$$
$$e_{n-2} + a_2 \, e_n = A e_{n-1}$$
$$\cdot$$
$$\cdot$$
$$\cdot$$
$$e_1 + a_{n-1} \, e_n = A e_2$$
$$a_n e_n = A e_1$$

hold. These can be satisfied by choosing e_n, and determining $e_{n-1}, \, e_{n-2}, \ldots, e_1$ in order. This program would fail only if, for some i, e_i is zero for every choice of e_n. But this last eventuality would signify that the minimal polynomial of A had degree less than n. This establishes the proposition that B is similar to A.

The example

$$A = \begin{bmatrix} 0 & 0 \\ 0 & 0 \end{bmatrix}, \quad R A R^{-1} = A,$$

shows that B is not the only canonical form needed. In case the degree of the minimal polynomial is less than n, the corresponding canonical form is a block diagonal form; see the first display in Appendix II.

APPENDIX IV

Sylvester's Determinantal Identity

A determinantal identity due to Sylvester has the following statement. Let A be any $n \times n$ matrix; let A_h be a principal $h \times h$ submatrix of A. Let S be the compound (square) matrix of order

$$\binom{n-h}{m-h},$$

the elements of which are those $m \times m$ matrices which contain A_h as submatrices. The value of $\det S$ is the product of the

$$\binom{n-h-1}{m-h}$$

power of $\det A_h$ by the

$$\binom{n-h-1}{m-h-1}$$

power of $\det A$. See [47] for a proof and a generalization to singular matrices.

BIBLIOGRAPHY

[1] Andronow, A. A., and Chaikin, C. E., *Theory of Oscillations*, Princeton Univ. Press, Princeton, 1949.

[2] Andronov, A. A., and Voznesenskiĭ, I. N., On the work of J. C. Maxwell, I. A. Vyshnegradskiĭ, and A. Stodola in the field of the theory of the control of machines. In Maxwell, J. C., Vyshnegradskiĭ, I. A., and Stodola, A., *Theory of Automatic Control*, (in Russian), Moscow, 1949, pp. 253–301.

[3] Bellman, R., *Stability Theory of Differential Equations*, McGraw-Hill, New York, 1953, Ch. 4.

[4] Birkhoff, G., On product integration, *J. Math. Phys.*, 16 (1937), pp. 104–132.

[5] Birkhoff, G. D., Equivalent singular points of ordinary linear differential equations, *Math. Ann.*, 74 (1913), pp. 134–139.

[6] Bôcher, M., *Introduction to higher algebra*. Macmillan, New York, 1907.

[7] Brauer, A., Limits for the characteristic roots of a matrix. IV. *Duke Math. J.* 19 (1952), pp. 73–91.

[8] Chebotarev, N. G., and Meĭman, N. N., The Routh-Hurwitz Problem for Polynomials and Entire Functions, (in Russian) *Trudy Mat. Inst. im. V. A. Steklova*, 26 (1949), p. 21.

[9] Chetaev, N. G., *Stability of motion*, (in Russian), Gostehizdat, 1946.

[10] Collatz, L., Einschliessungssatz für die charakteristischen Zahlen von Matrizen, *Math. Z.* 48 (1942), pp. 221–226.

[11] Courant, R., and Hilbert, D., *Methoden der Mathematischen Physik*, Vol. 1, 2nd ed., Berlin, 1931, pp. 19–23.

[12] Dmitriev, N. A., and Dynkin, E. B., Characteristic roots of stochastic matrices, *Doklady Akad. Nauk*, ser. mat., 10 (1946), pp. 167–194.

[13] Doeblin, W., Sur deux problèmes de M. Kolmogoroff concernant les chaînes dénombrables, *Bull. Soc. Math. France*, 66 (1938), pp. 210–220.

[14] Doob, J. L., Asymptotic properties of Markoff transition probabilities, *Trans. Amer. Math. Soc.*, 62 (1948), pp. 393–421.

[15] ———, Markoff chains – denumerable case, *Trans. Amer. Math. Soc.*, 58 (1945), pp. 465–473.

[16] ———, Topics in the theory of Markoff chains, *Trans. Amer. Math. Soc.*, 52 (1942), pp. 37–64.

[17] Erugin, N. P., Reducible systems, *Trudy mat. Inst. im. V. A. Steklova*, 13 (1946).

[18] Erugin, N. P., Sur la substitution exposante pour quelques systèmes irrégulières, *Mat. Sbornik* 42 (1935), pp. 745–753.

[19] ———, Exponential substitution in irregular systems of linear differential equations, *Doklady Akad. Nauk. S.S.S.R.*, 17 (1937), pp. 235–236.

[20] Feller, W., Introduction to probability theory and its applications, Vol. 1, 2nd ed., Wiley, New York, 1957.

[21] Frobenius, G. Über Matrizen aus positiven Elementen, *Sitzber. Akad. Wiss. Berlin, Phys. math. Kl.*, 1908, pp. 471–476; 1909, pp. 514–518.

[22] ———, Über Matrizen aus nicht negativen Elementen, *Sitzber. Akad. Wiss. Berlin, Phys. math. Kl.*, 1912, pp. 456–477.

[23] ———, Über das Tragheitsgesetz der quadratischen Formen, *Sitzber. Akad. Wiss. Berlin, Phys. math. Kl.* (1894), 241–256, 407–431.

[24] Gantmacher, F. R., and Kreĭn, M. G., *Oscillating matrices and small oscillations of mechanical systems*, Akademie-Verlag, Berlin, to be published.

[25] Gantmacher, F. R., and Kreĭn, M. G., Sur les matrices oscillatoires et complètement non-negatives, *Compositio Math.* 4 (1937), 445–476.

[26] Gobulchikov, A. F., On the structure of the automorphisms of complex simple Lie groups, *Doklady Akad. Nauk S.S.S.R.* 27, 1 (1951) pp. 7–9.

[27] Hermite, C., Sur le nombre des racines d'une équation algébrique comprise entre des limites données, *J. reine angew. Math.* 52 (1856), pp. 39–51.

[28] Hurwitz, A., Über die Bedingungen, unter welchen eine Gleichung nur Wurzeln mit negativen reellen Teilen besitzt, *Math. Ann.* 46 (1895), pp. 273–384, also in *Mathematische Werke*, Basel, 1933, 2, pp. 533–545.

[29] Ince, E. L., Ordinary differential equations, Dover, New York, 1956 (1926).

[30] Jacobi, C. G. J., Über eine elementare Transformation eines in Bezug auf jedes von zwei variablen Systemen linearen und homogenen Ausdrucks, *J. reine angew. Math.* 53 (1857), pp. 265–270, also in *Gesammelte Werke*, Berlin, 1884, 3, pp. 583–590.

[31] Jacobson, N., *The theory of rings*, Mathematical Surveys, no. 2, Amer. Math. Soc., New York, 1942.

[32] Karpelevich, F. I., Characteristic roots of matrices with non-negative elements, *Izvest. Akad. Nauk S.S.S.R.*, ser. mat., 15 (1951), pp. 361–383.

[33] Kolmogorov, A. N., *Foundations of the theory of probability*, Trans. ed. by N. Morrison. Chelsea, N. Y., 1950.

[34] Kolmogorov, A. N., Markoff chains with a countable number of possible states, *Bull. Univ. Moscow* (A) 1 : 3 (1937).

[35] Kotelyanskiĭ, D. M., Some properties of matrices with positive elements, *Mat. Sbornik* 31 (73) (1952), pp. 497–506.

[35a] Kravchik, M. F., and Gol'dbaum, Ya. S., The equivalence of singular pencils of matrices, *Trudy aviac. inst., Kiev*, 1929, pp. 73–98; 1936, pp. 12–23.

[36] Kronecker, L., Algebraische Reduction der Schaaren bilinearen Formen, *Sitzber. Akad. Wiss. Berlin*, (1890), pp. 1225-1237.

[37] Lappo-Danilevskiĭ, I. A., *Mémoires sur la théorie des systèmes des equations differentielles linéaires*, Chelsea, New York.

[38] Ledermann, W., Bounds for the greatest latent root of a positive matrix, *J. London Math. Soc.* 25, (1950), pp. 265–268.

[39] ———, Reduction of singular pencils of matrices, *Proc. Edinburgh Math. Soc.* (2) 4, (1935), pp. 92–105.

[40] Lefschetz, S., *Lectures on Differential Equations*, Princeton Univ. Press, Princeton, 1948, Ch. IV.

[41] Liénard, A., and Chipart, M. H., Sur la signe de la partie réelle des racines d'une équation algébrique, *J. Math. Pures Appl.* (6) 10 (1914), pp. 291–346.

[42] Liapounoff, A., *Problème générale de la Stabilité du Mouvement*, Princeton, Univ. Press, Princeton, 1947, Sec. 20.

[43] MacDuffee, C. C., *Vectors and matrices.* Carus Mathematical Monographs no. 7, Mathematical Association of America, The University of Buffalo, Buffalo.

[44] Malkin, I. G., *The Theory of Stability of Motion*, (in Russian), Moscow, 1952.

[45] Markov, A. A., *Selected Works*, Moscow, 1948, (in Russian), p. 95ff.

[46] Maxwell, J. Clerk, On Governors, *Proc. Roy. Soc. London* 16, (1868), pp. 270–283 (also in *Scientific Papers*, Cambridge, 2, (1890), 105–120).

[47] Mohr, Ernst, Einfacher Beweis des verallgemeinerten Determinantensatzes von Sylvester nebst einer Verschärfung, *Math. Nachr.* 10, (1953), pp. 257–260.

[48] Morinaga, K., and Nôno, T., On the complex orthogonal transformations, *J. Sci. Hiroshima Univ.* Ser. A 18, (1955), pp. 349–377.

[49] Murnaghan, F. D., *The theory of group representations*, Johns Hopkins, Baltimore, 1938.

[50] Naĭmark, Yu. I., *The Stability of Linearized Systems* (in Russian), Leningrad, 1949.

[51] Orlando, L., Sul problema di Hurwitz relative alle parti realli delle radici di un'equazione algebrica, *Math. Ann.* 71 (1911), pp. 233–245.

[52] Ostrowski, A., Bounds for the greatest latent root of a positive matrix, *J. London Math. Soc.* 27 (1952), pp. 253–256.

[53] Peano, G., Intégration par séries des équations différentielles linéaires, *Math. Ann.*, 32 (1888), pp. 450–456.

[54] Perfect, H., On positive stochastic matrices with real characteristic roots, *Proc. Cambridge Phil. Soc.* 48 (1952), pp. 271–276.

[55] Perron, O., Grundlagen für eine Theorie des Jacobischen Kettenbruchalgorithmus, *Math. Ann.* 64, (1907), pp. 1–76.

[56] ———, Zur Theorie der Matrices, *Math. Ann.* 64 (1907), pp. 248–263.

[57] Rasch, G., Zur Theorie und Anwendung des Produktintegrals, *J. reine angew. Math.* 171 (1934), pp. 65–119.

[58] Romanovskiĭ, V. I., Recherches sur les chaînes de Markoff, *Acta Math.* 66 (1935), pp. 147–251.

[59] Routh, E. J., *Stability of a Given State of Motion*, London, 1877; *The Advanced Part of a Treatise on the Dynamics of a System of Rigid Bodies*, 6th ed., London, 1930; Dover, New York, 1955.

[60] Schlesinger, L., *Vorlesungen über lineare Differentialgleichungen*, Berlin, 1908.

[61] ———, *Einführung in die Theorie der gewöhnlichen Differentialgleichungen auf funktiontheoretischer Grundlage*, Berlin, 1922.

[62] Schreier, O., and Sperner, E., *Introduction to modern algebra and matrix theory*, Chelsea, New York, 1951.

[63] Shohat, J. A., and Tamarkin, J. D., *The problem of moments*, Mathematical Surveys no.1. American Mathematical Society, New York, 1943.

[64] Suleĭmanova, H. R., Stochastic matrices with real characteristic numbers, *Doklady Akad. Nauk S.S.S.R.* 66 (1949), pp. 343–345.

[65] Turnbull, H. W., On the reduction of singular matrix pencils, *Proc. Edinburgh Math. Soc.*, (2) 4, (1935), pp. 67–76.

[66] Volterra, V., Sui fondamenti della teoria delle equazioni differenziali lineari, *Mem. Soc. Ital. Sci.* (3), 6, (1887), pp. 1–104; (3), 12 (1902), pp. 3–68.

[67] Volterra, V., and Hostinsky, B., *Opérations infinitésimales linéaires*, Gauthier-Villars, Paris, 1938.

[68] Vyshnegradskiĭ, J., Sur la théorie générale des régulateurs, *Compt. Rend. Acad. Sci. Paris*, 83 (1876), pp. 318–321.

[69] ———, Über direkt wirkende Regulatoren, *Der Civilingenieur* (2) 23 (1877), pp. 95–132.

[70] Weierstrass, K., Zur Theorie der bilinearen und quadratischen Formen, *Monatsh. Akad. Wiss.*, Berlin, (1867), pp. 310–338.

[71] Wellstein, J., Über symmetrische, alternierende und orthogonale Normalformen von Matrizen, *J. reine angew. Math.*, 163, (1930), pp. 166–182.

[72] Wielandt, H., Unzerlegbare, nicht negative Matrizen. *Math. Z.* 52, pp. 642–648 (1950).

INDEX